ELECTRIC
RAILWAY ENGINEERING

McGraw-Hill Book Co., Inc.

PUBLISHERS OF BOOKS FOR

Electrical World ▽ Engineering News-Record
Power ▽ Engineering and Mining Journal-Press
Chemical and Metallurgical Engineering
Electric Railway Journal ▽ Coal Age
American Machinist ▽ Ingenieria Internacional
Electrical Merchandising ▽ Bus Transportation
Journal of Electricity and Western Industry
Industrial Engineer

PURDUE UNIVERSITY TEST CAR.

(Frontispiece)

ELECTRIC RAILWAY ENGINEERING

C. FRANCIS HARDING, E. E.

Professor, Electrical Engineering; Director, Electrical Laboratories, Purdue University; Fellow American Institute Electrical Engineers; Associate American Electric Railway Association; Member Society for Promotion of Engineering Education; National Electric Light Association, Etc.

ASSISTED BY

DRESSEL D. EWING, E. E., M. E.

Professor, Electric Railway Engineering, Purdue University; Fellow American Institute Electrical Engineers; Member American Electric Railway Association; Member Central Electric Railway Association; Member Society for Promotion of Engineering Education

THIRD EDITION
FULLY REVISED, ENLARGED, AND RESET

McGRAW-HILL BOOK COMPANY, Inc.
NEW YORK: 370 SEVENTH AVENUE
LONDON: 6 & 8 BOUVERIE ST. E. C. 4
1926

The Maple Press Company, York, Pa.

PREFACE TO THIRD EDITION

Although the fundamental principles underlying the operation of electric locomotives, cars and trains have not changed materially since the publication of the second edition of this book in 1915, the variety and type of their applications to practice during the past decade as well as the new statistical data now available seem to warrant a completely revised and enlarged third edition.

A new chapter has been added in order to introduce some of the economic problems involved in motor-bus transportation, although an exhaustive treatise upon the mechanics of bus design and operation is considered to be without the scope of this book.

Following the trend of the present period, the chapter on "Power Station Location and Design" gives way to that entitled "Sources of Electrical Energy," containing in detail one of the most recent and complete contracts for electrical energy which has ever been negotiated.

All of the chapters involving applications, engineering practices or the results of new research or developments have been completely revised, augmented and illustrated with recent photographs or drawings. The developments in automatic substations and the results of braking tests on interurban cars carried on under the direction of Professor D. D. Ewing of Purdue University should be listed among the important innovations.

As in the case of the second edition, the very able assistance of Professor Ewing is acknowledged, particularly upon the chapters having to do with electric locomotives, electrification of steam railroads and braking. The assistance of Mr. G. C. Sharma, formerly a graduate student at Purdue University and now instructor in electrical engineering at Notre Dame University, is also gratefully acknowledged.

Many applications of electric traction are changing rapidly. Several important electrifications of steam railroads are taking

vii

place, motor-bus design and operation by railroads are being sta-
bilized, while the use of the mercury-vapor converter and the
various requirements with regard to automatic train control
and carrier-current dispatching are being tried out, more or less
experimentally, pending a permanent solution of the many local
problems, if not a standardization of methods and systems.   In
their present stage however, they are considered to be too much
in state of flux to warrant detailed treatment herein.

It is the intention of the authors to include in subsequent
editions such applications as they become generally adopted,
thereby warranting the continued use of the book, both as a
college text and as an electrical railway instruction and reference
book.

C. F. H.

LaFayette, Ind.
  December, 1925.

PREFACE TO SECOND EDITION

A most gratifying reception of the three impressions of the first edition of this text by the large number of technical institutions in which it has been adopted, and the rapid development of electric traction during the last few years, warrant a second edition.

Although but one entirely new chapter, that entitled "Locomotive Train Haulage," has been added, practically every chapter in the book has been completely revised and further illustrated. Tabulated data representing actual operating conditions in railway practice have been increased by 50 per cent and more than 50 illustrations have been added.

The author has been very ably assisted in this revision by Prof. D. D. Ewing, also of Purdue University, whose experience with both steam railroads and electrification projects has well fitted him to discuss the problems of heavy electric traction which have been especially augmented in this edition.

This opportunity is also taken to express appreciation of the assistance given by Mr. E. A. Bureau, graduate student in electrical engineering at Purdue University, whose research revealed many of the advancements in the profession which have been incorporated in this volume.

It is hoped that the new edition will prove its added worth to both the educators and railway executives whom the book has been privileged to serve in the past, and that in addition its field of usefulness may be broadened by its more thorough treatment of this rapidly advancing profession.

C. F. H.

LaFayette, Ind.
December, 1915.

PREFACE TO FIRST EDITION

To students in technical universities who wish to specialize in the subject of electrical railway engineering and to those who understand the fundamental principles of electrical engineering and are interested in their application to electric railway practice it is hoped that this book may be of value.

While it is planned primarily for a senior elective course in a technical university, it does not involve higher mathematics and should therefore be easily understood by the undergraduate reader.

The volume does not purport to present any great amount of new material nor principles, but it does gather in convenient form present-day theory and practice in all important branches of electric railway engineering.

No apology is deemed necessary for the frequent quotations from technical papers and publications in engineering periodicals, for it is only from the authorities and specialists in particular phases of the profession that the most valuable information can be obtained, and it is believed that a thorough and unprejudiced summary of the best that has been written upon the various aspects of the subject will be most welcome when thus combined into a single volume.

The author wishes to express his appreciation of the assistance of Mr. Emrick, instructor in electrical engineering at Purdue University, in preparing illustrations for the book and to those students who by thesis investigations have added to its value.

LaFayette, Ind.
September, 1911.

CONTENTS

PART I

PRINCIPLES OF TRAIN OPERATION

CHAPTER I

CHAPTER II

CHAPTER III

CHAPTER IV

CHAPTER V

CHAPTER VI

CHAPTER VII

CHAPTER VIII

CHAPTER IX

CHAPTER X

CHAPTER XI

PART II

POWER GENERATION AND DISTRIBUTION

CHAPTER XII

CHAPTER XIII

CHAPTER XIV

PART III

EQUIPMENT

CHAPTER XIX

PART I

PRINCIPLES OF TRAIN OPERATION

ELECTRIC RAILWAY ENGINEERING

CHAPTER I

HISTORY OF ELECTRIC TRACTION

Although it is not the purpose of this treatise to relate facts, but rather to study the engineering and economic problems encountered in electric traction, yet it seems advisable to review briefly the history of the development of the electric railway by way of introduction.

Two distinct epochs were encountered in the brief period in which electric traction has come to the front. The first was that in which the experimental designs were hardly more than models operated with primary batteries. Occasionally during this period, however, enthusiasts who did not realize the insuperable financial drawbacks of primary-battery operation constructed and experimented with cars of considerable size operated in that manner. Such was the car constructed by Page in 1851 for the Washington & Baltimore R. R., which made use of a 16-hp. motor supplied with power from two large Grove cells made up of platinum plates 11 in. square. This first epoch was soon brought to a close, however, partly by the foresight of the investigators, who realized the limitations of the primary battery, and partly by the failure of all attempts to commercialize the primary-battery car by those who had continued to experiment therewith.

The second epoch opened, after a brief interval of inactivity, simultaneously with the development of the reversible dynamo. In the development of this machine, progressive experimenters could foresee the beginnings of electric traction upon a practical basis. Bearing in mind the existence of these two periods, the history of electric traction will be considered, greatly abstracted, but as nearly as possible in chronological order.

Since electric traction has ever been dependent upon the electric motor and the latter upon the discovery by Faraday, in 1821, that electricity could be made to produce mechanical motion, the latter date rather indirectly and vaguely marks the birth of the subject under consideration. America has the honor of first applying the electric motor to a car, model though it was, while later developments vibrated from America to Europe and back to America with a rapidity difficult to follow with accuracy. A poor blacksmith of Brandon, Vt., by the name of Thomas Davenport, has the honor of first making this application of an electric motor to a car in 1835, the motor having been constructed by him several years previous. During the short period of 6 years it is said that Davenport constructed over 100 electric motors of various designs. That which was described as having been exhibited by him upon a car at Springfield and Boston, Mass., consisted of a revolving commutated magnet which was caused to attract stationary armatures arranged around the periphery of its path of revolution. The car thus equipped was operated upon a small circular track.

About the year 1838 Robert Davidson of Aberdeen, Scotland, built a much larger motor placed upon a battery car 16 by 5 ft. in dimensions of the gage then standard and operated it with 40 cells of battery consisting of iron and amalgamated zinc plates immersed in dilute sulphuric acid. It is of interest to note that, after several successful trips over Scotland railways, this car was purposely wrecked by steam railway engineers, who were afraid it would supersede types in use at that time.

Two rather fundamental patents were issued in England about this time, one in 1840 to Henry Pinkus, involving the use of the rails for current conductors, and another in 1855 to Swear, which, although applied to telegraphic communication with moving trains, comprised the basis of the present current-collecting trolley. Patents were also granted in 1855 by both France and Austria to Major Alexander Bessolo, which covered the same fundamental principles but which described more in detail the third-rail conductor, the insulated trolley, and even suggested central-station supply.

In this country the experimental work of Prof. Moses G. Farmer in 1847 and Thomas Hall in 1850 might be considered in particular, because of the use for the first time of the rail as a conductor and the adoption of a geared speed reduction between motors and driving axle. The work of Page, previously noted, deserves prominent mention at this time. For many years after these experiments, investigations in electric traction seemed to be dormant, largely due to the general realization of the impracticability of the battery as a source of energy.

The second era of electrical railway development opened about 1861, when Pacinotti invented the reversible continuous-current dynamo. From this invention may be said to have arisen all modern generators and motors. While these were gradually developed by Gramme and Siemens, Wheatstone and Varley, Farmer and Rowland, Hefner-Alteneck, and others—Wheatstone and Siemens having almost simultaneously developed self-exciting generators equipped with shunt and series windings, respectively—yet a considerable period of time elapsed before these developments were effectively applied to traction.

The work of George F. Green, a poor mechanic of Kalamazoo, Mich., has been quoted as the connecting link between the two eras. Although he began his experiments as late as 1875, after the development of the dynamo, his first model road reverted to the battery delivering current to the car over the operating rails. Although Green proposed the trolley for his experimenal track, he did not make use of it. The subsequent work of this man is rather pathetic, in that he constructed a car, about 1878, large enough for two people, and realized the advantages of the dynamo for supplying energy for same. He did not understand how to construct this machine himself, however, and was not financially able to procure one of the few being constructed abroad at that time. He applied, in 1879, for patents which would probably have been of considerable value at that time, but, because of limited funds and because he was obliged to act as his own patent attorney, his claim was rejected and only finally granted in 1891 after a belated appeal to the circuit court of the District of Columbia.

The first electric road operating on a practical scale was the one exhibited by Siemens and Halske at the Berlin Exposition in 1879. This consisted of an oval track, about ⅓ mile in length, upon which an electric locomotive was operated with three small trailers accommodating from 18 to 20 passengers. The motor was mounted with its axle lengthwise of the car and power was transmitted to the car axle through a double-bevel gear speed reduction. A speed of about 8 m.p.h. was attained. The current was supplied by means of a third rail located between the running rails.

The year 1880 marked the exhibition by Egger, in Vienna, of another model electric railway, which used the running rails for conductors. In this year, also, the study of a method of replacing the pneumatic dispatch system of Paris by miniature electrically propelled carriages was carried on. Siemens proposed a commercial road for Berlin at this time and endeavored to obtain a franchise for it.

The first electric road to be installed apart from an exposition was that at Lichterfelde, near Berlin, which was opened in 1881. A single motor car, using cable drive between motors and axles, operated upon this road, which was 1½ miles in length, at a speed of about 30 m.p.h. It was sufficiently large to accommodate 36 passengers. Although this road was a third-rail road when installed, it was changed over 12 years later to a double-trolley system. This road has remained in continuous operation. During this year, also, the horse railroad between Charlottenburg and Spandau was changed to electric traction.

At the Paris exposition of 1881, Siemens and Halske demonstrated the use of the overhead trolley for current distribution to cars, the conductors consisting of metal tubes slotted on the underside, mounted upon wooden insulators, in which tubes metal contactors, electrically connected with the car, were allowed to slide. In 1883, a 6-mile third-rail road was opened at Portrush, Ireland, which was worthy of note because of its operation from a central station driven by water power.

Turning again to this country, Thomas Edison and Stephen D. Field began experimenting about 1880. Edison was principally interested in the development of the incandescent and arc lamps at this time and, aside from building a short road at his laboratory at Menlo Park and taking out a few patents, he did little in this line. Field did considerable pioneer work. He had made plans in 1879 for a railway to be supplied with power by means of a conductor enclosed in a conduit and using the rails as a return circuit. In 1880–1881 he constructed and put inot operation an experimental electrical locomotive at Stockbridge, Mass. Patents were applied for by Field, Siemens, and Edison within 3 months of each other early in 1880. Since Field had filed a *caveat*, however, the year before, his papers were given priority. Field's plans, however, remained on paper until the latter part of . 1880, which was a year later than the installation of the Berlin road.

Little more was accomplished in the United States until 1883, when the interests of Edison and Field were united and the Electric Railway Company of the United States was organized. This company exhibited an electric locomotive at the Chicago Railway Exposition in 1883, which operated on a track about ⅓ mile long in the gallery of the exposition building. The motor operated a central driving shaft by means of bevel gears, this shaft being belted to one of the axles. The speed was varied by the use of resistances. Reverse motion was accomplished by throwing into service an extra set of brushes by means of a lever, only one set of brushes, of course, being upon the commutator at any one time.

Charles J. Van Depoele, a Belgian sculptor, who was destined to play an important part in the later development of electric traction, entered the field in 1882–1883 when he operated a line in connection with the industrial exposition at Chicago. After installing equipments at the New Orleans exhibition and at Montgomery, Ala., and putting roads in operation at Windsor, Ont., Detroit, Mich., Appleton, Wis., and South Bend, Ind., the company which Van Depoele had formed was absorbed in 1888 by the Thomson-Houston Company, which had recently been organized. The name of Leo Daft is one that cannot be neglected in the development of this period, for, after considerable work with stationary motors, in 1883 he constructed a locomotive capable of hauling a full-sized car. The control in this car was brought about by varying the resistance of the motor field, for which purpose some of the coils were wound with iron wire in place of copper. The company organized by Daft at Greenville, N. J., installed roads at Coney Island, N. Y., and the Mechanic's Fair in Boston, and in 1885 equipped the Baltimore Union Passenger Ry. Co., with electric locomotives. During this year electric traction was applied by this company to the Ninth Avenue lines in New York, but after a few experimental runs of the locomotive termed the "Benjamin Franklin" the experiment was abandoned.

In 1884 Bentley and Knight installed a system in Cleveland, Ohio, which was probably the first to come into active competition with a horse-car line. Two miles of track were operated with an underground conductor in a wooden slotted conduit. Motors were connected with car axles through the agency of wire cables.

The railroad installed in Kansas City, Mo., in 1884, by J. C. Henry, was noteworthy for its departure from other designs and its adoption of features which have since become standard practice in electric railroading. Henry claims to have introduced the use of the overhead trolley. Whether this be true or not, the word "trolley" was first coined by the employees upon this road as a contraction for "troller," the word first applied to the four-wheeled carriage which was used on the overhead wire as a current collector and connected with the car by means of a flexible cable. The use of the trolley rope for replacing the trolley was of much more significance than it would at first appear, because it was formerly customary to hire a boy to ride on top of the car to keep the trolley on the wire. The present system of span construction and feeder installation was first developed by Henry on this road. His overhead conductors consisted of two No. 1 B. & S. bare copper wires spliced every 60 ft., for this was the greatest single length procurable at this time. The rails used were those which had been installed 12 years before for horse-car service and weighed but 12 lb. per yard. They were at first bonded by driving horseshoe nails between the fish plates and the rails. The motor was a 5-hp. Van Depoele type connected with the axles by means of a clutch and a five-speed differential gearing. The generator was a series arc machine of 10 hp., developing a voltage up to 1,000 volts. Although Henry was able to mount 7 per cent grades without difficulty, the Cleveland road was the only other practical road operating in America at that time and it was extremely difficult to gain the confidence of the public.

Of the roads that were installed during the next few years, the one which gave the greatest impetus to electric traction and the one often quoted as the first electric road in the United States was that in Richmond, Va., equipped in the year 1888 by Frank J. Sprague. At this time Mr. Sprague was already prominent in the railway field, although much of his time had been given to the development of the stationary motor. In a paper before the Society of Arts of Boston in 1885 he had advocated the equipment of the New York Elevated Railway with motors carried upon the trucks of the regular cars. In 1886 a series of tests were carried on upon the tracks of the 34th Street branch of this road. These experiments, like many previous ones, however, were finally suspended because of the impossibility of interesting the railway management sufficiently to launch out upon a commercial installation.

The motor design and suspension used by Sprague in these tests were the forerunners of present construction, and therefore worthy of a brief description. The motor frame contained bearings mounted upon the car axle, thus permitting the former to swing slightly about the axle as a center, keeping the gear and pinion always in mesh on rough track. The other side of the motor frame was hung from the truck frame by means of springs. Single-reduction gearing was used. Two motors were used on each truck, but they were open to the weather. The first designs were shunt wound, but later types made use of a series compensating winding. Control was obtained by resistance in both armature and field circuits. The motors were used for returning energy to the line as well as for braking.

Before considering further the rather important installation at Richmond, it is well to take census of electric traction development early in 1887. In Europe at this time there were but nine installations, including but 20 miles of track, taking into consideration every type of electric traction, including that in mines. In the United States there were 10 such installations, involving 40 miles of track and 50 motor cars. Public prejudice had not been overcome and no system of any size had been operated commercially.

The Sprague Electric Railway & Motor Co. contracted for installations at St. Joseph, Mo., and Richmond, Va., during the year 1887, the latter contract covering a complete new road, including generating station, overhead lines, and the equipment of 40 motor cars with two 7½-hp. motors each. It was placed in operation in February, 1888, and many were the new experiences and amusing anecdotes connected with this installation. The distribution system consisted of an overhead conductor mounted over the center of the track with a second parallel conductor on the pole line supplied with feeders from the power station and extending to various distributing points. The power station was equipped with six 40-kw., 500-volt Edison generators driven by three 125-hp. engines. Upon each axle of the car was mounted an exposed motor in the manner previously described. The single-reduction gearing employed at first was later replaced by the double-reduction type. The speed control was effected by two separate switches, one changing the field connections from series to parallel and the other making similar changes in the armature circuit. The cars could be operated in either direction from either end and the entire weight of the car was available for traction. Motors were operated in both directions, at first with laminated brushes fixed at an angle and later with radial solid metallic brushes. The success of this road at Richmond, in the face of many reverses and new engineering problems which had to be overcome, was probably largely due to the fact that Mr. Sprague was the first man with a competent education to enter the field. With this technical training together with his familiarity with the failures of other experiments and the development of the stationary motor with which he was closely allied, he was able to solve the many difficult problems which arose and to place this road on a practical operating basis.

From this date electric traction became firmly seated and its future development was rapid, the natural tendency being toward heavier equipment. After investigation of the Richmond system the West End Ry. of Boston soon adopted electric traction. In 1890 the South London road was equipped with electric locomotives and 3 years later the Liverpool overhead electric railway was put in operation. Third-rail trains of four motor cars, equipped with hand control, hauling three trail cars, were used at the Chicago World's Fair, in 1893, and in 1896 the Nantasket branch of the New York & New Haven Ry. was electrified. September of the same year saw the Lake Street Elevated of Chicago begin electrical operation and 2 months later electric service was begun on the Brooklyn Bridge.

Since it is impossible further to list the new electric roads coming into existence Table I will be of value in pointing out the remarkable growth of the electric railway in the United States.

Figures 1 and 2, reproduced from the *Electric Railway Journal*, indicate recent increases in track mileage and rolling-stock additions respectively.

The most important changes in motor design that came with this progressive movement of the electric railway were the

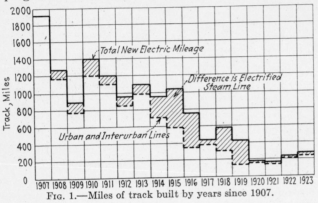

FIG. 1.—Miles of track built by years since 1907.

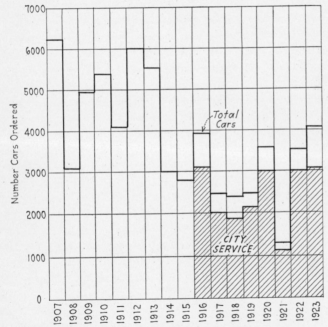

FIG. 2.—New cars and locomotives ordered by years.

enclosing of the frame to protect the motor from the weather, the replacing of cast iron by steel, the change from two to four poles, the use of form-wound coils and carbon brushes, and the return to the old single gear reduction between motor and axle. The control system of 1892 made use of the combined resistance and series-parallel connection, which is recognized as good practice today, while the introduction of the blow-out magnet was a long step forward in controller design.

TABLE I.—GROWTH OF ELECTRIC TRACTION IN THE UNITED STATES

Year	Number of electric roads	Miles of track
1889	50	100
1890	200	1,200
1891	275	2,250
1894	606	7,470
1895 (July)	880	10,863
1902	739	22,000
1907	904	34,000
1912	975	40,800
1916	1,045	47,562
1917	1,029	48,175
1918	991	48,484
1919	841	48,325
1920	831	47,704

The more recent developments in electric traction comprise the use of alternating current for transmission to substations, the multiple-unit control of the various cars of a train from a single master controller, field control of motors, the use of alternating-current and commutating-pole, direct-current motors on the car, the electrification of steam roads with the more powerful electric locomotives, regenerative braking, and the use of high-voltage, direct-current systems. These problems are of such a broad nature and so important in the study of modern practice that they will be taken up more in detail elsewhere. Suffice it to say, by way of historical comment, that the rapid introduction of interurban railways beginning about 1894, together with the advances made in transformer design by Stanley, in polyphase transmission by Ferraris and Tesla, and in the synchronous converter by Bradley and others, brought about the first of the above-mentioned changes, *i.e.*, the use of alternating current for transmission purposes. Probably the first proposal to use such a system with substations was the one made by B. J. Arnold in

1896 for an interurban road to run out of Chicago. Although this particular line was not built, a similar system was installed about 2 years later. The multiple-unit system was developed by F. J. Spraque, who proposed its application to the New York Elevated Ry. in 1896. After several vain endeavors to secure its adoption, it was finally installed the following year by the South Side Elevated R. R. of Chicago and is now in common use on elevated systems and is used to some extent in interurban traction.

Summarizing briefly, the most prominent names in the development of the electric railway are found to be those of Faraday, Davenport, Farmer, Hall, Pacinotti, Siemens, Green, Field, Van Depoele, Daft, Bentley, Knight, Henry, and Sprague. While gradual developments have been going on more or less irregularly since 1835, the practical electric railroad, operating upon a commercial scale, dates back to about 1888. Vast strides have taken place since that date, however, until at the present time electric traction is the recognized transportation system in practically all cities and towns. It has tied together the larger cities with facilities for rapid passenger transit and for the transportation of both express and freight. It has opened up the city markets for the farmer of the small town, and the country suburbs for the residences of the city business man. It has competed successfully with the steam roads on interurban lines; it has found a foothold in the city terminals of the former, and is at present being seriously considered and in some particular cases has been adopted and successfully tried out for trunk-line service. Rightly has it been said that its growth is without a parallel in the history of American invention and industrial progress.

CHAPTER II

TRAFFIC STUDIES (PREDETERMINED)

One of the first considerations in connection with the planning of a new railroad or of an extension to an old system, whether it be within the limits of a city or an interurban line, is the study of probable traffic. Upon such a study is based the predetermination of gross income, train schedules, and power-station demand. The importance, therefore, of an accurate and detailed study of all the factors which may affect the traffic upon a given road need not be emphasized further.

Population.—A study of the railway census will disclose the fact that there is a fairly dependable relation between passenger traffic and population for both urban and interurban railroads. In the latter case, of course, the population under consideration must be that of the two terminal cities and, in most cases, a portion of the intermediate population which may be considered as tributary to the line. The determination of this tributary population is rather difficult, being largely dependent for its accuracy upon the experience and judgment of the engineer. In general, however, it is usually taken as the population of a strip of territory from $1\frac{1}{2}$ to 2 miles in width on either side of the proposed railroad and parallel thereto. The population of such a strip may be determined by actual canvass, or it may be assumed that the township or county through which the road extends is evenly populated throughout the rural districts. If this be true, the tributary population may be found from the following proportion:

$$\frac{\text{Tributary population}}{\text{Township population}} = \frac{\text{Area strip}}{\text{Area township}}.$$

The township population may be obtained from the census reports and the required areas scaled from a map of the territory in question.

While it will be found advisable to make an analysis of the relation between population and passenger traffic per year,

14

TABLE II.—ELECTRIC RAILWAY STATISTICS[1]

Company	Total passengers	Miles track	Terminal population	Total population towns served	Passengers per capita Terminal Population	Passengers per capita Total Population	Miles track per 1,000 Terminal Population	Miles track per 1,000 Total Population
Boston & Worcester Street Railway Co..	10,989,391	79.58	816,571	898,796	13.49	12.24	0.0976	0.0886
Worcester Consolidated Street Railway Co..	40,654,742	167.69	251,322	297,704	16.2	13.68	0.667	0.563
Grand Rapids, Grand Haven & Muskegon Ry. Co..	927,139	49.31	142,489	142,489	6.5	6.5	0.346	0.346
Cedar Rapids & Iowa City Railway & Light Co..	590,787	30.50	42,902	42,902	13.8	13.8	0.711	0.711
Terre Haute, Indianapolis & Eastern Traction Co..	23,335,689	384.63	382,468	435,632	60.9	53.5	1.005	0.883
Fort Wayne & Northern Indiana Traction Co..	17,041,491	211.73	112,500	168,237	151.6	101.2	1.88	1.256
Union Traction Co. of Indiana..	16,021,263	378.12	291,259	407,918	55.0	39.3	1.3	0.927
Aurora, Elgin & Chicago Railway Co....	12,224,852	154.46	2,241,066	2,252,935	5.45	5.43	0.0688	0.0686
Rockford & Interurban Railway Co....	8,005,775	101.80	59,295	101,103	135.2	79.2	1.726	1.008
Milwaukee Electric Railway & Light Co..	9,524,636	183.06	418,504	481,109	22.8	19.81	0.4365	0.38
Western Ohio Railway Co..	1,031,472	110.95	62,736	88,492	16.5	11.69	1.778	1.256
Ohio Electric Railway Co..	17,720,779	504.17	1,031,264	1,208,676	1.72	1.47	0.489	0.417

[1] Taken from Railway Census, 1907.

mileage of track economically operated, gross income, etc., for the entire country, a table or series of curves covering such data obtained from the particular locality in which the proposed road is to be operated will be found of more value. The nearer the conditions of installation and operation of these roads approach those of the proposed road, the more dependable will be the results based thereon.

A table giving data of value in predetermining the traffic and gross income for a proposed road is given herewith.

Whereas such a table offers more opportunity for the correct comparison of traffic, etc., for an urban road or for extensions to such a system than for the predetermination of interurban traffic, yet the methods outlined may be used to advantage in interurban developments, provided they are applied with conservative judgment based upon successful interurban experience. As an example of such adaptation of data to interurban practice it should be noted that a different proportion of terminal population will be tributary to the traffic of the proposed road in each case under consideration. If a road is the first to enter a relatively small terminal city, a large portion of the population of the city will avail itself of the road, but if the road is the fifth or sixth to enter such a city as Indianapolis or Chicago, a relatively small portion of the population of the terminal city can be counted upon for passenger traffic. It follows directly from this, therefore, that with a large terminal city the earnings of the road per capita of terminal population will be small and the earnings of a successful road per mile of track will be relatively large, and *vice versa.*

Growth in Population.—It is necessary, however, to know more than the present terminal and tributary population. The growth of both for several years to come must be predicted. In order to do this intelligently it is necessary not only to know the growth in the past, but to study the causes of any eccentricities in the growth curve. It is only after such a detailed study that the population curve may be accurately extended to determine the population to be expected 40 or 50 years hence.

Bion J. Arnold, consulting engineer of Chicago, in his "Report on the Chicago Transportation Problem," points out very clearly the fallacy of predicting the population for any considerable term of years by any rate of growth which has existed in the past, if the law of "yearly decrease in the rate of increase" be neglected. For example, by referring to the curve of Fig. 3, which represents the population of the city of Philadelphia during a long term of years, it is seen at once that, had the future population of that city been predicted in 1860 from the rate of increase during the previous decade, the result would have been far from

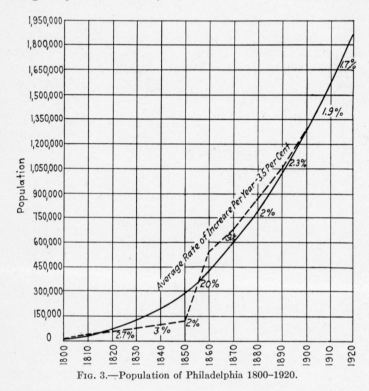

Fig. 3.—Population of Philadelphia 1800–1920.

the fact. As a matter of fact, the rate of increase in the population of Philadelphia dropped in 5 years from 33 to 9.7 per cent per annum, and in another 5 years to 2.9 per cent. Although this marked change in the rate of increase of population is exceptional in the case of Philadelphia, Arnold found that in the eight largest cities of the world which he studied the average rate of increase in population is gradually decreasing. It is obvious, therefore, that, even if the average rate of increase in population over a long term of years were applied to the future growth of a city, the results would still be too high. As an illustration, the average rate of increase in Chicago from 1837 to 1902 was 8.6 per cent per annum, from 1892 to 1902 it was 4.9 per cent, and during the year 1902 it was 7.7 per cent.   Beginning with the year 1900 and compounding the population at 5 per cent, the resulting value for the year 1952 would be 18,500,000, while an 8 per cent increase, compounded,

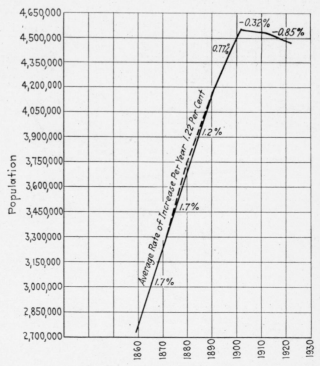

Fig. 4.—Population of city of London 1860–1920.

would give this city a population of 26,500,000 in only 35 years. With the use of the more correct method, however, which takes into consideration the fact that the rate of increase is continually on the decline, the population is compounded with a constantly decreasing percentage. Such a method applied to the city of Chicago and beginning with the 1902 rate of 7 per cent results in a predicted population of 13,250,000 for the year 1952. It is probable that this will mark the upper limit of the actual population curve, while the minimum limit of the area within which the population will fall in the next 50 years will be determined by a similar method of reasoning beginning with an increase rate of 3 per cent, which represents the average growth of the large Euro-

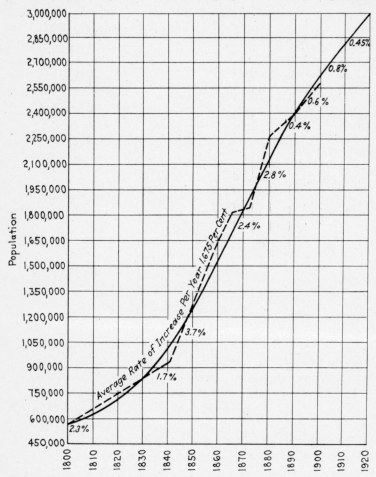

FIG. 5.—Population of city of Paris 1800–1920.

pean cities. The result of the latter calculation gives Chicago a population of 5,250,000 in 1952.

Reference to Figs. 4, 5 and 6 will give an idea of the changing rates of increase in population of the cities of London, Paris, and New York respectively. Several decades will be noted in these curves, during which these rates have been abnormal; these rates, if used as a basis for the predetermination of future population, would lead to very erroneous results.

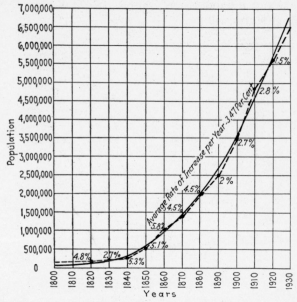

FIG. 6.—Population of city of New York.

Riding Habit.—The proper determination of the "riding habit" for a given community or the number of passengers per capita of population per annum is important if the traffic of a proposed road is to be correctly predicted. This is always a local problem, dependent upon the geographical and industrial features of the country or city under consideration, as well as upon the customs of the people, the existing or possible forms of recreation, etc. In the case of the interurban road little aid can be obtained from tabulated results upon other roads, for the possibility of comparison with a road where the conditions outlined above are the same is very small. For urban roads, however, reference may well be made to a curve (Fig. 7) plotted between "passengers per capita per annum" and population throughout the country. This curve has been shown by one author[1] to rise from approximately 70 passengers per capita per annum in cities of 15,000 population to a constant value of 240

[1] See vol. 2. ASHE, S. W., "Electric Railways."

in cities of 1,000,000 inhabitants and over, although Arnold's results in Chicago show an increase from 150 to 182 passengers per capita per annum from 1891 to 1901. An interesting comparison of the riding habits of several foreign countries with that of the United States will be found in Fig. 8.[1]

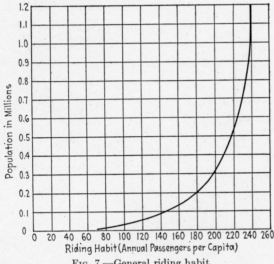

Fig. 7.—General riding habit.

Competition.—The question of competition with steam roads is a vital one with most interurban and suburban railroads, whereas most urban systems are practically monopolies.

If the proposed road is to parallel a steam line, it is usually advisable to make a study of the traffic conditions on such an existing line, either from authentic records or by actual counting of passengers on all trains in the various seasons of the year. Such records must be applied with great caution, however, for it has been found that a well-equipped interurban line with frequent and high-speed service not only often takes away much local traffic from the parallel steam lines, but, in addition, creates a traffic of its own. In other words, if the public can make a trip at any time of the day desired, if the cars are clean, free from smoke and cinders, and comfortable, and if the time lost *en route* is a minimum, it has been found that many ride who would otherwise remain at home. It is difficult to obtain more than a very

[1] See Elec. Ry. Jour., Aug. 16, 1921.

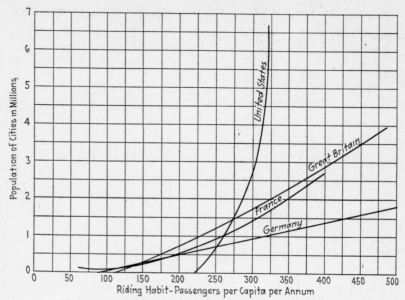

FIG. 8.—Comparative study of riding habits.

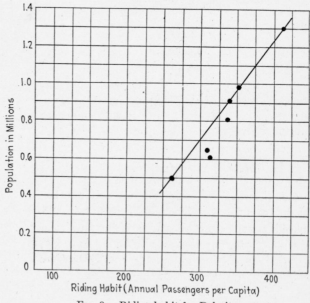

FIG. 9.—Riding habit for Delroit.

rough approximation, therefore, of future traffic from steam rail-road statistics.

Bus Competition.—In recent years, however, the new problem of competition from motor busses has arisen for both urban and interurban railway systems. Comfortable and even luxuriantly appointed gasoline-propelled busses are now to be found running between many important cities within 60 miles or less of one another upon schedules and with rates of fare comparable with those available on interurban electric roads. In city service the motor-bus competition will be found to range from the so-called individually owned jitney service on the street-car lines or paral-lel routes to extensive long-distance suburban systems organized by relatively large motor-bus corporations.

TABLE III.—ANALYSIS OF PARTIAL NUMBER OF BUSSES PUT IN SERVICE IN 1923

Motor busses	Total No.	Capacity		
		12 to 20	21 to 25	Over 25
Street-car type:				
By bus companies................	810	185	495	135
By railway companies..............	588	80	433	75
By hotels......................	5			
By school districts................	90			
Sedan or stage type:				
By bus companies................	248	175	68	5
By railway companies..............	14	5	9	
By sight-seeing companies..........	106			
Double-deck type:				
By bus companies................	264			
By railway companies.............	32			
Total busses....................	2,157			
Trolley busses by railway companies.....	17	5	12	

Although the problem of bus competition is large and inter-esting, varied in type and method of solution with nearly every locality in which it has arisen, the extent of this rapidly growing transportation service in the year 1923 may be approximated from Table III. Such a list is of only temporary and comparative value because of the state of transition which exists at present as the result of the elimination on the part of the electric railways of

much of this competition, either by Public Service Commission
or municipal enactments or by purchase and operation of the bus
systems as feeders to the railways. The problem has been considered of sufficient importance, however, to warrant a chapter by
itself, which will be found in the subsequent pages.

Gross Income.—After having studied all statistics and local
conditions which may possibly have a bearing upon the future

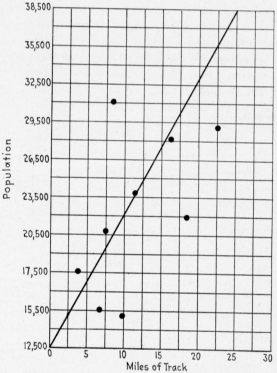

Fig. 10.—Relation of miles of track to population in Middle West.

traffic of a proposed road and having approximated from such
study, combined with the riding habit of the people, the total
traffic that may be expected with its hourly, daily, and season-
wide fluctuations, it will be necessary to determine the gross
income possible from such a road. This may be done either by
applying the average fare paid per passenger to the above traffic
figures, which total may be augmented in some cases by express,

freight, and mail receipts; or a comparison may be made with other similar roads operating successfully in the same locality and under similar conditions. Such a comparison based upon units of gross income per capita of terminal or tributary population or per mile of track gives very satisfactory results, as will be seen from the following example.

Electric railways from the beginning have handled more or less freight, mail, and express, but only within the last few years have the managements of electric railways begun to look on such traffic as an important source of revenue. Very few electric railways can afford the equipment necessary to carry on interchange traffic with steam roads. By reason of the quick service they offer, electric railways have found favor with shippers of package freight destined for local points. They often cooperate with steam roads, serving as gatherers and distributors of carload-lot freight, gathering carloads of grain, fruit, sand, stone, etc., along their lines and turning them over to steam roads with which they make physical connection, and receiving from the steam roads carloads of coal, oil, and similar freight for distribution. The revenues from freight traffic of the various electric railways differ greatly, varying with the different roads from 1 to 50 per cent of the gross earnings. According to the United States Railway Census for 1912, the number of electric cars used for hauling freight, express, mail, and baggage increased from 1,114 in 1902 to 7,794 in 1912 and the revenues from $1,871,-849 to $14,577,203. Only after a very careful study of local conditions can an estimate be made of the probable freight revenues of a proposed road. This estimate should be checked, when possible, by comparison with the actual revenues of other electric railways operating under similar conditions.

In determining the gross income for a proposed 50-mile electric interurban line in Texas, connecting cities of 34,000 and 58,000 inhabitants, comparison was made with two other roads operating under similar conditions, with the following results:

One of these roads, in the same state, connected cities of 15,000 population each with 16 miles of track, returning a gross income in 1905 of $3.48 per capita of terminal population, while the second road, 81 miles in length, connecting cities of 26,000 and 52,000 population, earned a gross income of $8.45 per capita. Taking the more conservative value of $3.48 from the former road as a basis, the minimum return from the new road should be approximately 92,000 × $3.48, or $321,000, representing an earning of $6,420 per mile. This figure compares very favorably with the corresponding values of $8,160 and $6,540 per mile for the two roads previously referred to.

In order to determine the net income, it would be possible, of course, to approximate the operating expenses, fixed charges, etc., in detail, and subtract them from the gross income. A fair average ratio of net to gross income is often taken as 45 per cent, however. This figure applied to this particular road shows a net income of $144,500 annually and therefore a possible operating expense of $176,500.

Number and Capacity of Cars.—The determination of the number and, therefore, the necessary carrying capacity of cars is sometimes arrived at as follows:[1]

A well-conducted road may safely be assumed to earn 20 cts. per car-mile. The car mileage per year may, therefore, be roughly obtained by dividing the gross income by the factor 0.2. The number of car-miles per hour is, of course, readily deduced from the above quotient by dividing by the hours of actual car operation per year. If, then, the average schedule speed is specified by city ordinance or is decided upon by the railway officials, the number of cars may readily be determined from the equation

$$\text{Number of cars} = \frac{\text{Car-miles per hour}}{\text{Schedule speed in miles per hour}}$$

However, the above result can be more satisfactorily and correctly obtained in most cases from train schedules. When the total traffic to be expected has been calculated as explained above, the headway or schedule speed of cars is usually readily decided upon with a view toward carrying this amount of traffic or in order to meet successfully the competition of parallel steam roads. The graphical train schedule sheet explained in detail in Chap. IV may then be plotted, whereupon the number of cars necessary to maintain the proposed schedule immediately becomes apparent.

It would be possible, of course, to determine the seating capacity and size of cars to be purchased for a given road from the theoretical calculation of the probable number of passengers per trip at various times of day and at various seasons of year,

[1] See ASHE, S. W., "Electric Railways," vol. 2, p. 16.

but such calculations seldom, if ever, become controlling features in the purchase of cars for a given road. For interurban roads the size and capacity of cars have been very well standardized by custom, the increased traffic at times being handled by changes in schedule or by the operation of two or more cars together in a train on the same schedule. As will be seen in the following chapter, however, cars are seldom operated at their exact seating capacity, and in spite of the fact that standing in cars on interurban trips becomes most tedious and oppressive, and granting the conclusions discussed more at length in the following pages that a considerable percentage of passengers stand in cars by preference, yet it is a regrettable fact that the size and the headway of cars on many roads, especially in urban traffic, are determined with but little consideration of the ratio of seating capacity to passenger traffic.

On interurban railways, mail, express, and milk are often carried in the baggage compartments of the regular passenger cars. Freight is carried in motor cars designed for the purpose and in standard freight cars hauled either by locomotives or motor cars. No general rule can be given for the calculation of the number of freight cars necessary to handle the freight traffic of a proposed road, but a careful study of the country traversed by the road will furnish data valuable for estimating purposes.

Freight Transportation.—The development of freight business is, without question, an important subject which should be given serious consideration by the electric interurban railways at this time, both from the standpoint of rendering the maximum service to the public and because of the financial benefits to be derived.

Existing operating facilities, including roadway, track, power plant, etc., are idle a large part of the time, or are employed to the extent of only a fraction of their capacity. Much tonnage can be handled at night and during these idle periods and off-peak hours, thus making unnecessary any further investment in power facilities, and at the same time utilizing this idle equipment in revenue-producing service.

It may be truthfully stated that net earnings of from 15 to 40 per cent on the freight investment may be expected, depending on the location of the line, the class of tonnage available, methods and efficiency in handling, and the facilities provided.

The most urgent need of the lines today is trail box cars. It is believed that in the Central Electric Railway Association territory 500 additional cars of this type could be absorbed in the service at once. One result of this shortage of rolling stock is the tendency to load the present cars beyond their capacity. This is not only dangerous, but increases equipment maintenance costs, causes a loss in the revenue while cars are out of service for repairs, and is a practice which should be strictly regulated.

Another outstanding and serious disadvantage to the proper development of the freight traffic on the interurban railroads is the lack of adequate station and terminal facilities, including team tracks and sidings. At practically any terminal of its size, shipper's conveyances are delayed, sometimes for several hours, in unloading shipments at the platform. These delays, to say the least, are costly to the patrons and, as a result, many shippers take advantage of the electric line service only to non-competitive destinations and often resort to the use of the more expensive motor vehicle in order to satisfy their desire of pleasing the customers, when, as a matter of fact, the interests of all concerned would be better served by the electric line.

Another matter worthy of serious consideration is the possibility of materially reducing train operating costs. The greatest items in freight handling are station and train labor. Both train labor and power costs could be materially reduced through the use of motive power capable of hauling longer trains.

CHAPTER III

TRAFFIC STUDIES (EXISTING)

The necessity of making a careful study of existing traffic upon urban, interurban, and even steam railroads for the purpose of comparison with the conditions of a proposed line and in order intelligently to predetermine the probable income from, and therefore the advisability of financing and building, a new line has already been set forth. Further than this, those responsible for the successful operation of present and future lines must continually study the condition and tendencies of traffic. Quoting from an editorial in the *Electric Railway Journal* upon this point:

The managers of city railway systems which do not embrace more than a half dozen routes usually feel that they know every detail of the traffic distribution so well that it is unnecessary to go to the trouble of preparing graphic records. The correctness of this point of view, however, is not proved by the experience of those who have had occasion to prepare traffic curves, even for cities of less than 40,000 population, as they have found that such curves will betray the riding peculiarities of the public much more clearly than a mere tabulation. From such a record, for example, it is easy to observe whether the passengers take kindly to short-trip cars or neglect them in favor of through cars even when they do not ride to the end of the line.

Traffic curves, furthermore, are not only of value to the company in making up its schedule, but are also an aid in its relations to the public. When a complaint is made about the service on a certain line, it is surely convenient to be able to prove graphically that in the course of the day's operation the number of seats furnished far exceed the passengers and that the schedules adopted are based strictly upon the amount of traffic which the line brings.

While reports of traffic investigations have been made public from time to time, especially as the results of studies by consulting engineers in connection with proposed improvements in the railway system for the purpose of reducing congestion of traffic by means of subways, elevated lines, rerouting of cars, introduction

29

of prepayment cars, etc., yet little has been said regarding the best method of making such detailed studies with any degree of accuracy. In fact, the difficulty in obtaining accurate and dependable results has often been given as an excuse for not undertaking such a study. It is also true that, where conditions of traffic are most variable, and these difficulties, therefore, most pronounced, the need of such an investigation is usually greatest and, when undertaken, results in the greatest possible improvement in service.

It has been found where these traffic studies have been successfully made that it is necessary to obtain data entirely independent of the daily returns of employees and that these data should be obtained by a crew of technically trained observers who understand the significance of every reading taken. The average car employee, no matter how loyal and conscientious, usually not understanding the use to be made of the data collected and the relative accuracy with which the various readings should be taken, has been found unsatisfactory for this work.

It is usually advisable to subdivide the city roughly into districts, such as business, manufacturing, residence, etc., and then to make a detailed study of the riding habits of the people and the loading of the cars on a single route or division at a time. It will at once be observed that the day may readily be divided into several periods of peak load, usually four. One city whose traffic conditions were investigated by the Wisconsin State Commission was found to have its four periods of peak load extending from 6 to 9 a.m., 11 a.m. to 2 p.m., 5 to 8 p.m., and from 10 to 11 p.m., respectively.[1] The last was, of course, the theatre period and was, therefore, limited to a small district of the city.

In studying the problem further, it is usually found that the public at large has a very well-defined habit of travel which does not vary greatly from one end of the year to another. Pleasure seekers and shoppers, of course, are irregular in their movements, but the majority of passengers will soon be found to follow not only a definite route in their traveling, but certain classes may be depended upon to ride during certain periods of the day. The above-mentioned residence districts of the city and the passengers as well may, therefore, be still further subdivided as follows:

[1] HARRIS, R. W., Graduate Thesis, Purdue University, 1910.

1. Business or professional.
2. Clerks and shoppers.
3. Laborers.

With such classifications in mind, it is necessary that the inspectors ride over the route or division under investigation a number of times during all periods of the day and in all kinds of weather to note roughly the effects of time of day, weather, and all local conditions upon maximum traffic. Especial notice should be taken of the stops which are of most importance, *i.e.*, those at which most passengers leave and board cars.

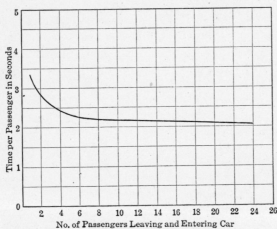

No. of Passengers Leaving and Entering Car

FIG. 11.—Duration of car stop per passenger.

After such preliminary study the number of inspectors necessary, the particular stops to be studied, data to be recorded, and the number of readings to be taken in the detailed investigation may be decided upon. These readings may be taken by inspectors, provided with stop watches, located at the principal stopping points; or, if the number of cars is not too great, an inspector may be assigned to each car on the route. In general the observations to be made at the most important stops are as follows:

1. Line (route).
2. Period of day.
3. Exact time.
4. Direction of car.

5. Number of car.

6. Total number of people on car.

7. Number of people standing in front vestibule.

8. Number of people standing in rear vestibule.

9. Duration of stop.

10. Number of people getting off car.

11. Number of people getting on car.

12. Class of passengers.

13. Conditions of vehicular traffic.

14. Conditions of pedestrian traffic.

With symbols to represent many of the above conditions upon data sheets carefully prepared in advance and with a little experience on the part of the inspector, the above data have been found to be readily and accurately taken. In fact in the investi-

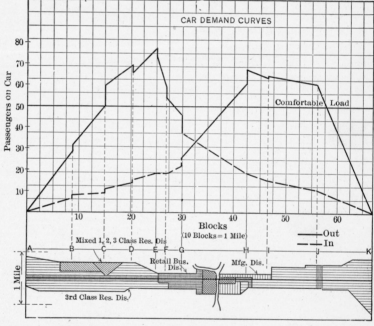

Fig. 12.

gations above alluded to check observations, taken independently but at the same time and place, varied less than 5 per cent. This is sufficiently accurate for the determinations desired. A convenient curve resulting from such data is found in Fig. 11.

The results of an extensive investigation carried on in this way in one of the large cities of the West are typified by the single example represented by Fig. 12, in which the shaded areas represent the various districts served by the particular car line under consideration, while the ordinates of the upper curve represent the passengers on the car during the period of maximum traffic extending from 5 to 8 p.m. The abscissæ of both curves represent the distance in miles on either side of the center of the city, while the full lines and dotted lines of the upper curve represent outgoing and incoming cars, respectively. It will be readily seen that the traffic at this time of day is largely from the city outward, as would be expected. Another point of significance is the fact that outgoing cars from G to A take on the greater portion of their passengers between G and E, which is the retail business district of the division, and deposit them principally between C and A, which is in the mixed residence district. These passengers may properly be classed, therefore, as "clerks and shoppers." On the other hand, the cars running from G to K take on their passengers between G and H within the wholesale business and manufacturing districts and deposit them between I and K in the third-class residence district. This fact results in classifying this traffic as "laborers." In a similar manner it is possible to determine from curves resulting from careful investigation the tendency and the amount of traffic on each division at all times of day.

In order to determine, however, whether or not sufficient cars of ample capacity are being supplied, the "comfortable load" per car must be decided upon. During such investigations in several of the larger cities it has been found that a considerable number of the passengers on a car stand by preference. In Fig. 13, curves A and A' show the total and percentage increase respectively of passengers standing by preference as the number of passengers on the car increases in a city of 25,000 population, while curves B and B' show curves of similar tendency for a city of 330,000 in the Middle West. Referring to curve B and with the knowledge that the cars operated in this city will seat 42 passengers, it will be noted that when the car is fully loaded eight will, on the average, stand by preference. The comfortable load has, therefore, been taken as 50 passengers and the variation of the "car-demand" curves of Fig. 12 above and below the "comfortable-load" line indicates at once the quality of service being rendered.

It cannot be reasonably expected by the public that sufficient cars shall be furnished to enable everyone to have a seat at all times of day, for many of the peak loads come on so suddenly and often so unexpectedly that it would be impossible to have

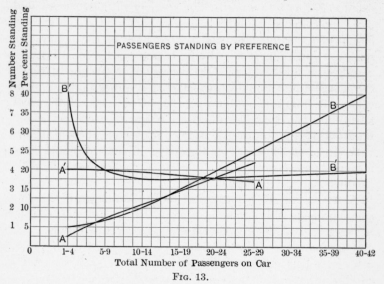

FIG. 13.

the necessary cars at the proper time and place if it were the policy of the company to accommodate the peak traffic with seats. Most progressive companies, however, endeavor to meet the just demands of the riding public and, therefore, should determine those demands from time to time by methods similar to those outlined above.

CHAPTER IV

TRAIN SCHEDULES

Having studied in the two previous chapters the important elements underlying the determination of probable traffic on a new railway line or upon the extension of an old system, it becomes necessary to establish the train schedule. As has been previously inferred, this is often a question of judgment to be exercised by the executive head of the road in view of the necessity of meeting competition. That is to say, the engineer who plans the details of the train schedule is instructed to arrange for hourly or half hourly interurban service, as the case may be, or the headway expressed in minutes or distance between cars in feet may be specified in the urban system. In both types of system the limiting schedule speed is usually stipulated, often by the municipalities involved. The interurban system is usually limited to two or more different schedule speeds, the higher velocities being confined to operation over private right-of-way and the lower within city limits or upon particularly dangerous sections of track, such as trestles, drawbridges, and temporary construction.

Whereas the hours of train arrival and departure are usually placed in the hands of the public in the form of time tables, the most convenient and common form for the study of these data by railway engineers is the graphical chart. Many factors entering into the proper construction and successful operation of a road are at once apparent from such a chart or graphical train schedule. This train schedule is often plotted with time of day in hours and minutes as ordinates and distances expressed in miles as abscissæ. It is convenient if the ordinates representing the hours be designated by heavy lines on the coordinate paper and if the hourly sections be subdivided into sixths or twelfths, representing 10- and 5-min. intervals, respectively. Upon the distance scale it is customary to designate the distance between stations and the location of any points of especial engineering interest along the line, such as branch lines, railway crossings, city and township limits, etc. With the scales of coordinates thus determined, a series of slanting lines (Fig. 14) may be drawn to represent the progress of the train from station to station. The slope of these lines is, of course, dependent upon speed, the cotangent of the angle which they make with the horizontal representing the schedule speed of the train. A chart made up of such straight lines representing each train leaving the terminals

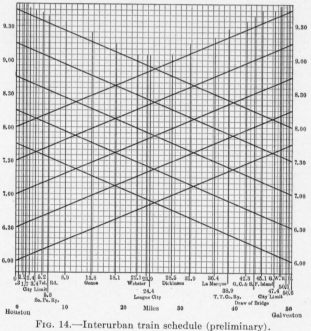

FIG. 14.—Interurban train schedule (preliminary).

of the line in either direction is sufficiently accurate for a rough preliminary study of traffic possibilities, power requirements, and substation locations, but before exact time tables can be adjusted and meeting points determined a very much more accurate and detailed graphical train schedule must be drawn. Such a schedule, involving three different schedule speeds over the various sections of road, as well as the representation of the time elapsed in making station stops, is shown in Fig. 15, which is the proposed train schedule for a 50.6-mile interurban line now connecting the cities of Galveston and Houston, Tex., within whose limits the schedule speed was to be confined to 10 m.p.h. It should be noted that speeds of 30 and 55 m.p.h. are adopted for portions of the private right-of-way, while 1 min. has been allowed for the average station stop. Such a graphical schedule enables one to predetermine not only the number of cars necessary to maintain a given schedule and the position of those cars at any moment, but it locates the meeting points, which are

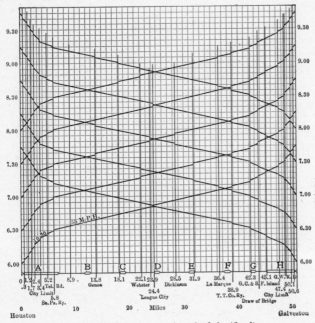

Fig. 15.—Interurban train schedule (final).

designated by the crossing of the schedule lines, and, when used in conjunction with the power curves of the various cars, it aids in locating substations and in determining the average and maximum loads on substations and power station. Comparing Figs. 14 and 15 it will be noticed that, while the former has the same through schedule speed as the latter and while all considerations based upon the headway and the time of leaving and arrival at terminal cities, taken from Fig. 14, are quite as accurate as those taken from the more detailed chart (Fig. 15) yet it is clear that nothing of value can be learned from the former regarding the meeting points nor the positions of trains at any moment.

A convenient way in which to study the possible changes in schedule upon a given line is to stick pins into the drafting board at points corresponding with the various stations and the hours of leaving and arrival at terminals or way stations. A number of strings stretched over these pins indicate immediately the relative speeds and meeting points required to make the desired schedule. The ease with which the strings may be changed from one minute of time to another, or from station to station, immediately commends the method to the busy traffic supervisor.

Although local conditions will prevent any extensive comparison of train schedules of different roads or even the schedules of the same road at different seasons of year, yet it is believed that the principal factors to be borne in mind in plotting schedules can best be outlined by a more detailed study of the particular schedule of Fig. 15.

This schedule is one proposed for maximum summer traffic. It will be noted that the first trains in the morning leave both terminals simultaneously at 6 a.m., and make the run in 1 hr. and 45 min., requiring a through schedule speed of $\dfrac{50.6 \times 60}{105} = 29$ m.p.h. Further reference to the schedule will show that of this total time only 43 min. are spent on the private right-of-way, where the maximum speed of 55 m.p.h. is possible. While all trains stop at all stations within the city limits, there are a number of flag stops between these limits which tend to make the operating schedule irregular, but which for convenience in plotting can be represented fairly accurately by allowing three flag stops for each train between the Southern Pacific Railway crossing and that of the T. C. T. Co., at which crossings all trains are required to stop.

The corresponding points of meeting as graphically determined fall sufficiently close together to be provided for by the six sidings shown at B, C, D, E, F, G, which are approximately 1 mile in length. These could be materially shortened by varying the running time slightly. The meeting places within the city limits are so numerous that a double track extending from

6 to 7 miles out of the city terminals would seem advisable from this preliminary study.

The time table below, which was taken from the graphical schedule represented by Fig. 15, will be self-explanatory and a comparison of the table and the chart will illustrate the advantages of the graphical method, even if the time table were to be the only result obtained therefrom.

TABLE IV.—TIME TABLE (PREDETERMINED)

Stations	North			South		
Houston.......	6.00	7.00	8.00	7.40	8.40	9.40
Genoa.........	6.35	7.35	8.35	7.05	8.05	9.05
League City....	6.50	7.50	8.50	6.50	7.50	8.50
Dickinson......	6.54	7.54	8.54	6.45	7.45	8.45
La Marque....	7.06	8.06	9.06	6.33	7.33	8.33
Galveston......	7.40	8.40	9.40	6.00	7.00	8.00

The interurban road whose schedule was predetermined in accordance with the charts of Figs. 14 and 15 has now been in operation for several years, and its time table of first-class passenger cars is indicated in Table V. This is of interest in determining the accuracy with which such schedules can be predicted for a proposed road.

TABLE V.—TIME TABLE (OPERATING)

Stations	North					South				
Houston.......	6.00	6.30	7.00	7.30	8.00	7.45	8.15	8.45	9.15	9.45
Genoa........	6.39	7.08	7.39	8.09	8.38	7.04	7.35	8.05	8.34	9.05
Webster.......	6.48	7.18	7.48	8.18	8.49	6.55	7.27	7.56	8.26	8.56
League City...	6.52	7.21	7.52	8.22	8.52	6.52	7.23	7.52	8.23	8.52
Dickinson.....	6.56	7.25	7.57	8.26	8.56	6.47	7.19	7.48	8.18	8.48
La Marque....	7.05	7.36	8.06	8.35	9.06	6.38	7.09	7.38	8.09	8.39
Galveston.....	7.45	8.15	8.45	9.15	9.45	6.00	6.30	7.00	7.30	8.00

It has been previously stated that one of the advantages of the modern interurban system in competition with steam roads is its ability to transport the passenger to more nearly the exact point in a terminal city to which he wishes to go and often gives him transfer privileges upon the local railway system if necessary. When comparing, therefore, the graphical train schedule of the interurban line with that of the competing steam road, especially with regard to the relatively long time required by the former within the city limits, it is often advisable to add to the steam schedule the walking time from terminal station to a point representing the average destination of the traveling public, if such can be found. Such "walking schedule" lines added to the train schedule often bring out very striking facts in favor of the electric railway as a popular choice of means of transportation.

The particular schedule taken for illustration is a relatively simple one. With the addition of limited and local service and possibly freight and mail trains, and, in some cases, the necessity of meeting the schedules of trunk or branch lines, the graphical chart often becomes rather complicated. The use of a large-scale drawing, however, usually permits such a solution to be made with little difficulty. In fact, such schedules have been very satisfactorily used with the varied types of service outlined above, but with the additional requirement that the train be made up of a varying number of cars controlled by the multiple-unit system, the various cars being feeders to the trunk line from the branches *en route* and being joined together at the junction stations, thus forming the trains to enter the terminal city. The trains leaving the terminal city would operate in the reverse order, dropping car after car to the various branches and having relatively few through cars from terminal to terminal.

In steam railway electrification studies, graphic time tables are of considerable assistance in the analysis of operating conditions with existing steam motive power and in the determination of possible savings in time, number of trains, and train schedules with electric motive power. Graphic time tables for days of average and maximum traffic are usually plotted from data obtained from the dispatcher's train sheets. These diagrams show the points along the line at which congestion occurs and give a much clearer conception of train movements than does a mass of tabulated information such as is found in a dispatcher's train sheet.

CHAPTER V

MOTOR CHARACTERISTICS[1]

It will be readily recognized that the ordinary operation of a car, whether it be from block to block in the city or for a 5- to 10-mile run between stations on an interurban private right-of-way, may be subdivided into periods of acceleration, constant-speed running, coasting retardation, braking retardation, and stop. The conditions of particular runs as to length, grades, curves, etc. may materially vary or even eliminate some of these periods, but if all problems of car operation are to be solved, a detailed study of each of these portions of the so-called "speed-time curve" must be undertaken.

The principal factors entering into the determination of such a curve will be given detailed consideration in the following order, the present chapter dealing only with the first two functions:

Motor characteristics.

Gear ratio.

Weight of car.

Bearing and rolling friction.

Air resistance.

Rotative inertia of wheels and armatures.

Grades.

Curves.

Brake friction.

Motor Characteristics.—In studying the characteristics of motors, in order to determine those best fitted for traction service, it may be found convenient to classify all motors into the following types:

Direct-current:

Series.

Shunt.

Compound:

Cumulative.

Differential.

[1] See also chap. XXIII and "Standardization Rules," *Trans.* A. I. E. E. vol. 33.

Alternating-current, polyphase:
  Induction.
  Synchronous.
Alternating-current, single-phase:
  Series.
  Induction.
  Synchronous.
  Repulsion.

If the speed characteristics of all these motors be compared, it will be found that with varying loads within the rating of the motor the synchronous motors, both single and polyphase, maintain constant speed, while all the other direct- and alternating-current motors, except the series type, operate at nearly constant speed, the speed falling off slightly, usually in accordance with a straight-line law, as the load increases. The speed characteristics of the compound motor may be made to approximate those of either the series or the shunt motors by varying the relative strength of the series and shunt fields, respectively. Since with constant-potential motors, particularly of the direct-current type, the current input to the motor varies approximately with the load, the speed-current curves of Fig. 16 may be taken as typical of the three classes of motors designed for commercial service.

The torque of a motor, which is defined as the tangential force that the armature is capable of exerting at a radius of 1 ft. from the center of the shaft, is proportional to the product of armature current and field strength. Since the field strength of a shunt-type, constant-potential motor is constant, the torque varies directly with the armature current and approximately in proportion to the load. From the above reasoning, it would be expected that the torque of a series motor would vary with the square of the current, since the field current and the armature current are the same. In the actual design of series motors for railway service, however, the magnetic circuit is nearly at the point of saturation, except at very light loads. The torque-current curve, therefore, while slightly concave upward at light loads, is nearly a straight line for practically all operating current values, since the field strength varies but slightly with change of current. In Fig. 16 a comparison of the torque-current curves of the three types of direct-current motors will also be found.

A study of the alternating-current motors will reveal the fact that all types except the series have approximately the same inherent characteristics as the shunt-type, direct-current motor, if the starting conditions of some of the former be disregarded. The series alternating-current motor, as constructed at present for railway and hoisting service, has characteristics very closely approximating those of the series direct-current motor.

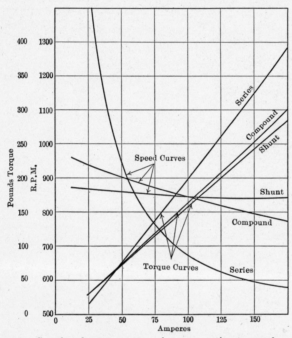

Fig. 16.—Speed and torque curves of representative types of motors.

In order to determine the best class of motor for traction purposes, therefore, it is only necessary to apply the characteristics of typical shunt and series direct-current motors to the conditions of railway service. Such characteristics may be found in Fig. 17 where *A* and *A'* are the speed and torque curves of a series motor while curves *B* and *B'* represent respectively the corresponding characteristics of the shunt motor. The motors from which these characteristics were taken were designed for the common maximum speed of 22.8 m.p.h. with the particular gear ratio used.

Tractive effort may be defined as the tangential pull in pounds exerted at the periphery of the car wheel.

It should be noted that, whereas the torque curves of Fig. 16 were plotted with values of the torque, or tangential pull at 1-ft. radius, as ordinates, the torque of Fig. 17 is expressed as tractive

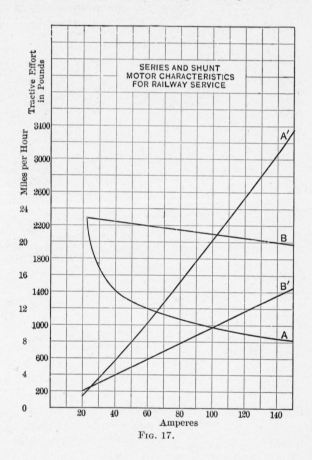

FIG. 17.

effort. As it is much more convenient in applying motors to railway service to have the pull of the motor expressed in terms of tractive effort, the characteristic curves of railway motors are universally plotted in this manner. In each case, however, the diameter of wheels and the gear ratio involved must be stated, for it is evident that the same motor will give quite different values of tractive effort at a given current input if the size of wheel or gear ratio be changed. The variation of tractive effort of a motor for a given current with change of gear ratio or wheel diameter is indicated under Gear Ratio.

It will be realized at once that a car under most conditions found in practice must be able to operate at variable speed. Conditions of grades, curves, pedestrian and vehicular traffic, necessary stops, etc. demand this. With the geared or direct connection between motors and car axles usually adopted,

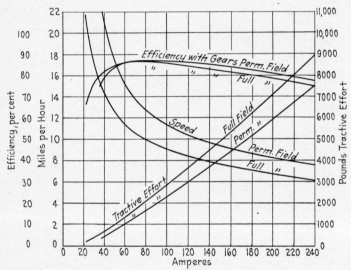

Fig. 18.—Characteristic curves of GE–272, 600-volt railway motor. Gear reduction, 4.26; wheel diam., 33 ".

therefore, a variable-speed motor seems desirable. Furthermore, a much larger torque is required to start and accelerate a car than is necessary to maintain the car at full speed. As the power taken by a motor is roughly proportional to the product of torque and speed, if large values of torque cannot be obtained at low speeds the power taken by the motor will be excessive. Reference to Fig. 17 will show that with the series motor a large torque is available at low speeds, the torque and the current both falling off as the car accelerates and, therefore, as the demand for torque decreases. Assuming a concrete example, if a tractive effort of 1,200 lb. per motor is required to accelerate a car, the series motor of Fig. 17 will require but 68 amp. of current while the corresponding shunt motor will draw 125 amp. Assuming that they are both operating on the same line the power demand in the latter case will be nearly double that of the series motor.

For the above reasons the series, direct-current motor has come into almost universal use for traction service. During the last few years, however, the single-phase, series motor, with practically

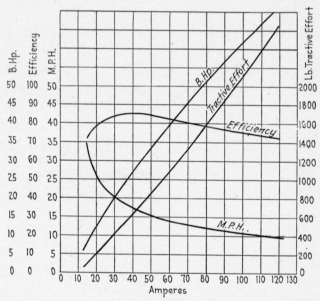

Fig. 19.—Characteristic curves of Westinghouse No. 56, 500-volt railway motor. Gear reduction, 3.56; wheel diam., 24 ".

the same characteristics as the direct-current, series motor, has been installed in a number of instances. In many cases in Europe and in several instances in this country the polyphase induction motor has been adopted where conditions seemed to be particularly favorable for constant-speed operation.

Confining the discussion to series motors, the characteristics already considered are the torque and speed curves plotted in terms of current input. To these should be added the curves of efficiency, often plotted both with and without gears, temperature rise, and, in the case of alternating-current motors, the power factor. These characteristics (Fig. 20) may be obtained either from design data before the motor is built or by test after its completion.

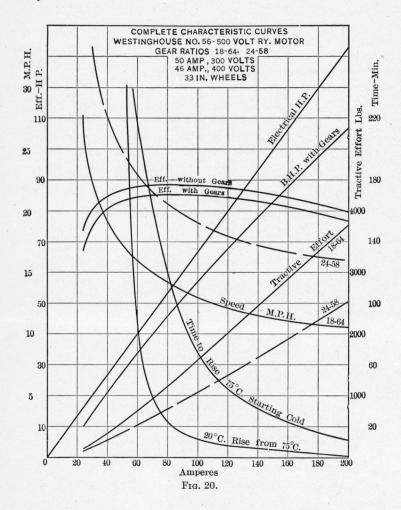

COMPLETE CHARACTERISTIC CURVES
WESTINGHOUSE NO. 56 - 500 VOLT RY. MOTOR
GEAR RATIOS 18-64· 24-58
50 AMP, 300 VOLTS
46 AMP., 400 VOLTS
33 IN. WHEELS

Fɪɢ. 20.

Assuming that the design of a proposed motor has been tentatively made and its dimensions and winding data known, the speed, torque, and efficiency characteristics may be found as follows:

$E =$ impressed voltage.

$e =$ counter e.m.f.

$I =$ current in amperes.

$T =$ torque at a 1-ft. radius in pounds.

R_a and $R_f =$ resistance armature and field, respectively.

$V =$ speed in revolutions per minute.

$N_a =$ total conductors on surface of armature.

$N_f =$ turns on one field pole.

$\phi =$ flux per pole in maxwells.

$p =$ number of poles.

$b =$ number of paths in parallel on armature.

$A =$ area cross-section magnetic circuit at air gap.

$l =$ length magnetic circuit.

$\mu =$ equivalent permeability magnetic circuit.

$P =$ power delivered to the shaft of motor expressed in watts.

From the experimental definition of the volt:

$$e = \frac{N_a \phi p V}{60 \times 10^8 b} \tag{1}$$

or

$$V = \frac{60 \times 10^8 b e}{N_a \phi p}, \tag{2}$$

but if leakage and armature reaction be neglected,

$$\phi = \frac{4\pi N_f I A \mu}{10 l}. \tag{3}$$

Substituting

$$V = \frac{47.7 \times 10^8 b e l}{N_a p N_f I A \mu}, \tag{4}$$

but

$$e = E - I(R_a + R_f), \tag{5}$$

therefore,

$$V = \frac{47.7 \times 10^8 b l [E - I(R_a + R_f)]}{N_a p N_f I A \mu}. \tag{6}$$

As all factors in the right-hand side of Eq. (6) are either constants of the design or dependent upon current, a series of assumed values of current will give corresponding values of speed V, from which the speed characteristic may be plotted. It will be seen from Eq. (2) that, if ϕ be constant because of field saturation, the speed V will vary directly with the counter e.m.f. e. Since, however, the voltage drop due to resistance is a small percentage of the impressed voltage, it may be said that the speed of a series motor varies with the voltage impressed upon it if load conditions remain the same. This fact is of importance in the design of car-control systems.

With reference to the torque characteristic and neglecting iron losses,

$$P = eI \tag{7}$$

$$P = \frac{2\pi VT \times 746}{33,000} \tag{8}$$

whence
$$T = \frac{33,000eIN_a\phi p}{2\pi \times 746 \times 60 \times 10^8 be} \tag{9}$$

or
$$T = \frac{0.117IN_a\phi p}{10^8 b}. \tag{10}$$

If the flux ϕ be assumed constant, which would be the case with the magnetic circuit saturated, Eq. (10) proves that the torque of a series motor will vary directly with the current as previously stated.

While the efficiency and the temperature characteristics can be very closely approximated in advance by means of empirical formulas, it is usually customary to determine these values roughly by comparison with other machines of similar design which have been previously constructed and to await the test for accurate results.

Several methods of testing are available for the determination of all the characteristics of the motor when constructed. Three methods will be briefly outlined, of which the one involving the apparatus most available may be selected.

Prony-brake Test.—This test is probably the simplest of the three and may be used where plenty of power is available for the operation of the motor up to 50 or 100 per cent overloads. As the name implies, the motor is loaded by means of a prony brake from which the torque may be directly determined, while the current and the speed are read directly by means of an ammeter connected in series with the motor, and a tachometer. A resistance may be inserted, if necessary, to maintain constant voltage across the motor. The efficiency curve may be obtained by making a series of calculations from the following Eq. (13) with varying currents. It is believed that the derivation of the formula is self-explanatory.

If T' represents torque at pulley at a radius of 1 ft.

$$\text{Output (hp.)} = \frac{2\pi V T'}{33,000} \tag{11}$$

$$\text{Input (hp.)} = \frac{EI}{746} \tag{12}$$

$$\text{Efficiency} = \frac{0.142 V T'}{EI}. \tag{13}$$

Pumping-back Test.—For this test two motors, identical in design and construction, are necessary, but the method has the advantage of a relatively small power demand, as the losses alone are supplied from outside sources.

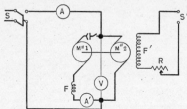

FIG. 21.—Connections for pumping back test.

Two motors are placed in alignment with shafts end to end and mechanically clutched together. They are so connected (Fig. 21) that one machine, acting as a motor with a separately excited field, drives the other as a generator. The latter has a series-connected field. By varying the field strength F' by means of the resistance R the current A' may be controlled from no load to overload. The output of motor No. 2, if the losses are supplied from the external source S, is the product of the readings V and A'. This value of power,

$$EI = \frac{2\pi V T' \times 746}{33,000}, \tag{14}$$

whence the torque

$$T' = \frac{33,000 EI}{2\pi \times 746 V} = \frac{7.05 EI}{V}. \tag{15}$$

Speed and torque plotted against current in amperes read from meter A' furnish the two principal motor characteristics.

In order to find the efficiency, for which a knowledge of the losses is necessary, the assumption is made that the combined iron and friction losses of the two machines are equal. Since the field I^2R loss of No. 2 has been eliminated from the calculation by the fact of its separate excitation, the losses represented by the power AV must be made up of the following:

Friction losses of both machines.
Iron losses of both machines.
I^2R losses of both armatures.
I^2R losses of No. 1 field.

If the resistances of both armatures and fields are known, the I^2R losses can be readily calculated for the various values of current. These losses subtracted from AV leave the total iron and friction losses of the two machines, one-half of which, according to the above assumption, is chargeable to each motor. Thus the losses, and therefore the efficiency of the motor under test, become known and the efficiency characteristic may be plotted. If a more detailed analysis of iron and friction losses is desired, additional tests with different connections must be made.[1]

The two temperature curves of Fig. 20 showing respectively the time required for the motor to rise 75°C. above the room temperature when starting cold and the time to rise 20°C. above the temperature of 75°C. for the various currents in the motor circuit, are of the greatest value not only in selecting the proper motor for a given service, but for determining the temperature rise corresponding to various overloads which the motor will usually be called upon to carry for short intervals of time. The values from which these curves may be plotted can best be obtained by actual test, preferably with the connections of Fig. 21, separate runs being made, of course, for each value of current. Thermometers placed on the various parts of the machine during the run indicate when the desired temperature has been reached and the time for such rise may then be plotted against the constant value of current maintained during the test.[2] Additional thermometers may be applied to determine the temperature of rotating parts at the end of the test and the hot resistance of the windings taken to determine by calculation the internal temperatures of the coils.

Test Using One Motor as a Generator.—In this case the motors are mechanically clutched together as in the "pumping-back" test, one being used as a motor to drive the other as a generator. The latter is loaded by means of a water rheostat,

[1] KARAPETOFF, V., "Experimental Electrical Engineering," pp. 406–407.
[2] See Rating, chap. XXIII.

as shown in Fig. 22. The calculations for losses and efficiency are very similar to those in the previous test, this method differing from the former principally in the type of load used. These connections are often used by the manufacturing companies for the heat run usually applied to railway motors.

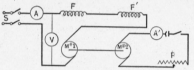

FIG. 22.—Connections for motor used as generator.

Gear Ratio.—Since a suitable design for a railway motor demands a speed much higher than that at which the car axle should be driven in ordinary installations, single-reduction gearing is introduced between the motor shaft and the car axle, a pinion upon the former engaging a gear keyed to the latter.

It has become customary in railway practice to express this gear ratio as an integer, or

$$\text{Gear ratio} = \frac{\text{Number teeth in gear}}{\text{Number teeth in pinion}}. \qquad (16)$$

As it is most convenient to plot the characteristic curves of railway motors in terms of forces at the periphery of the car wheel and speeds in miles per hour traveled by the car, it is obvious that a given group of such curves is dependent upon a single definite car-wheel diameter and gear ratio. With a change of gear ratio, however, the motor speed remaining the same, the speed of the car will change in the inverse proportion while the tractive effort will, of course, vary in direct proportion to the change in gear ratio.

The torque and speed characteristics may, therefore, be changed to apply to a new gear ratio by the use of the proportions given in Eqs. (17) and (18).

$$\frac{\text{New speed}}{\text{Old speed}} = \frac{\text{New gear ratio}}{\text{Old gear ratio}}. \qquad (17)$$

$$\frac{\text{New tractive effort}}{\text{Old tractive effort}} = \frac{\text{New gear ratio}}{\text{Old gear ratio}}. \qquad (18)$$

Motor characteristics thus changed are represented by the broken lines of Fig. 20.

Since the tractive effort increases and the speed decreases for a given current as the gear ratio is increased, it is clear that more rapid acceleration may be obtained with a given equipment with greater gear ratios. Where frequent stops are necessary and the equipment can maintain schedule speed without difficulty, the question of possible increase of gear ratio may be studied to advantage.

More than this, if the required tractive effort can be maintained with a reduced current by increasing the gear ratio and if the high speeds obtainable with a low ratio are not required to make schedule time, a very material decrease in the power taken by the car or train may often be secured by more careful selection of gears.

A concrete example of the accomplishment of both of the preceding improvements is indicated in the following test:

	Gear ratios	
	3.58	4.12
Stops per mile (average)......................	7.2	10.3
Schedule speed, m.p.h.......................	8.2	8.1
Watt-hours per car mile......................	2,762.0	2,640.0
Watt-hours per ton mile......................	150.6	134.6

An increase was made in the number of stops in this case with but slight decrease of schedule speed, while the power taken by the car was materially reduced. In many such instances a careful selection of the proper gears will result not only in better service but in less operating cost as well.

CHAPTER VI

SPEED-TIME CURVES (COMPONENTS)

Weight of Car.—From the familiar relation Force = Mass × Acceleration, expressed in the formula

$$F = ma, \tag{19}$$

it is clear that the weight of the car, complete with its equipment and load, will enter into the calculations for the speed-time curve as an important factor. The above equation may, however, be reduced to a form more convenient for railway application as follows:

$$m = \frac{w}{g}, \tag{20}$$

where w represents the weight in pounds and g the acceleration of gravity (32.2). Equation (19) becomes with this substitution

$$F = \frac{wa}{32.2}. \tag{21}$$

Changing to the more convenient units of miles per hour in place of feet per second by means of the constant 1 m.p.h. $= \frac{5,280}{3,600} =$ 1.467 ft. per second or $a = 1.467\,A$, when A is expressed in miles per hour per second, and substituting 2,000 W in place of w expressed in pounds, Eq. (21) becomes

$$F = \frac{WA \times 2,000 \times 1.467}{32.2} = 91.1WA. \tag{22}$$

In order, therefore, to accelerate a car at a rate of 1 m.p.h. p.s., a net force of 81.1 lb. must be exerted for every ton weight of car. It must be remembered that this net force available for acceleration is only that which remains after all resistances to the motion of the car have been overcome.

It is now possible to obtain relation between the tractive effort of the motors comprising the car equipment and the acceleration that this tractive effort will produce for a given weight of car.

This will obviously depend upon whether a two- or four-motor equipment is used. Equation (22) may be written

$$A = \frac{p_m n}{91.1W},\tag{23}$$

if $n =$ number of motors on car.

$p_m =$ net tractive effort per motor.

From the above equation it will be seen that the acceleration is inversely proportional to weight of car.

Bearing and Rolling Friction.—In studying the various retarding forces which have to be overcome by the motors in car operation and which must, therefore, be subtracted from the gross tractive effort of the motors in order to determine the net effort available for acceleration, it seems logical to consider first those forces acting under the normal conditions of a straight level track. Among these forces are found the friction of armature and axle bearings. The axle friction, which is usually the greater of the two, varies with the pressure on the bearing and, therefore, with the weight of the car for a given truck arrangement. Both frictional resistances vary very nearly in proportion with the speed. In building up an empirical formula for train resistance, therefore, expressed in pounds train resistance per ton weight of car, it would be expected that bearing friction would be represented therein by a constant term added to a term varying with speed.

In the operation of a car, however, other frictional forces are exerted between the wheels and rails. These forces have been termed "rolling friction." They are caused partly by the rubbing of the wheel flange against the head of the rail and partly by the fact that there is apparently a slight depression in the rail under each wheel out of which the wheel must be forced against an appreciable resistance. This effect is more marked with a greater distance between ties or where rail spikes have become loosened, allowing considerable vertical motion to the rail as the car passes over it. Since the flange friction previously mentioned is considerably increased if the track gage is not maintained constant, the entire item of rolling friction may vary greatly with the condition of the track. As this resistance will also vary with the speed and weight of the car for a given track, both bearing and rolling friction may be represented by a single constant plus a second term varying with speed.

Air Resistance.—The amount of resistance offered to the motion of the car by the air is very surprising, especially single cars at relatively high speeds. Not only is considerable resistance offered to the front cross-section of the car as it cuts through the various strata of air, but the friction of the air upon the sides of the car and the eddies and suction produced at the rear cause a considerable retarding effect upon the motion of a train. This suction phenomenon may readily be observed at the rear of a high-

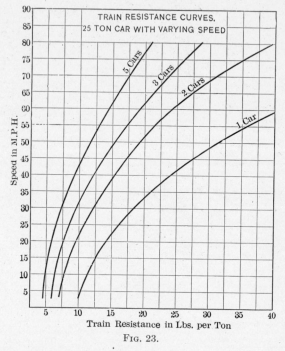

Fig. 23.

speed train by noting the motion which it conveys to cinders and light objects found along the track.

This air friction upon the various portions of the car has been more or less successfully measured in train-resistance tests, but there still exists a wide difference of opinion regarding its absolute value. It is generally conceded, however, that the front- and rear-end resistances are proportional to the cross-sectional area of the car from car axle to roof and that the side resistance of a single car is approximately one-tenth of the sum of the head and rear resistances. Since the side resistance is much smaller than the end resistance, it would be expected that the total air resistance per ton weight of car would be very much greater for a single car than for a train.   This has been found to be so marked in the tests carried out that it is usually impractical to operate a single car much over 60 m.p.h., while a train of many cars may be operated at much higher speeds without serious loss.   While this air resistance is a comparatively small quantity at low speeds, it is generally considered to vary with the square of the speed and is, therefore, a very formidable factor at high speeds.

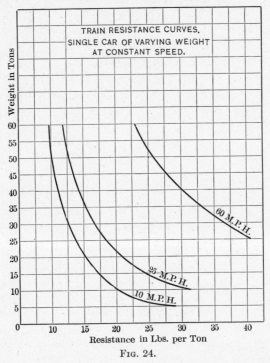

TRAIN RESISTANCE CURVES.
SINGLE CAR OF VARYING WEIGHT
AT CONSTANT SPEED.

Fig. 24.

As a result of the various train-resistance tests which have been made by determining the retardation of cars and trains while coasting from different initial speeds to a standstill on a straight, level track, a number of empirical formulas have been suggested and used with varying degrees of accuracy in train calculations. The test which have been made comparatively recently with electric equipment, with which the power is much more accurately measured than in steam-locomotive tests, may be represented by the curves of Fig. 23, plotted in pounds per ton train resistance for 25-ton cars against speed in miles per hour. This train resistance includes bearing and rolling friction and air resistance upon the entire car or train.

The empirical formula[1] from which these curves were plotted and which probably approximates most closely the true train resistance in practice of short, high-speed trains is represented below:

$$f = \frac{50}{\sqrt{W}} + 0.03V + \frac{0.002}{W} V^2 a \left(1 + \frac{n-1}{10}\right) \qquad (24)$$

f = total train resistance in pounds per ton weight of train.
W = weight of train in tons.
V = speed of train in miles per hour.
a = area of cross-section of front end of car or locomotive above axle expressed in square feet.
n = number of cars in train.

In this formula the first two terms express the rolling and bearing friction, while the last term determines the resistance due to air friction and suction.

The effect of increased weight of cars upon train resistance at constant speed is very clearly shown in the curves of Fig. 24, which are plotted from the same formula. It must be remembered that this effect is entirely separate from the extra tractive effort necessary to accelerate the heavier cars and, therefore, represents an additional negative force or resistance which the motors are called upon to overcome when operating heavy rolling stock.

Rotative Inertia of Wheels and Armature.—It will be remembered from mechanics that if two different rotating masses of different inertia are acted upon by similar propelling and similar resisting forces respectively, the mass having the greater inertia will have the lower value of acceleration of retardation, as the case may be.

From this fact it would be expected that the relatively large inertia of the rotating elements of the car, including motor armatures, gears, pinions, axles, and wheels, would tend to reduce the acceleration when the car is starting and the retardation when coasting and braking. This inertia factor must be taken into

---

[1] ARMSTRONG, A. H., "Electric Traction."

consideration in the accurate calculation of speed time curves as follows:

The energy of rotation

$$E = \frac{\omega^2 I}{2} = \frac{M\omega^2 k^2}{2}, \tag{25}$$

since

$$I = Mk^2 \tag{26}$$

where ω = angular velocity.

I = moment of inertia.

M = mass.

k = radius of gyration.

These fundamental formulas will be applied to this particular problem with the following nomenclature:

n_w = number of pairs of wheels on car.

n_a = number of armatures on car.

W_w = weight of each pair of wheels and axle in tons.

W_a = weight of each armature in tons.

k_w = radius of gyration of wheels and axle.

k_a = radius of gyration of armature.

r = radius of wheels in feet.

A = acceleration of car in miles per hour per second.

V = velocity of car in feet per second.

v = velocity at extremity of radius of gyration.

g = acceleration of gravity.

G = gear ratio.

W = weight of car in tons.

p = net tractive effort at periphery of wheel.

Considering first the wheels and axles:

From Eq. (25)

$$E_w = \frac{n_w W_w (k_w \omega)^2}{2g}. \tag{27}$$

But

$$k_w \omega = v. \tag{28}$$

Substituting,

$$E_w = n_w \frac{W_w v^2}{2g}. \tag{29}$$

Since the velocity of the periphery of the car wheel is the same as that of the car, if it be assumed that no slipping occurs,

$$E_w = n_w \frac{W_w}{2g} \left(\frac{k_w}{r} V \right)^2, \tag{30}$$

or, in other words, replace $n_w W_w$ with the equivalent weight $\left(\dfrac{k_w}{r}\right)^2 n_w W_w$ if V is used in Eq. (29).

In a similar manner, remembering that in transferring armature values to those at the periphery of the wheel the gear ratio G must be introduced,

$$E_a = n_a \frac{W_a}{2g}\left(\frac{k_a}{r}GV\right)^2, \tag{31}$$

from which the equivalent weight is $\left(\dfrac{k_a}{r}G\right)^2 n_a W_a$.

By adding the new values of equivalent weight, expressed in tons, necessary to overcome rotational inertia, therefore, Eq. (22) may be corrected to read

$$F = 91.1A\left[W + n_w W_w\left(\frac{k_w}{r}\right)^2 + n_a W_a\left(\frac{k_a G}{r}\right)^2\right]. \tag{32}$$

Since the radius of gyration

$$k = \sqrt{\frac{I}{M}} \tag{33}$$

and all revolving parts to be considered in electric traction may be assumed to be cylinders revolving about their axes,

$$I = M\frac{r^2}{2} \tag{34}$$

$$k = \frac{r}{\sqrt{2}}. \tag{35}$$

In order to determine approximately the magnitude of the inertia of rotating parts, the following concrete values, which are often found in practice, may be assumed:

$n_w = n_a$		$= 4$
$W_w = 1,500$ lb.		$= 0.75$ ton
$W_a = 700$ lb.		$= 0.35$ ton
$r = \dfrac{33 \text{ in.}}{2 \times 12}$		$= 1.375$ ft.
$k_w = \dfrac{33 \text{ in.}}{2 \times 12\sqrt{2}}$		$= 0.97$ ft.
$k_a = \dfrac{14 \text{ in.}}{2 \times 12\sqrt{2}}$		$= 0.412$ ft.
$A = 1$ m.p.h. per sec.		
$G = 19/52$		$= 2.74$
$W = 25$ tons.		

Substituting in Eq. (32)

$$F = 91.1(25 + 1.49 + 0.944) = 2{,}500 \text{ lb.,}$$

or 100 lb. per ton. In other words, the net tractive effort necessary for translation must be increased approximately 89. per cent for this car in order to overcome the inertia of rotating parts for an acceleration of 1 m.p.h. per second.

For approximate calculations, 100 lb. per ton is often assumed for the net tractive effort without calculation of rotative inertia. The following table taken from the "Standard Handbook" will give other values which may be assumed under varying conditions:

TABLE VI.—PER CENT OF TOTAL TRACTIVE EFFORT CONSUMED IN ROTATING PARTS

	PER CENT
Electric locomotive and heavy freight train	5
Electric locomotive and high speed passenger train	7
Electric high-speed motor cars	7
Electric low-speed motor cars	10

Grades.—Whenever a grade is encountered, it is not only necessary to provide an additional tractive effort to overcome linear and rotational inertia, but it is also necessary to make use of some of the tractive effort of the motors in actually lifting the car through the vertical distance represented by the grade. In

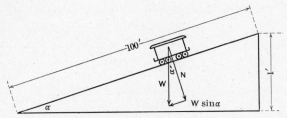

FIG. 25.—Forces existing as result of grades.

other words, referring to Fig. 25, the weight of the car W may be resolved into the two forces N and $W \sin a$, which are normal and parallel to the track, respectively. The reaction of the track balances the former, while a force proportional to the latter must be supplied by the motors of the car. As the angles a and a' are equal, it is obvious that this force is proportional to the grade and amounts to 0.01 × 2,000 = 20 lb. per ton weight of car for each per cent of grade. If the car is on a down grade, this force is available for producing acceleration and is, therefore, added to the tractive effort of the motors.

The ruling grade of a road is that grade which limits the weight of the train or car to be operated upon a given schedule. It is not necessarily the steepest grade upon the road, for the momentum of the train may often be sufficient to prevent a short, steep grade which is advantageously located from becoming a determining feature in the weight of train for a desired schedule. The ruling grade can be determined only by careful calculation of operating characteristics upon all large grades on the road or by actual test runs over the road with trains of varying weight.

Curves.—Before it is possible to consider the resistance offered to the passage of a car or train by curves in the track, it is neces-

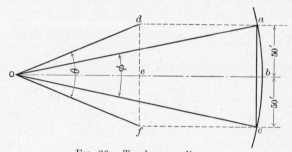

FIG. 26.—Track curve diagram.

sary to understand clearly the method of rating curves. In city streets, sharp curves are usually designated by their radii, *e.g.*, a curve of 30-ft. radius. On private rights-of-way, however, in suburban and interurban construction, it has been customary to designate curves in degrees of central angle subtended by a chord of 100 ft. Referring to Fig. 26, if angle ϕ is drawn so that it is subtended by the chord *ac* of 100 ft. and ϕ = 1 deg., then the radius *Ob* necessary to make this assumption correct is found as follows:

$$\tan 30' = 0.0087 = \frac{50}{Ob}, \text{ or } Ob = 5,730 \text{ ft.}$$

The radius of a 1-deg. curve is, therefore, 5,730 ft.

If, now, ab be moved toward O such a distance as to make $Oe = eb$

$$\tan \frac{\theta}{2} = \frac{50}{2,865} = 0.0175 = \tan 1° \text{ or } \theta = 2°.$$

Therefore, curvature in degrees $= \dfrac{5,730}{\text{radius}}$.

As a car enters a curve there is, of course, a tendency to ride over the outer rail and there occurs between the flange of the car wheel and the head of the rail considerable frictional force, tending to cause the car to follow the rail but at the same time retarding the motion of the car. This force must be considered as an additional resistance which manifests itself in frictional heat.

The amount of this resistance has been approximated from test data and it is conceded that it is directly proportional to the curvature in degrees. Values ranging from 0.52 to 1 lb. per ton weight of car per degree curvature have been obtained, but good practice at present stipulates 0.6 lb. per ton weight of car per degree curvature. When the car is on a curve, therefore, an additional force of $0.6W \times$ degrees curvature must be subtracted from the gross tractive effort in addition to all resistances previously considered.

Probably the best method of summarizing the discussion of train resistance is to express in terms of a formula the derivation of the net tractive effort available for acceleration from the gross tractive effort obtained from the motors, thus

$$p = P - f \pm g - c, \tag{36}$$

where P = gross tractive effort of motors in pounds per ton.

p = net tractive effort available for acceleration in pounds per ton.

f = train resistance due to bearing and rolling friction and air resistance in pounds per ton.

g = resistance due to grades in pounds per ton.

c = resistance due to curves in pounds per ton.

The use of this net tractive effort p in calculating the acceleration of a car or train will be discussed in detail in the following chapter.

CHAPTER VII

SPEED-TIME CURVES (THEORY)

Having considered in detail the various factors entering into the speed-time curve, the methods of plotting same may now be considered. Two methods are in general use, the so-called "cut-and-try" method which involves considerably more time

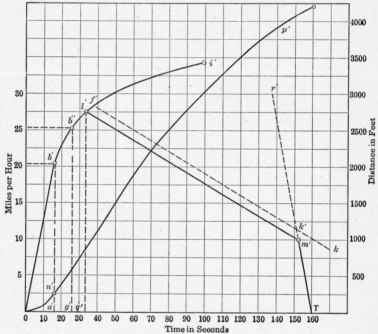

FIG. 27.—Speed and distance curves.

for its performance, but which is the more accurate, and the "straight-line" method which assumes all portions of the diagram made up of straight lines, thereby simplifying the calculation at the expense of the introduction of slight errors. The former and more accurate method will first be considered, for

64

only through the complete analysis of the correct curves can a thorough understanding of electric-car performance be obtained.

The distance between the two consecutive stops having been determined, it is next necessary to select the proper schedule speed for the run, *i.e.* the average speed which, if maintained constant throughout the run, would bring the car to its destination in the required time. This speed is usually determined from traffic studies and is, of course, dependent upon the train schedule of the entire system. With the distance and schedule speed determined, the time required for the run can be calculated and the limits of the curve laid off graphically to scale as OT in Fig. 27.

The nomenclature which will be used is as follows:

$T.E.$ = gross tractive effort per motor in pounds.

P = gross tractive effort at periphery of car wheel in pounds per ton.

p = net tractive effort in pounds per ton.

v = speed corresponding to $T.E.$ in miles per hour.

I = current corresponding to $T.E.$ in amperes.

A = acceleration in miles per hour per second.

D = retardation in miles per hour per second.

V = average speed in miles per hour.

S = length of run in feet.

s, s', etc. = distances in feet.

T = time for entire run in seconds.

t, t', etc. = time for portions of run in seconds.

f = train resistance in pounds per ton.

g = grade resistance in pounds per ton.

c = curve resistance in pounds per ton.

b = braking resistance in pounds per ton.

W = weight of car in tons.

n = number of motors on car.

W_1 = weight of car per motor in tons.

Referring to Fig. 27

$$OT = T = \frac{S}{V \times 1.467}.$$ (37)

The acceleration A must be assumed sufficiently large to enable the desired schedule to be made and yet not so great as to be of inconvenience to passengers. Values may be taken from

Table VII for the class of service under consideration. The method of calculating the net tractive effort p has been previously explained in formulas and it will, therefore, be considered as a known quantity.

TABLE VII.—ACCELERATION RATES

Type of service	Acceleration in m.p.h./sec.
Electric passenger locomotives...................	0.3 to 0.6
Interurban cars.................................	0.8 to 1.3
City cars.......................................	1.5 to 2.0
Highest practicable rate........................	2.0 to 2.5

The gross tractive effort per ton may now be found:

$$P = (p + f \pm g + c). \tag{38}$$

The sign of the grade resistance g depends, of course, upon whether the car is ascending or descending the grade; in the latter case the sign is negative and the gross tractive effort necessary is decreased by the presence of the grade.

The weight of car which must be accelerated by each motor is

$$W_1 = \frac{W}{n}. \tag{39}$$

The gross tractive effort which the motor must exert is, therefore-

$$T.E. = PW_1 = \frac{W}{n}(p + f \pm g + c). \tag{40}$$

Referring to the characteristic curves of the motor which has been assumed as probably of the correct design for this service, the gross tractive effort $T.E.$ is found to correspond to a current I (Oa, Fig. 28) and at this current the speed is v (ab, Fig. 28). The motors of the car will be able to maintain this rate of acceleration A as long as they can be supplied with current $I = Oa$. As the speed increases, however, the current, and therefore the tractive effort, will decrease unless the voltage applied to the motors is increased. This is the function of the control equipment, whether it be of the rheostatic, series-parallel, or autotransformer type. Until such time as the voltage impressed upon the motors reaches the maximum value possible with the particular control equipment in use the assumed value of acceleration A may be used for calculation. In other words, the acceleration portion of the speed-time curve may be drawn as a straight line from O with a slope of $\left(\dfrac{dv}{dt} = A\right)$ until a speed is reached corresponding to $v = ab$ (Fig. 28). This line is drawn as Ob' in Fig. 27 where $a'b' = ab$ (Fig. 28).

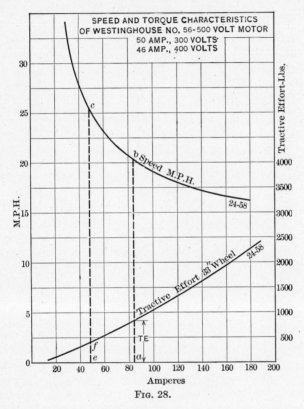

FIG. 28.

Beyond the point b' the "cut-and-try" method using increments of speed and time must be used. The time, $t = Oa'$ corresponding to point b', can readily be calculated from the equation

$$t = \frac{v}{A} = \frac{a'b'}{A}. \tag{41}$$

Assuming a small increment of speed beyond point $b' = dv$, the new speed is $v + dv = ec$. Referring to the characteristic curves (Fig. 28), this speed ec corresponds to a gross tractive effort $T.E.' = ef$. It is now necessary to determine what acceleration this tractive effort can produce as follows:

$$\text{Net tractive effort } p' = \frac{T.E.'}{W_1} - f' \pm g' - c'. \qquad (42)$$

If the speed increments are selected sufficiently small, the value of f' will not be materially different from f, although for accurate work substitution should be made of the resistance from the train-resistance curves (Fig. 23) for the average speed represented by the increment dv. The distance curve explained below will determine the portions of track corresponding to various points on the speed-time curve, thus permitting correct values of g and c to be selected. In many cases these latter values do not change materially throughout the calculation.

Having determined the new value of net tractive effort p',

$$A' = \frac{p'}{p} A, \qquad (43)$$

where A' is the new acceleration for the increment of speed dv. The time required to traverse the distance ds may be calculated from the equation

$$dt = \frac{dv}{A'}. \qquad (44)$$

The coordinates of the next point upon the acceleration curve are, therefore, known to be $v + dv = g'b''$ and $t + dt = Og'$, and the point may, therefore, be plotted as b''.

If this procedure be continued, assuming new increments of speed and calculating the corresponding values of the time increments, the complete acceleration curve may be plotted. This curve will become horizontal when the acceleration reaches zero; or, in other words, when the gross tractive effort of the motors is completely balanced by the resistances so that no net tractive effort remains to produce acceleration. With no change in grade or curvature of track the car will continue running at constant maximum speed until the power is shut off.

Coasting.—The amount of coasting permissible in a given run varies widely. In some instances where schedules are very conservatively planned and the equipment more than adequate for the demands made upon it, excessive coasting is introduced, while in heavy suburban and elevated service braking is often begun as soon as power is shut off, the coasting portion of the curve being entirely eliminated. In order to be able to make up time in case of delay, however, some coasting should be provided for in the speed-time curve, the time involved in this portion of the run acting as a storage reservoir for a hydraulic plant, since it may be drawn upon if necessary to maintain normal schedules.

In order to plot an absolutely accurate coasting curve, the "cut-and-try" method should be used, since the average speed during the coasting period, from which the train-resistance factor f is obtained, is difficult to predetermine, and for the further reason that the resistance f does not vary directly with the decrease in speed. It is customary, however, to consider the coasting portion of the diagram as a straight line, i.e., to assume the retardation constant, and to select the value of f from appropriate resistance curves (Fig. 23) for an approximate average speed during coasting, or even to assume f directly. This value is often taken arbitrarily at 15 lb. per ton.

With the value of f known, the retardation is

$$D_c = \frac{-(f \pm g + c)}{p}A, \tag{45}$$

from which the increment of time dt corresponding to an assumed change of speed dv may be calculated as follows:

$$dt = \frac{dv}{D_c}. \tag{46}$$

The coasting line may then be drawn through f', (Fig. 27) with a slope $D_c = \frac{dv}{dt}.$ Such a line is $f'k$, (Fig. 27), f' being any point arbitrarily selected upon the acceleration curve. The line $f'k$ determines the slope, but not necessarily the exact position of the coasting line.

Braking.—Since the speed-time curve must cut the time axis at T (Fig. 27) in order that the run may be completed in the predetermined schedule time, the braking line can best be drawn back from T, the slope being determined by the assumed braking retardation, as in the case of the coasting curve. As in the case of acceleration, this rate must be selected sufficiently high to enable the schedule to be maintained and yet not prove disagreeable to passengers. In heavy suburban and elevated traffic where speed is relatively high and headway short, the braking rate must necessarily be high. Braking rates as high as 2.5 m.p.h./sec. may be attained in extreme cases with high-speed passenger trains, although rates for freight trains do not exceed 0.7 to 0.8 m.p.h./sec. An average figure often assumed is 1.5 m.p.h./sec. The braking line in Fig. 27 is represented by Tr'.

The area under the speed-time curve obviously represents the distance traveled during the run. In plotting the curve, therefore, especially if the distance-time curve is not simultaneously plotted, it is advisable to determine the area of the diagram occasionally by means of a planimeter as a check upon the distance. In closing the diagram, also, after the braking line has been drawn, the coasting line $l'm'$. must be so located parallel to $f'k$ that the area of the diagram will correspond to the distance traveled between the stops under consideration. The completion of the diagram is, therefore, a "cut-and-try" method.

In order that this method of plotting speed-time curves may be more clearly understood, a concrete example of a typical problem will be found in Chap. IX.

CHAPTER VIII

DISTANCE-, CURRENT-, AND POWER-TIME CURVES (THEORY)

The speed-time curve having been determined, the secondary curves which are dependent thereon may now be given consideration.

Distance-time Curves.—The distance-time curve, which is usually plotted simultaneously with the speed-time curve, is also obtained by the "step-by-step" method, the series of increments of time determined for the speed-time curve together with the corresponding average speeds during the increment being used to calculate the increments of distance as follows:

$$ds = \frac{v_1 + v_2}{2} \times 1.467 dt. \tag{47}$$

These increments of distance when plotted form the curve $On'p'$ (Fig. 27), having ordinates expressing distance in feet corresponding to abscissæ of time in seconds. Such a curve rises slowly as the speed increases, maintains a constant slope, and gradually approaches the horizontal during the coasting and braking periods.

Current-time Curve.—In order that the power which will be taken by a car on a given run may be predetermined, the current- and voltage-time curves must be plotted. Since the voltage is usually assumed constant at some average value which may reasonably be expected to obtain over the entire line, its graphical representation is merely a straight horizontal line.

With the current, however, it will be remembered that the control equipment is expected to maintain practically constant-current values in each motor until the net tractive effort falls below that necessary for the initial assumed acceleration. This point, which is represented by b' (Fig. 27), has its time coordinate definitely fixed. The current per motor I, as found from the characteristics for this particular speed, might be plotted as constant from the start to a point $t = oa'$. Since, however, the series-parallel control is ordinarily used and the current con-

71

sumption for two motors is the important consideration, it is usually assumed that during the first half of the time oa' (Fig. 27) the motors are in series and during the latter half period in parallel. The current consumption for two motors is, therefore, double the value in the latter or parallel half that it is in the first or series half of the constant acceleration portion of the run. Thus two of the motors of a four-motor equipment would have a current-time curve during the constant acceleration period represented by $OO'afg$ (Fig. 29), while the current of all four motors or, better, the current per car for the same period may be deter-

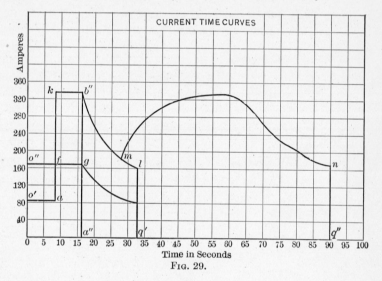

Fig. 29.

mined at any instant from the curve $OO''fkb''$ of the same figure. Since the two sets, of two motors each, are in parallel with each other, the total current per car in the series connection OO'' is double OO' and the corresponding "parallel" current $a''b''$ is double OO''.

Beyond the point b'', because of the increase of speed, the current begins to decrease, each point on the curve being readily determined by referring back to the motor-characteristic curve (Fig. 28) for the current values corresponding to the various coordinates of speed and time on the speed-time curve. The complete current curve up to the time oq' (Fig. 27) where the current is shut off, may then be plotted as $OO''fkb''lq'$ (Fig. 29).

Power-time Curve.—The power taken at various times during the run can be very readily represented graphically with the same abscissæ as the above current curve but with ordinates which are the products of the current-curve ordinates and the average assumed voltage. Since the voltage is constant, the power diagram $O_1O_1''f_1k_1b_1''l_1q_1'$ (Fig. 30) will take the same form as the current curve.

If alternating-current, series motors are being considered, with which the series-parallel control is seldom used, the current per motor and also per car will remain fairly constant throughout the

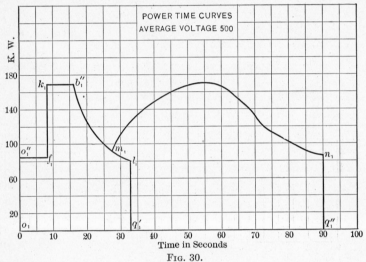

FIG. 30.

constant acceleration period, *i.e.*, during the time Oa'' (Fig. 29). Since the voltage impressed upon the motors during this period is usually varied by means of an autotransformer or induction regulator, neither of which involves the power losses incurred by the direct-current rheostatic and series-parallel control systems, the voltage curve is assumed as a straight line between the starting voltage and maximum operating secondary voltage. This starting voltage, or the voltage necessary to produce the initial tractive effort, may be determined from motor tests, while the maximum operating secondary voltage is usually that at which the motors are designed to operate.

If the product of the ordinates of the current and voltage curves for each of the time increments be plotted to a scale reduced in the ratio of 1,000 to 1, a kilovolt-ampere curve results which is quite as useful in determining substation and distribution-system requirements as the kilowatt curve. Figure 31 illustrates such a kilovolt-ampere curve for a proposed interurban line operating 72-ton, two-car trains, made up of a 44-ton motor car and a 24-ton trailer with rotative weight of 4 tons, equipped with four 125-hp., 200-volt, 25-cycle, single-phase, alternating-current, series motors with a 2.33 gear ratio.

Whereas the kilovolt-ampere-time curve is of great value as explained above, it is usually necessary to know the actual power

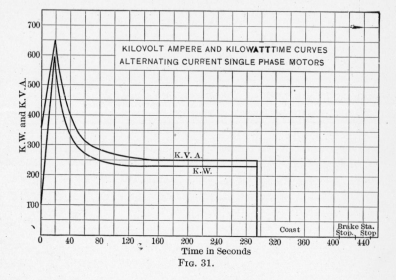

FIG. 31.

consumption expressed in kilowatts at any time during the run. This is rendered possible by plotting the kilowatt-time curve (Fig. 31), which is related to the kilovolt-ampere curve at any instant by the expression

$$\text{Kilowatts} = \text{Kilovolt-amperes} \times \text{power factor.} \qquad (48)$$

Reference to Fig. 170 will show that the power factor of an alternating-current railway motor varies with the current. In order to fix accurately a point on the kilowatt-time curve of Fig. 31, therefore, it is necessary to select a given instant of time, find the current in the motor at that instant from the current-time curve, determine the corresponding power factor from the motor-characteristic curve and substitute in Eq. (48). In many cases, however, it will be found sufficiently accurate to assume an average power factor for the entire curve, with the possible exception of the starting value, which is usually considerably lower than the average operating power factor.

The area enclosed by a kilowatt-time curve is a measure of the energy consumed by the car or train during the run; thus,

$$E = \frac{\text{Area of diagram}}{3,600} \tag{49}$$

$$E_1 = \frac{\text{Area of diagram} \times 1,000 \times 5,280}{3,600 WS} \tag{50}$$

where E = energy in kilowatt-hours.

E_1 = energy in watt-hours per ton-mile.

W = weight of car or train in tons.

S = length of run from station to station in feet.

If this energy be expressed in kilowatt-hours E it will be found to be in convenient form for calculating substation demands, while if expressed in "watt hours per ton-mile" E_1 it will be found useful in comparing various runs with different types of equipment and under different service conditions, since it has become customary to express the results of power-time curve calculations for the purpose of simplicity in terms of this unit.

CHAPTER IX

SPEED-DISTANCE, CURRENT, AND POWER CURVES
(CONCRETE EXAMPLES)

In order that the use of the formulas and the method of plotting curves outlined in the previous chapters may be thoroughly understood, a typical concrete problem will be considered. Although this particular case has been considered because of its rather exceptional changes in grade, involving the most difficult phase of the problem, the curves will first be plotted using the distances listed in Table VIII, but assuming the track a level tangent. Comparative curves will later be calculated and plotted to illustrate the effect of grades.

TABLE VIII.—DISTANCES AND GRADES OF TYPICAL RUN

Street crossings	Grade (per cent)	Distance from last stop (feet)	Distance from start (feet)
A to B.........	0.0	600	600
B to C.........	6.0	880	1,480
C to D.........	5.0	400	1,880
D to E.........	2.0	320	2,200
E to F.........	0.5	1,240	3,440
F to G.........	1.0	760	4,200

A 25-ton interurban car, equipped with four Westinghouse No. 56, 50-hp., direct-current railway motors and series-parallel control, is to be operated over this road with a gear ratio of 24 to 58 at a schedule speed of 18 m.p.h. The characteristics of this type of motor are found in Fig. 17.

The initial constant acceleration will be assumed as 1.25 m.p.h. /sec., which is a fairly representative figure in electric-railway practice.

A force of 100 lb. per ton will be considered as the necessary tractive effort to overcome the inertia of both translation and rotation in accelerating the car at a rate of 1 m.p.h. /sec. The

76

resistance curves found in Fig. 23 are plotted for a car of this weight and will, therefore, be used in this problem.

The values which must be substituted for the symbols listed in Chap. VII (page 65) are, therefore, as follows:

$$p = 125$$
$$A = 1.25$$
$$V = 18$$
$$S = 4,200$$
$$W = 25$$
$$n = 4$$
$$W_1 = 6.25$$

Using Eq. (38), the time of run is

$$T = \frac{4,200}{18 \times 1.467} = 159 \text{ sec.}$$

In order to substitute in Eq. (36) for gross tractive effort the value of train resistance f must be approximated. This may be done sufficiently accurately by selecting the value from Fig. 23 corresponding to the average speed which must be assumed for the constant acceleration period.

Taking this average speed at 10 m.p.h., $f = 11$ lb. per ton. From Eq. (38)

$$P = (125 + 11) = 136 \text{ lb. per ton.}$$

The gross tractive effort is, therefore,

$$T.E. = 6.25 \times 136 = 850 \text{ lb.} \tag{40}$$

Referring to the characteristic curves of this motor (Fig. 17), the current and the speed for this tractive effort are

$$I = 84 \text{ amp.}$$
$$V = 20.4 \text{ m.p.h.}$$

The average speed from the start is, therefore, 10.2 m.p.h., which proves the assumption of 10 m.p.h. used in obtaining the value of train resistance f was sufficiently accurate. Had this assumption been much in error a corrected calculation of tractive effort should have been made.

The time required for the period of constant acceleration is calculated from Eq. (41):

$$t = \frac{20.4}{1.25} = 16.3 \text{ sec.}$$

The line Ob' (Fig. 27) may now be plotted.

The corresponding distance covered is

$$s = O + \frac{20.4}{2} \times 1.467 \times 16.3 = 244 \text{ ft.} \tag{47}$$

This determines one point n' on the distance curve.

In order to determine the first point b'' on the curved portion of the acceleration diagram, an increment of speed must be assumed.

Let $dv = 5$ m.p.h. or $v + dv = 25.4$ m.p.h.

The gross tractive effort on the characteristic curve corresponding to 25.4 m.p.h. is

$$T.E. = 400 \text{ lb.}$$

The average speed of this increment being 22.9, the new value of train resistance f' will be found from the resistance curves to be

$$f' = 15 \text{ lb. per ton.}$$

The new value of net tractive effort is, therefore,

$$p' = \frac{400}{6.25} - 15 = 49 \text{ lb. per ton.} \tag{42}$$

The corresponding value of acceleration is

$$A' = \frac{49}{125} \times 1.25 = 0.49 \text{ m.p.h. / sec.} \tag{43}$$

$$dt = \frac{5}{0.49} = 10.2 \text{ sec.} \tag{44}$$

The coordinates of the point b'' are, therefore,

$$V + dv = 25.4 \text{ m.p.h. and } t + dt = 26.5 \text{ sec.}$$

The corresponding point on the distance curve is found as follows:

$$ds = \frac{20.4 + 25.4}{2} \times 1.467 \times 10.2 = 342 \text{ ft.} \tag{47}$$

$$s = 244 + 342 = 586 \text{ ft. from start.}$$

Neglecting the grade which is encountered at a distance of 14 ft. beyond the above point and continuing the above "step-by-step" method, the values listed in Table IX may be determined and the acceleration portion of the diagram plotted to the point i', where the speed becomes constant.

TABLE IX.—CALCULATED DATA, SPEED AND DISTANCE-TIME CURVES

dv	$V + dv$	dt	$t + dt$	ds	$s + ds$
5	25.4	10.2	26.5	342	586
3	28.4	10.7	37.2	421	1,007
3	31.4	22.2	59.4	974	1,981
3	34.4	49.1	108.5	2,370	4,351

Assuming the total braking resistance including train resistance $b = 150$ lb. per ton which, of course, will produce a retardation of 1.5 m.p.h. / sec., a straight line may be drawn back from $T = 159$ sec. with the above retardation as its slope. Such a line is Tr' (Fig. 27).

The train resistance during coasting should be selected as nearly as possible to the value which, on the train-resistance curves (Fig. 23), corresponds to the average speed expected during the coasting period. The value of 15 lb. per ton is often taken arbitrarily to represent this resistance and will, therefore, be used in this problem. Since this corresponds to a retardation of 0.15 m.p.h. / sec., a line with this slope is drawn in the position $f'k$, cutting the braking line at point k'.

If the area of the diagram $Ob'b''f'k'T$ be measured with the planimeter it will be found to contain approximately 123 section squares. With the particular scales of speed and time used each square is equivalent to a distance of 36.6 ft. The diagram, therefore, represents a distance of 123×36.6 ft. $= 4,500$ ft., which is greater than the length of the run. The coasting line must, therefore, be redrawn parallel with itself but starting with a lower initial speed until, by the "cut-and-try" method, the area of the diagram is found to correspond to the length of the run in feet. Such a diagram is that bounded by the lines $Ob'b''$-$l'm'T$ (Fig. 27). If the true coasting resistance be now determined it will be found to be 13.5. The assumption of 15 was, therefore, conservative.

The distance-time curve will be of value in approximating the correct area of the diagram. The values of distance from Table IX plotted against time would produce the curve of distance covered by the car if it were to be allowed to reach constant speed. However, since the power is shut off and coasting begun at a speed of 27.5 m.p.h., a new distance curve must be determined beyond this point.

The distance corresponding to point l' is found as follows:

$$\text{Average } V = \frac{27.5 + 25.4}{2} = 26.5 \text{ m.p.h.}$$

$$t = 33 \text{ sec.}$$

$$ds = 26.5 \times 1.467 \times (33 - 26.5) = 252 \text{ ft.} \qquad (47)$$

$$s = 586 + 252 = 838 \text{ ft. from start.}$$

Continuing the calculations of distance corresponding to the coasting and braking portions of the diagram, the distance-time curve $On'n''p'$ is determined which at 159 sec. checks very closely the length of the run.

Speed and Distance Curves for Actual Grades.—If the actual grades listed in Table VIII be considered, the curves take quite a different and more complex form. Since it was found in the previous calculations that the point b'' corresponded to a distance but 14 ft. short of B (Table VIII) where the grade changes to 6 per cent, it will introduce little error and simplify the calculations considerably to consider the grade beginning at this point.

Since the 6 per cent grade will cause an immediate reduction in speed, a decrement of 3 m.p.h. will be assumed.

$$dv = 3 \text{ m.p.h.} \quad V = 22.4 \text{ m.p.h.} \quad \text{Average } V = 23.9 \text{ m.p.h.}$$

$$f'' \text{ at } 23.9 \text{ m.p.h.} = 15.4 \text{ lb. per ton}$$

$$T.E. \text{ at } 22.4 \text{ m.p.h.} = 600 \text{ lb.}$$

$$p'' = \frac{600}{6.25} - 15.4 - 120 = -39.4 \text{ lb.} \qquad (42)$$

$$\text{Retardation} = 0.394 \text{ m.p.h. / sec.} \qquad (43)$$

$$dt = \frac{3}{0.394} = 7.6 \text{ sec.}$$

New point on curve has coordinates as follows:

$$V = 22.4 \text{ m.p.h.} \quad t = 26.5 + 7.6 = 34.1 \text{ sec.}$$

$$ds = 23.9 \times 1.467 \times 7.6 = 266 \text{ ft.} \qquad (47)$$

$$s = 586 + 266 = 852 \text{ ft.}$$

The corresponding point on the new distance-time curve is, therefore, determined.

Following this method, being careful to observe every change of grade at its correct distance from the start, the rather irregular curve $Ob'b''s''l''m''T$ (Fig. 32) results. If the distance corresponding to each of the steps assumed for the speed-time curve be calculated, the distance-time curve $On'n''p''$ may be plotted. If it be remembered that the slope of the distance-time curve $\dfrac{ds}{dt}$ represents speed, the effect of grades in reducing speed will readily be detected if the two distance curves are compared.

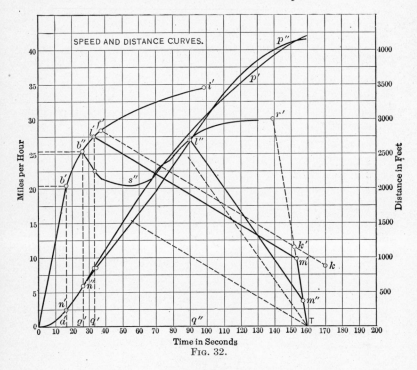

SPEED AND DISTANCE CURVES.

FIG. 32.

While the amounts of coasting in both of the speed-time curves considered are very generous, the effects of grades both in reducing the possible coasting and in increasing the coasting retardation in the second case are marked. If stops were necessary in this distance the coasting period would be greatly shortened and possibly eliminated if the same schedule speed were maintained.

Current and Power Curves.—The gross tractive effort during the constant acceleration period Oa' (Fig. 32) was found to be

850 lb., which requires a current value per motor of 84 amp. During the first half of this same period plotted to the same scale on Fig. 29, therefore, the current per pair of motors in a four-motor equipment is 84 amp. while the current per car is 168 amp. In the second or parallel half of the period, however, the corresponding values of current are 168 and 336 amp., respectively. In determining the other points on the current curve, such as the current after 20 sec. have elapsed, for example, it is found from Fig. 32 that the speed is 22.5 m.p.h. Referring to the speed characteristic (Fig. 20) the corresponding current is found to be 64 amp. per motor, or 16 amp. per car, since all four motors are now operating in parallel. This value is plotted against a time abscissa of 20 sec. in Fig. 29. Following out this method, the current required for operating the car over the level track will be represented by curve $OO''fkb''lq'$ (Fig. 29), while the corresponding current with the actual grades introduced is illustrated in curve $OO''fkb''mnq''$.

As an average voltage of 500 volts has been assumed on this road, the ordinates of the two similar curves of Fig. 30 are 500 times those of Fig. 29 reduced to the convenient scale of kilowatts. If these curves be compared with the speed-time curve (Fig. 32), the increased values of power required as the car enters the grades will be noted.

The areas of the two kilowatt-time diagrams (Fig. 30) are 3,960 and 12,100 kw.-sec., respectively. Applying Eq. (49), the energy requires by the level run is

$$E = \frac{3,960}{3,600} = 1.1 \text{ kw.-hr.,} \tag{49}$$

while that of a run involving the existing grades is

$$E = \frac{12,100}{3,600} = 3.36 \text{ kw.-hr.} \tag{49}$$

The energy consumptions for the two runs expressed in watt-hours per ton-mile are

$$E_1 = \frac{3,960 \times 1,000 \times 5,280}{3,600 \times 25 \times 4,200} = 55.3 \text{ watt-hr./ton mile.} \tag{50}$$

$$E'_1 = \frac{12,100 \times 1,000 \times 5,280}{3,600 \times 25 \times 4,200} = 169 \text{ watt-hr./ton mile.} \tag{50}$$

TABLE X.—WATT-HOURS PER TON-MILE AT CARS, FROM ACTUAL TESTS [1]

	N.Y., N.H. & H.R.R.	N.Y.C. & H.R.R.	N.Y., N.H. & H.R.R.	N.Y.C. & H.R.R.	N.Y., N.H. & H.R.R.	N.Y., N.H. & H.R.R.	N.Y.C. & H.R.R.	N.Y.C. & H.R.R.	N.Y., N.H. & H.R.R.	Interborough Subway, N.Y. (Express)	Interborough Subway, N.Y. (Local)	Northern Texas Traction Co.	Northern Texas Traction Co.	Urban trolley lines
Service	P	P	P	P	P	P	P	P	F	P	P	P	P	P
A.C. or D.C.	A.C.	D.C.	A.C.	D.C.	A.C.	A.C.	D.C.	D.C.	A.C.	D.C.	D.C.	D.C.	D.C.	D.C.
Locomotive or cars	L	L	L	L	L	L	L	L	L	C	C	C	C	C
Train weight, tons	316	266	285	250	477	493	432	434	1438	310.6	310.6	25.4	25.4	4-12
Length of run, miles	20.6	23.9	20.6	23.9	20.6	20.6	17.1	17.1	16.8	12.9	6.6	28.4	28.4	......
Average grade, per cent	+0.053	+0.129	-0.053	-0.129	+0.053	-0.053	+0.129	-0.129	-0.52	0	0	0	0	......
Schedule speed, m.p.h.	22.1	23.2	22.1	22.8	44.7	49.0	44.1	43.9	35.9	20.2	12.4	28.6	29.6	2-0
Stops per mile	0.68	0.84	0.68	0.75	0.048	0.048	0.059	0.059	0.06	0.62	1.76	0.32	0.27	......
Watt hours per ton mile	85.4	81.6	74...	59.4	35.0	30.0	29.2	17.6	25.9	58.2	78.6	75.5	72.5	100 to 160

Note.—While single-phase and direct-current service are given above in adjacent columns, the operating conditions are not identical and these figures are not intended to bring the two systems into comparison. Abbreviations: P = passenger; F = freight; L = locomotive; C = cars.

[1] Taken from American Handbook for Electrical Engineers.

Since the rolling stock and the equipment in this case are rather lighter than that of average interurban practice, the value of 55.3 watt-hr./ton-mile for the level track is rather a low figure, while the steep grades in the latter case render the figure 169 for E_1 rather above the average. The very fact, however, that these values of energy vary over so wide a range illustrates the marked effects which may be attributed to local conditions and emphasizes the necessity of a complete and detailed study of each proposed road before accurate estimates can be made of its cost of construction or dependable conclusions drawn regarding the advisability of its installation.

In Table X will be found results of actual tests upon cars and locomotive-propelled trains for various types of service.

CHAPTER X

SPEED-TIME CURVES (STRAIGHT-LINE)

The method of plotting speed-time curves outlined in the previous chapter is most desirable for final calculations where considerable accuracy is necessary. For preliminary approximate results, however, it is not necessary to go to this refinement and the so-called "straight-line" speed-time curve described below is therefore used.

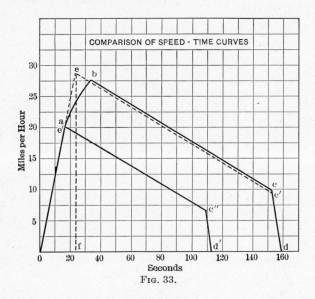

COMPARISON OF SPEED - TIME CURVES

Miles per Hour

Seconds

Fig. 33.

In Fig. 33 will be found reproduced the speed-time curve *oabcd* calculated in Chap. IX for a straight, level track (Fig. 27). If, now, the time *Od* and the distance, represented by the area *Oabcd*, are kept constant and the acceleration be assumed constant, *i.e.*, the acceleration portion of the figure a straight line, the diagram *Oaec'd* may be drawn with the same area and with the average assumed coasting and braking retardations of

85

0.15 and 1.5 m.p.h./sec., respectively. Such a chart, although it may vary considerably in some details from the more accurately drawn curve previously considered, is extensively used for rapid calculations of possible schedules for a given road and for the rough determinations of required equipment and preliminary estimates.

Granted that the straight-line diagram is sufficiently accurate for most practical purposes, an unlimited number of similar speed-time diagrams may be plotted for the same distance and time by varying the rate of acceleration but with constant coasting and braking retardations. Such a series of diagrams for a 1-mile run in 120 sec. appears in Fig. 34,[1] in which *OBC* represents

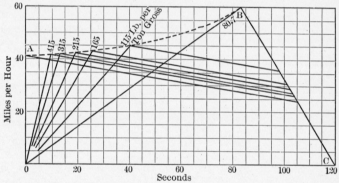

FIG. 34.—Typical speed time curves. (Varying rates of acceleration.)

a run with no coasting and, therefore, the lowest possible rate of acceleration, while the other extreme case, which is, of course, theoretical only, is represented with an acceleration *OA* infinitely great. Between these two limiting values there are a number of possible selections to be made, the gross tractive efforts listed on the chart including the net effort necessary for acceleration plus the 15 lb. per ton train resistance assumed for all diagrams. It should be noted that the dotted line *AB* is the locus of maximum speeds for all diagrams.

Furthermore, if the distance still remain constant at 1 mile and the time for the entire run be varied, the more complete chart (Fig. 35)[1] results, which is made up of a series of charts like Fig.

[1] Taken from ARMSTRONG, A. H., "Electric Traction."

34, each having its own acceleration variations for a fixed distance and time. The dotted curve of Fig. 35 represents the locus of maximum speeds necessary to cover the distance of 1 mile in any given time represented as an abscissa. For example, if it be desired to cover the mile run in 150 sec., the braking line terminating at 150 sec. shows the maximum speed with any acceleration to be 48 m.p.h. corresponding to a gross tractive effort of 51.2 lb. per ton. If other rates of acceleration are possible, the particular chart designated by the point 51.2 may be treated as outlined in Fig. 34.

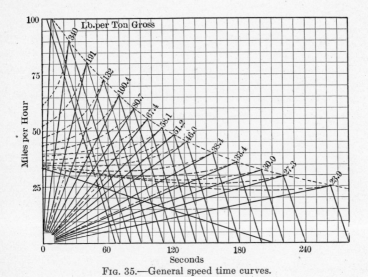

Fig. 35.—General speed time curves.

These charts are of little use, however, unless readily applicable to various lengths of run. Such application may be made in the following manner.

It can be readily proved geometrically that the ratio of the altitudes or bases of two similar trapezoids is that of the square root of their areas. The speed-time diagrams which have been considered in this chapter are trapezoids with altitudes representing maximum speeds, bases representing time, and, therefore, with areas expressed in terms of distance. If the length of run be changed, keeping the same acceleration and coasting and braking retardations, the diagrams for the two lengths of run will remain

similar and the following formulas may be derived for the calculation of maximum speed and time.

T = schedule time for original run.
T' = schedule time for new run.
S = distance of original run.
S' = distance of new run.
V_m = maximum speed of original run.
V'_m = maximum speed of new run.

$$\frac{T'}{T} = \sqrt{\frac{S'}{S}} \tag{51}$$

$$\frac{V'_m}{V_m} = \sqrt{\frac{S'}{S}}. \tag{52}$$

As an illustration of the use of these formulas, it will be
assumed that the speed-time diagram is desired for a run one-half
the length of that considered in the previous chapter (2,100 ft.)
(Fig. 33) with the same rate of acceleration, coasting, and braking.
From the diagram the following values may be scaled:

$$T = Od = 159 \text{ sec.}$$
$$V_m = ef = 28.5 \text{ m.p.h.}$$
$$S = 4,200 \text{ ft.}$$

Substituting in Eqs. (51 and (52),

$$T' = 159\sqrt{0.5} = 112.4 \text{ sec.} \tag{51}$$
$$V'_m = 28.5\sqrt{0.5} = 20.1 \text{ m.p.h.} \tag{52}$$

Plotting these values, the diagram $Oe'c''d'$ results and, therefore, represents fairly accurately a speed-time curve for a distance
of 2,100 ft. with a minimum of labor involved in its determination.

Energy Calculations.—As the acceleration was assumed constant in the above diagrams, it is usually not sufficiently accurate
to derive from them the current and kilowatt-time curves as was
done in Chaps. VIII and IX. The energy required for the run
may be closely approximated, however, by the following method,
which may also be used to advantage as a check on the power-
time curves when the latter are plotted by the "step-by-step"
method.

Assume the following nomenclature:

V = average speed in miles per hour.
V_c = initial coasting speed in miles per hour.

V_b = initial braking speed in miles per hour.

r = total train resistance in pounds per ton including $(f \pm g + c)$.

E_1 = energy in watt-hours per ton-mile.

m = mass of car = $\dfrac{2{,}000W}{g}$.

b = braking force at periphery of car wheel in pounds per ton.

S_c = distance traveled from beginning of coasting period to stop with no braking.

S_b = distance traveled from beginning of braking period to stop.

t_c = time of coasting in seconds.

t_b = time of braking in seconds.

$$E_1 = \frac{V \times 5{,}280 \times r \times 746}{60 \times 33{,}000V} = 1.99r. \tag{53}$$

This may be considered with little error to be $2r$.

This represents in simple form the net energy at the wheels of the car. To obtain the gross input to motors this must be divided by the efficiency of the motors with gears included.

Energy during the Braking Period.—Furthermore, it should be noted that neither Eq. (53) nor the formulas of Chap. VIII includes the power required to stop the car. To determine this power exerted during the braking period, proceed as follows:

$$e = \frac{m(V_b \times 1.467)^2}{2} \tag{54}$$

but

$$e = S_b(b + r)W, \tag{55}$$

therefore,

$$WS_b(b + r) = \frac{2{,}000W(1.467V_b)^2}{2g}. \tag{56}$$

The power during the braking period is, therefore,

$$\text{Hp.} = \frac{\text{Foot-pounds per minute}}{33{,}000} = \frac{60WS_b(b + r)}{33{,}000t_b},$$

or simplified

$$\text{Hp.} = \frac{60 \times 2{,}000W(1.467V_b)^2}{32.2 \times 2 \times 33{,}000t_b} = 0.121\frac{WV^2_b}{t_b}. \tag{57}$$

Coasting Energy and Train Resistance.—If, however, the above reasoning be applied to the results of a coasting test in which the car or train is allowed to coast to a standstill from various initial speeds, the train resistance may be calculated thus:

$$WS_c r = \frac{2,000W(1.467V_c)^2}{2g}, \tag{58}$$

whence

$$r = 66.8\frac{V^2_c}{S_c}. \tag{59}$$

If, however, the portion of the coasting line to the point where brakes are applied is being considered, Eq. (59) becomes

$$r = 66.8\frac{V_c{}^2 - V_b{}^2}{S_c}. \tag{60}$$

By thus combining the straight-line, speed-time charts with the calculation of energy from the above formulas, a rapid although approximate method of calculating train performance is provided which will be found of great convenience.

PART II

POWER GENERATION AND DISTRIBUTION

CHAPTER XI

LOCOMOTIVE TRAIN HAULAGE

In the previous chapters, the problems that apply particularly to motor-car train haulage have been studied. This chapter will be devoted to a study of the application of electric locomotives as a source of motive power for railway trains.

Drawbar Pull.—The drawbar pull of a locomotive is the force exerted by the locomotive on its drawbar. The more important of the factors on which this force depends are as follows:

1. Characteristics and capacity of the motors.
2. Gear ratio.
3. Diameter of drivers.
4. Train resistance of the locomotive.
5. Adhesive weight.
6. Coefficient of adhesion.

The characteristics of a 100-ton, direct-current, freight locomotive are shown in Fig. 36. The points marked C and "1 Hr." indicate respectively the continuous and 1-hr. ratings of the locomotive. It will be noted that tractive effort has been used for the abscissa of these curves instead of amperes, as in Fig. 20; the arrangement here used is believed to be more convenient for use in the solution of locomotive train haulage problems.

The effect of changing the gear ratio of the motors has been discussed in Chap. V, and, therefore, needs no further discussion here.

For a given motor speed, any increase in the diameter of the drive wheels of a locomotive causes a proportional decrease in the tractive effort, and, therefore, a decrease in the drawbar pull. Considerations such as stresses at contact area between driver and rail, tire wear, surface speed of journals, and track maintenance fix the minimum driver diameter for a given weight on driver axle.

As has been intimated in a previous chapter, it is a very difficult matter to secure consistent results in experimental determinations of train resistance. Authentic data on the subject of locomotive train resistance are scarce. The practice of engineers differs widely. Burch recommends that 22.2 lb. per ton on drivers be used for the frictional resistances and $0.24V^2$ for the total air resistance of the locomotive.[1] Some engineers use a constant value of 15 lb. per ton for all conditions of track,

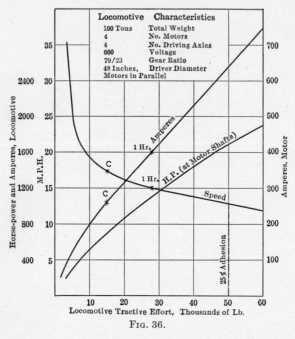

Locomotive Characteristics

100 Tons	Total Weight
4	No. Motors
4	No. Driving Axles
600	Voltage
79/23	Gear Ratio
48 Inches,	Driver Diameter
Motors in Parallel	

Locomotive Tractive Effort, Thousands of Lb.

Fig. 36.

weather, and speed. Equation (24) has for its basis the tests made on the New York Central electric locomotive No. 6000 during its 50,000-mile endurance run. The locomotive resistance may be calculated from a modification of Eq. (24)

$$f_1 = \frac{50}{\sqrt{W_1}} + 0.03V + \frac{0.002V^2 a}{W_1}, \qquad (61)$$

where f_1 = frictional and air resistances of the locomotive in pounds per ton.

V = speed in miles per hour.

[1] Burch, "Electric Traction for Railway Trains."

W_1 = weight of the locomotive in tons.

a = cross-section of locomotive above the axle in square feet.

This formula gives results which check very well with those secured in the New York Central tests with the locomotive running alone.[1] The curve in Fig. 37, giving the train resistance for the 100-ton freight locomotive whose characteristics are shown in Fig. 36, was plotted from this formula.

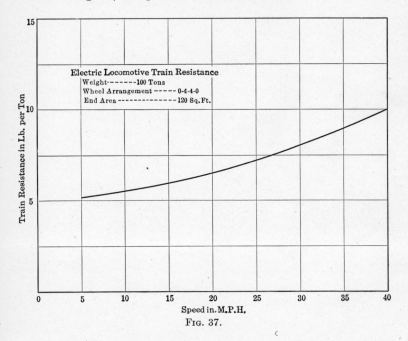

Electric Locomotive Train Resistance
Weight------100 Tons
Wheel Arrangement-----0-4-4-0
End Area------------120 Sq.Ft.

Speed in.M.P.H.

FIG. 37.

The adhesive weight of a locomotive is defined by the A. I. E. E. as "the sum of the weights on drivers and of the drivers themselves."[2] The ratio of the adhesive weight to the total weight of the locomotive varies from about 0.65 for large, high-speed passenger locomotives to 1.00 for freight and interurban locomotives. Interurban locomotive weights vary between the limits of 25 and 75 tons, 50 tons being an average weight. In heavy traction service, such as obtains on electrified steam lines, the

[1] See also "Standard Handbook for Electrical Engineers."

[2] *Proc.* A. I. E. E., August, 1914.

locomotive unit weights vary from 75 to 150 tons. A unit weighing about 100 tons seems to fit present requirements best.

The coefficient of adhesion is the ratio between the maximum tractive effort that can be exerted without slipping the drivers and the adhesive weight. Electric locomotives are often rated at 25 per cent adhesion; that is, the tractive effort which the motors can develop momentarily is 25 per cent of the adhesive weight. In Fig. 36 the dashed ordinate indicates the 25 per cent limit. When track conditions are bad, the maximum drawbar pull which a locomotive can exert is lowered because of the low coefficient of adhesion.

TABLE XI.—COEFFICIENT OF ADHESION[1]

	Per cent.		Per cent.
Most favorable condition	35	when sanded	40
Clean,dry rail	28	when sanded	30
Thoroughly wet rail	18	when sanded	24
Greasy,moist rail	15	when sanded	25
Sleet-covered rail	15	when sanded	20
Dry,snow-covered rail	11	when sanded	15

For a given speed, if

$T.E.$ = tractive effort of all motors on the locomotive,
$D.B.P.$ = drawbar pull of locomotive in pounds,
g = grade resistance in pounds per ton,
c = curve resistance in pounds per ton,
$r_1 = f_1 \pm g + c$,

the drawbar pull

$$D.B.P. = T.E. - W_1(f_1 \pm g + c) \qquad (62)$$
$$= T.E. - W_1 r_1.$$

Power Required for Train Haulage.—The power required for train haulage may now be calculated.

Let U = energy, in watt-hours, required to haul trailing load 1 mile (measured at drawbar).

U_t = energy in watt-hours, required to haul entire train 1 mile.

W = weight of trailing load in tons.

$r = (f \pm g + c)$ for trailing load.

P = power input required for the train, as measured at the drawbar, in kilowatts.

[1] BURCH, "Electric Traction for Railway Trains."

P_t = total power input to locomotive in kilowatts.

η = average efficiency from current collector to drive wheels.

From Eq. (53)

$$U = 1.99rW.$$

Therefore,

$$P = \frac{UV}{1,000} = \frac{1.99rWV}{1,000}. \tag{63}$$

The horsepower exerted at the drawbar will be

$$\frac{1,000P}{746} = \frac{1.99rWV}{746} = \frac{D.B.P. \times V}{375}. \tag{64}$$

If *T.E.* is substituted for *D.B.P.* in Eq. (64), the formula may be used to calculate the "horsepower at rim of drivers," or the brake horsepower of the locomotive. The total energy input required to haul the train 1 mile will be equal to the energy required to haul both cars and locomotive, divided by the efficiency of the locomotive, or

$$U_t = \frac{1.99rW + 1.99r_1W_1}{\eta} = \frac{1.99(rW + r_1W_1)}{\eta}.$$

The power input to the locomotive,

$$P_t = \frac{1.99V(rW + r_1W_1)}{1,000 \times \eta}. \tag{64.5}$$

For ordinary calculations $2r$ can be used instead of $1.99r$, in the preceding formulas, and η may be taken as 0.80. These formulas are based on the assumptions of constant speed and constant total train resistance, and therefore do not take into account the variable-speed and train-resistance conditions which obtain in practice. The average power input and the average energy input per train-mile for a given run calculated by using in these formulas the average speed and average total train resistance will be only approximate. Because of their convenience, however, the formulas are much used by engineers in making preliminary estimates and checking calculations. Where more accurate results are desired the power-time curve method, explained in Chap. VIII, may be used.

Determination of the Tonnage Rating of a Locomotive.—In order to assist the train crews and yardmaster in making up trains, and to prevent overloading of locomotives, railroad companies usually supply their operating men with a table of tonnage ratings which gives for each locomotive the number of trailing tons it can haul over the division of the road on which it is operated. The calculation of locomotive tonnage ratings is one of the common problems in train haulage. A solution of this problem can be best illustrated with an example.

It is desired to determine the tonnage rating of the locomotive whose characteristics are given in Fig. 36 for a section of road which has the following track conditions for a given direction of traffic:

Average grade............................ 0.2 per cent
Ruling grade............................ 1.1 per cent
Length of track section.................... 10   miles

The ruling grade which is located at the beginning of the section is 2,350 ft. in length, and the first 926 ft. of it is on a 3-deg. curve.

The average empty freight car weighs about 15 tons and the average loaded car on this road weighs about 60 tons. It is desired to calculate:

1. The number of loaded cars the locomotive can start on the ruling grade.

2. The number of empty cars the locomotive can start on the ruling grade.

3. The number of loaded cars the locomotive can haul at rated speed over the section.

4. The number of empty cars the locomotive can haul at rated speed over the section.

A solution of the problem, taking up its parts in the order above enumerated, follows:

1. The maximum tractive effort which the locomotive can momentarily exert (Fig. 36) is 50,000 lb. The train resistance of the locomotive at starting (Fig. 37) is 5.25 lb. per ton.

Experience has shown that, in order that a train may be started and brought up to speed under all ordinary track conditions, an accelerating force of about 15 lb. per ton of train weight must be allowed. The tractive force required by the locomotive at starting is

$$100(15 + 5.25 + 1.1 \times 20 + 3 \times 0.6) = 4,400 \text{ lb.}$$

(The curve resistance is here estimated at 0.6 per ton per degree of curve.)

The starting drawbar pull is, therefore,

$$50,000 - 4,400 = 45,600 \text{ lb.}$$

The train resistance f of a 60-ton freight car at starting (assumed to be equal to the resistance at 5 m.p.h.) is (Fig. 38)[1] 3.25 lb. per

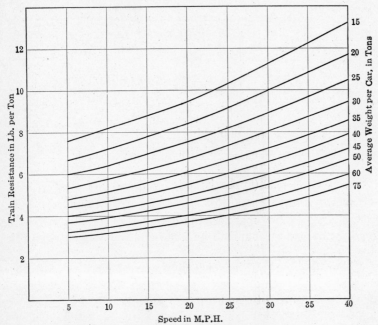

Fig. 38.—Freight car train resistance curves.

ton. The total train resistance r of one car for the given track conditions is

$$3.25 + 1.1 \times 20 + 3 \times 0.6 = 27.05 \text{ lb. per ton.}$$

The tractive force repuired at starting is

$$27.05 + 15 = 42.05 \text{ lb. per ton.}$$

$$\frac{45,600}{42.05} = 1,085 = \text{number of tons the locomotive can start}$$

on the ruling grade.

$$\frac{1,085}{60} = 18 \text{ (approximately)} = \text{number of cars.}$$

[1] From *Bull.* 43, Engineering Experiment Station, University of Illinois.

2. Proceeding in a similar manner, the empty-car tonnage and the number of empty cars will be found to be, respectively, 985 tons and 65 cars.

3. From Fig. 36 the continuous tractive effort of the locomotive is found to be 15,000 lb. and the corresponding speed, 17.4 m.p.h. The tractive force necessary to haul the locomotive at 17.4 m.p.h. is

$$W_1(f_1 + g) = 100(6.25 + \tfrac{2}{10} \times 20)$$
$$= 1,025 \text{ lb.}$$

The drawbar pull

$$D.B.P. = 15,000 - 1,025 = 13,975 \text{ lb.}$$

The tractive force necessary to haul 1 ton of the trailing load is

$$r = f + g = 3.9 + \tfrac{2}{10} \times 20 = 7.9 \text{ lb.}$$
$$\frac{13,975}{7.9} = 1,769 = \text{number tons trailing load.}$$
$$\frac{1,769}{60} = 29 \text{ (approximately)} = \text{number of cars.}$$

4. In a similar manner the number of trailing tons of empty cars will be found to be 1,065 and the number of empty cars 71.

Under adverse rail conditions the coefficient of adhesion would be less than 25 per cent and the values obtained in (1) and (2) would have to be decreased proportionately.

It is evident from the above results that the loaded-car tonnage rating of this locomotive for the given section of track is seriously limited by the ruling grade. Also, it is interesting to note that this locomotive can start on the ruling grade nearly as many empty cars as it can haul continuously at 17.4 m.p.h.

Since the motor current during the accelerating period is far above the continuous-current rating of the motors, it is usually necessary to check the motor heating for the run over a given section. A method of checking the motor heating will be explained under the heading of Speed,- Distance-, Current-, and Power-time curves.

Determination of the Locomotive Capacity Required for a Given Train.—This problem is the reverse of the preceding one, and, while ordinarily not so common, under present conditions of heavy electric traction where electric locomotives are required to haul over certain sections of road trains that are hauled over other sections by steam locomotives, it is a problem that the railway engineer is often called upon to solve.

With track and train conditions known, the drawbar pull and drawbar horsepower necessary to haul the train over the road can be readily computed by methods previously explained. The problem, then, is to find a locomotive which can develop the required drawbar pull at the required speed. The usual solution is a "cut-and-try" method. A locomotive which can develop the necessary drawbar horsepower (due allowance being made for excessive motor heating during accelerating periods) is selected and its gear ratio, or gear ratio and drive-wheel diameters, changed until a combination is found which will allow the locomotive to exert the required drawbar pull at the required speed.

Speed-, Distance-, Current-, and Power-time Curves.—In the solution of problems connected with locomotive train haulage, speed-time curves are used:

1. To determine whether or not a given locomotive hauling a given train can maintain a certain schedule speed.

2. To determine the running time required by a given locomotive to haul a given train over a given section of track.

3. To aid in the accurate determination of current-time and power-time curves and motor heating.

Since the runs of locomotive-hauled trains are usually much longer than those of motor-car-hauled trains, the time required for accelerating and braking is usually small as compared with the total time required to make the run. The "straight-line," speed-time curve, therefore, may be used with a very fair degree of accuracy in determinations (1) and (2), the constant-speed, or "balancing-speed," as it is often called, part of the curve being plotted for the speed at which the train resistance of the trailing load just balances the drawbar pull of the locomotive.

Determinations of the current- and power-time curves and motor heating require the use of the "cut-and-try" method of calculating the speed-time curves.

The heating of a series motor is proportional to the square of the current (copper losses only considered). The heating effect, then, for the time dt and current I will be proportional to $I^2 dt$. If these heating effect increments be integrated over the time t necessary to make a complete run and the summation be divided by the time t, the quotient will represent the square of a steady current which flowing for the time t would produce the same heating effect as was produced by the variable current that actually existed in the motor windings. As the continuous current rating of a motor for a given operating voltage can always be readily determined by test or secured from manufacturers' data, the root-mean-square current offers a convenient method of checking the motor heating of direct-current, series motors.

Concrete Example of Speed-, Distance-, Current-, and Power-time Curves and Motor-heating Calculations.—Given the following data:

100-ton, 600-volt locomotive (Fig. 36).

Trailing load of 18 sixty-ton cars or 1,080 trailing tons.

Track conditions and data as in paragraph on determination of tonnage rating.

Locomotive train resistance as in Fig. 37.

Car train resistance as in Fig. 38.

Braking rate 0.75 m.p.h./sec.

Required to determine:

1. Time necessary to make the run.

2. Average running speed.

3. The suitability of the locomotive from the standpoint of motor heating.

4. The energy input, in kilowatt-hours, required to make the run.

A force of 100 lb. per ton will be considered as necessary to accelerate the train 1 m.p.h./sec.

Let it be assumed that the motor connections during the "notching-up" period are (1) all motors in series, (2) motors in series parallel, (3) all motors in parallel, and that the "notching-up" time is equally divided among the three periods. It will also be assumed that the motor current is kept constant at 600 amp. during the "notching-up" period.

In dealing with locomotive-hauled trains it is more convenient to make this last assumption than to assume some definite rate of acceleration as was done in Chap. IX. Since those locomotives which are equipped with automatic controllers automatically keep the motor current constant during the notching-up period, and the ammeter equipment on locomotives not so equipped enables the engineman to keep the current constant during this period, the preceding assumption accords well with operating practice. It is also more convenient to use the tractive effort of the locomotive rather than that of a single motor in the speed-time curve calculations. Otherwise the method of calculating the various curves is the same as was explained in Chaps. VII and IX. Since the method was discussed in detail in Chap. IX, it has not been thought necessary to repeat the details of the calculations here. Table XII gives the results of the calculation and illustrates a convenient form of record for such calculations. If more accurate results are desired, average values of I, $T.E.$, and R may be used in the calculations.

It will be noted that the first and second total distance values do not quite correspond with the ends of the curve and 1.1 per cent grade respectively, but the error resulting from the assumption that they do so correspond is negligible. The braking time and distance were calculated from the known speed at the beginning of retardation and the rate of retardation.

The root-mean-square current as calculated is 251 amp. per motor, while the rated continuous current of the locomotive (Fig. 36) is 262 amp. This indicates that the loaded-car tonnage rating as previously calculated is all right from the standpoint of motor heating.

While the preceding calculations give all of the desired results, the various curves may be plotted if so desired and the areas under the speed-time and power-time curves used to check the values of total distance and energy consumption respectively.

Regenerative Braking.—By regenerative braking is meant the control of train speed by causing the motors to act as generators and to transform the kinetic energy of the moving train into electrical energy which is fed back into the trolley or contact line. The advantages and disadvantages of regenerative braking and the modifications necessary in the design of motors and control apparatus will be discussed in later chapters. In practice, regenerative braking has so far not been used in stopping trains but in controlling the speed of trains on heavy grades. If the trains are heavy and the descending grades long, considerable saving in electrical energy can be made, amounting in some particularly favorable instances to about 30 per cent.

TABLE XII.—SPEED, DISTANCE, CURRENT, POWER-TIME CURVE CALCULATIONS

Period	d_v	$V + d_v$	Motor I	Locomotive I	T.E.	Total resistance	Net T.E.	A	dt	$t + dt$	ds	$s + ds$	Motor $\frac{I^2dt}{1,000}$	Locomotive $\frac{EI}{1,000}$	$\frac{EIdt}{1,000}$
Notching up—															
Motors in series.....				600										360	13,500
Motors series parallel	13.2	13.2	600	1,200	46,200	32,400	13,800	0.117	112.5	112.5	1,090	1,090	40,500	720	27,000
Motors in parallel...				2,400										1,440	54,000
Acceleration on motor	1.3	14.5	455	1,820	33,000	30,600	2,400	0.020	65	177.5	1,320	2,410	13,500	1,092	71,000
characteristic.	2.0	16.5	295	1,180	18,000	9,370¹	8,630	0.073	27.4	204.9	624	3,034	2,390	708	19,400
	2.0	18.5	220	880	11,800	9,500¹	2,300	0.020	100	304.9	2,570	5,604	4,840	528	52,800
	0.5	19.0	205	820	10,600	9,675¹	925	0.008	62.5	367.4	1,720	7,324	2,630	492	30,700
Balancing speed.......		19.5	195	780	9,750	9,750¹	0,000	0.000	1,675	1,942.4	45,104	52,428	59,800	468	738,500
Braking.......		19.5	000	000	000	000	0,000	(−0.75)	26	1,968.4	372	52,800			
Totals.........									1,968.4		52,800	52,800	123,660		1,026,900

1,968.4 sec. = 0.546 hour = total time.
10/0.546 = 18.3 = average speed.
The square root of 123,660 × 1,000/1,968.4 = 251 = root-mean-square current.
1,026,900/3,600 = 285 = kw.-hr. required for run.
Balancing speed distance = 10 × 5,280 − (7,324 + 372) = 45,104 ft.

Balancing speed time = $\dfrac{45,104}{19.5 \times 14.67}$ = 1,575 sec.

¹ Calculated for average grade.

The power regenerated by a train descending a uniform grade at constant speed may be accurately calculated:

$$\text{Power output of locomotive} = \frac{1.99V(rW + r_1W_1)\eta}{1,000},$$

where the symbols used have the same significance as in Eq. (63).

As the grade resistance is negative, the result will have a negative sign, indicating that the transfer of energy is from the locomotive to the contact line instead of from contact line to locomotive. As this method does not take into account starting and stopping conditions, and the fact that most actual grades are more or less undulating, the general application of the formula gives results that are only approximate. On account of its convenience it is often used by engineers in making preliminary estimates and in checking the results obtained by other methods.

Where more accurate results are desired, speed-, distance-, current-, and power-time curves are plotted. The power-time curve should be plotted on the negative side of the axis for the periods during which the motors act as generators. The regenerated power at the various points along the line may then be read directly from the curve. The energy regenerated in descending a given grade may be calculated by integrating the power-time curve for that section of the track on which the grade occurs. Before these curves can be plotted, it will be necessary to secure curves similar to those shown in Fig. 20, but giving the characteristics of the motor when acting as a generator. These curves may be obtained either from design data before the motor is built or by test if the motor has been constructed. In plotting the speed-, distance-, current-, and power- time curves the curves for motor action must be used when the train is taking energy from the line and the curves for generator action when the train is supplying energy to the line.

CHAPTER XII

SUBSTATION AND POWER-STATION LOAD CURVES

Whereas the previous chapters have been devoted to the operation of cars and trains, with the ultimate object of determining the demands which they may make upon the power-distribution system, it is now necessary to study the combination of individual train demands and their connection with the average and maximum loads on the substation and power station.

The load curves of substation and power station have been treated simultaneously, since the substation of a large urban railroad or a relatively long interurban line acts as a source of power for the surrounding distribution system and therefore, as far as the determination of station output and capacity is concerned, it matters little whether the machines supplying the cars are in turn furnished with electrical power over a high-tension transmission line or whether they are driven by engines or turbines.

The most convenient units in which quickly to express the power demands of a train were found to be watt-hours per ton-mile. This demand was shown to vary greatly with schedule speed, weight of cars, condition and profile of track, length of run, etc. It is clear, therefore, that, except in very exceptional cases, a single value of energy cannot be applied for the entire length of an interurban run from terminal to terminal. Occasionally, however, with a straight, level right-of-way, with fairly constant schedule speed throughout the run, and with all cars of about the same size and weight, an average value of energy may be used for all cars for the entire run and the average substation demand for the day determined as follows:

U = energy in kilowatt-hours.

U_1 = energy of car in watt-hours per ton-mile.

W = weight of car in tons.

S_s = length of section supplied by station in miles.

N = number of trips in both directions over section per day
    determined from graphical train schedule.
$Eff.$ = efficiency of distribution system in per cent.

The energy demand upon the substation in a day is, therefore,

$$U = \frac{NWU_1S_s}{1,000 \times Eff.}.\qquad(65)$$

The average load on the station in kilowatts during the day is

$$L = \frac{U}{\text{Hours operation per day}}.\qquad(66)$$

If it were not for the excessive current taken during the acceleration period as compared with the full-speed running current,

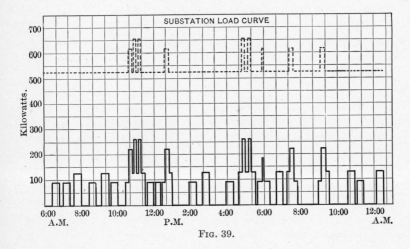

Fɪɢ. 39.

the maximum load on the station might be determined by multiplying the average power required per car (average ordinate of the kilowatt-time diagram, Fig. 30) by the maximum number of cars operating upon a single substation section at any one time. This method will usually give too low a maximum demand, however, and it is, therefore, necessary to find the maximum number of cars starting simultaneously on a single section. For such cars the maximum ordinate of the power-time curve (Fig. 30) must be used together with the average ordinate of the curves of such other cars as may be running upon the section at the same time. To determine correctly the number of cars starting at any one time, a great deal of judgment and knowledge of local conditions is necessary, in addition to a familiarity with the train schedule. If there be a siding located on the section, it is safe to assume at least two cars starting simultaneously.

While this method of determining average and maximum loads upon a substation has been successfully used in practice, especially where preliminary estimates only were involved and the runs between stations on a given section were quite similar in all respects, the more detailed method outlined below is usually finally adopted.

A series of speed-, current-, and kilowatt-time curves are plotted for the entire road, one curve for each run between stations. If more than one class of service, such as local, limited, freight, etc., is proposed, a similar series of curves must be plotted for each. From the kilowatt-time curves it is possible to scale off the area representing the energy taken by the car or train during any particular interval of time throughout the run. The combined areas of all these curves may readily be expressed in terms of kilowatt-hours per run or, better, the portion of the run which is shown by the time abscissa and train schedule to be on a given substation section may be thus treated. It is only necessary, therefore, to integrate all types of runs throughout the day on a given section in order to obtain the total energy and average load on the station in a similar manner to that of Eqs. (65) and (66).

The problem may be carried one step farther if necessary and the ordinates of kilowatt-time diagrams of all trains on the section for each increment of time may be added together to form the most accurate load diagram which it is possible to predetermine for the substation.

Many modifications of these two methods will present themselves to the engineer as best fitted to local conditions and to the degree of accuracy required. Figure 39, for example, is a load diagram made up of rectangular areas, each representing the average kilowatt-hour demand of all cars on one of the 12-mile substation sections of an existing interurban road at a given hour of the day. The average load on the station found by taking the average ordinate of this curve for the day is 69.3 kw., while the maximum demand from the upper curve plotted with reference to the possible number of cars starting simultaneously on the section is 655 kw.

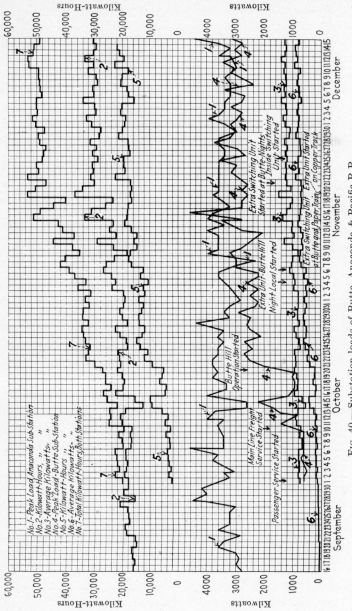

FIG. 40.—Substation loads of Butte, Anaconda & Pacific R.R.

In plotting station load curves by whatever method, it must be remembered that most roads have not only the daily fluctuations of load which will be shown by the peaks of the load-time curve

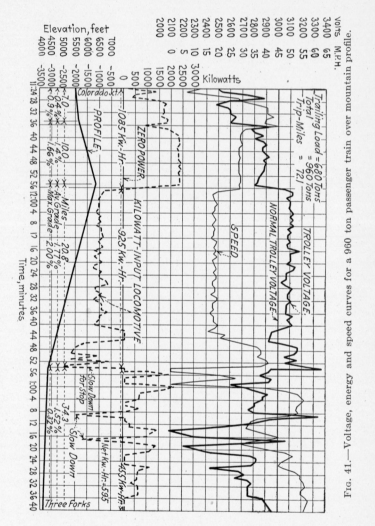

Fig. 41.—Voltage, energy and speed curves for a 990 ton passenger train over mountain profile.

plotted for a single day, but there is usually considerable difference between the load curves for the various seasons of the year, even the train schedule being changed for one of less headway in the summer season. This fact, together with the possibility of sudden daily demands due to special attractions along the line of the interurban road, especially upon holidays, must be given careful attention in applying load curves to the location and design of substations and power stations.

Such daily variations in power expressed in kilowatts and energy measured in kilowatt-hours throughout several months of the year are indicated for two of the substations of the Butte, Anaconda & Pacific Ry. in a very interesting manner in the chart of Fig. 40, which has been reproduced from the *General Electric Review*. The effect which starting the various types of electrified service has upon the load curves of each substation is made evident upon the chart by the indication of the dates upon which such services were started. The general upward trend of the total and average energy curves during the winter months, when additional demands occur, is also significant.

The demands for power made upon a substation from one minute to the next by an electrically operated 960-ton passenger train over the Rocky Mountain division of the Chicago, Milwaukee & St. Paul Ry. are plotted in Fig. 41. The effects of the grade as indicated by the profile traversed by the train at the moment the power log was made, and the indirect effect of the grade upon trolley voltage, are of particular interest. As the train coasts down the incline the reversal of power is noted, during which period the 2,400- and 3,000-volt electric locomotives generate electrical power and deliver it to the substation as indicated by the portion of the curve below the zero line. Incidentally, this is an excellent illustration of the regenerative braking principle described in the previous chapter.

Load Factor.—The "load factor" of a station or system is defined as the ratio:

$$\frac{\text{Average power} \times 100}{\text{Maximum power demand}} \text{ per cent.} \qquad (67)$$

Thus the load factor, as determined from the load curve of the substation in this particular case, is,

$$\frac{69.3 \times 100}{655} = 10.6 \text{ per cent.}$$

The load factor should be determined and expressed for a definite period of time, such as a day, month, or year, the power being averaged throughout the period of time for which the load factor is calculated. The maximum power demand is usually taken over a short interval representing the maximum load during the period in question.

The proper interval to select, such as a 15-min. or half-hourly maximum demand, and also the period over which the load factor is to be determined are subject to local conditions and the purpose for which the load factor is to be used. Perhaps the most common relation is the "half-hour monthly" load factor.

An equivalent definition of monthly load factor, making use of energy units, is sometimes more conveniently expressed as

$$\frac{\text{Kilowatt-hours output for month} \times 100}{\text{Maximum power demand} \times \text{hours in month}} \text{ per cent. (68)}$$

It is, of course, desirable to maintain as high a load factor as possible, since it follows that the greatest energy output for a given investment necessary to meet maximum demands is obtained under conditions of high load factor. Yet in interurban railway operation where traffic is relatively light and trains few in number, it is hardly possible to improve conditions of load factor to any great extent over the particular case which has been used as an illustration. An average load factor obtained from the railway census for 20 representative interurban systems was 28.8 per cent, while that of a similar number of large city railways was 32.6 per cent. However, the problem of higher load factors and more effective use of available station power throughout all hours of the day and all seasons of the year is rather intimately correlated with the following considerations.

Station or Plant Factor.—The load factor of a particular generating or substation is often confused with the so-called "plant factor" or "station factor," which is more correctly defined for a corresponding definite period as

$$\text{Station factor} = \frac{\text{Average power output} \times 100}{\text{Rated power capacity of station}} \text{ per cent. (69)}$$

Obviously, with adequate reserve capacity in the station, the station factor may be expected to be considerably lower than the load factor for the same period of time. With very large systems, however, with several interconnected power stations and substations, it has been possible to furnish a variety of classes of service having their maximum demands at different hours of the day or during different seasons, thereby greatly improving the load factor and the efficiency and economy of operation.

Diversity Factor.—Such operation involves the diversity factor, which is a measure of the variety of demands upon the system. It is defined as the ratio of the sum of the maximum power demands of the subdivisions of any system or parts of a system to the maximum demand of the whole system or of the part of the system under consideration, measured at the point of supply or, more concisely,

$$\text{Diversity factor} = \frac{\text{Sum of maximum demands}}{\text{Actual maximum demand}}. \quad (70)$$

Several such maxima occurring at different hours will not produce a single maximum demand equal to their arithmetical sum. In other words, the peaks of one type of load help to fill the valleys of the load curves of other types of service. Thus both the energy and the average power are greater for a given station maximum demand or for a particular rating of station capacity. The diversity factor, usually expressed as an integer, should, therefore, be as high as possible.

The arithmetical difference between the sum of several power demands and the corresponding single maximum demand upon a system is frequently expressed in terms of a diversity of power measured in kilowatts or horsepower. The greater such a difference can be made the more efficient and economical is the operation of the system.

One of the best examples in this country of economical generation and distribution of electrical energy resulting in very high load factors and diversity factors is that of the Commonwealth Edison Company of Chicago. The following abstract is taken from a recent address by Samuel Insull before the Western Society of Engineers, to illustrate the timely significance of high load factors and great diversity of loads upon a single generating system. The city railway, the elevated road, and some of the interurban roads in Chicago are supplied with electrical energy from the same system as the light and power demands of the city and surrounding territory. In 1922 about twice as much electrical energy was required to supply lighting and industrial demands in Chicago as it took to supply the railways. If the steam railroads entering Chicago were electrified they also would require about one-half the lighting and power needs. The coincident demand of all three types of service would be 959,500 kw., while the sum of the three individual maxima would be

1,110,500 kw.   Thus a diversity factor of 1.16 would be experienced between the various classes of loads or, in other words, an actual diversity of 151,000-kw. capacity of generating equipment would be conserved.

Mr. Insull went on to say:

If you will take that saving of 151,000 kw., and figure it out at $100 per kilowatt, which is a very low price for central stations at this time, and allow a 25 per cent reserve, that diversity would save an investment of $18,120,000.   And if you go a little further and include the diversity that exists between the city and country districts, the diversity is increased to about 170,000 kw.   The saving in serving all of these various organizations, with energy produced from the same source, would be upward of $20,000,000, not figuring anything for the electrification of the steam railroads outside the switching area.

Diversity factors must be considered with respect to the class of service with which it is associated before it may be classed as "satisfactory" or too low, for example, a diversity factor of 3 or 4 may be experienced between residence and industrial loads which will not effect the savings which this factor of 1.16 will provide between large blocks of wholesale industrial energy.   A carefully worded load-factor clause is, therefore, often to be found in contracts involving the sale of large amounts of energy.

CHAPTER XIII

DISTRIBUTION SYSTEM

The circuit which the propulsion current for a car follows extends from the feeder panel of the substation over the outgoing feeders and trolley to the car motors, thence through the rails back to the substation switchboard or, in some cases, directly to the negative terminal of the converter. The voltage at the substation is maintained constant, usually at 550 or 600 volts. The current flowing over the above circuit causes a drop of potential in proportion to the resistance of the entire circuit, in accordance with Ohm's law. This fall of potential subtracted from the substation potential determines the voltage at the car. As the latter voltage should be as high and as constant as possible if good service is to be maintained, it follows that the resistance of the feeders and track return should be carefully proportioned. The latter will be discussed in detail under the subject of Bonds and Bonding, Chap. XVII, while this chapter will be devoted to the study of the overhead trolley and feeder system.

On interurban roads and often in the city systems the trolley is sectionalized by the introduction of circuit breakers in the trolley wire which insulate one section from another. Cables from either side of the breaker are carried to a pole switch by means of which the sections may be connected together if necessary. Each section is generally supplied with power from a single substation through the agency of feeders paralleling the trolley for a portion of its length. The trolley wire itself for mechanical reasons is usually from No. 00 to No. 0000[1] B. & S. gage, hard-drawn copper, and is occasionally installed double with wires about 6 in. apart but electrically connected at every hanger. Where the current required is considerable this practice is very commendable, for the second trolley replaces an equal amount of copper which would otherwise be installed in the insulated feeder and, what is of greater consequence, it eliminates all overhead switches

[1] For standards and specifications, see manual A. E. R. A.

115

and frogs in the trolley wire at sidings, the wires being spread as the tracks are separated, the car trolley always remaining on the right wire.   With the size of trolley given, together with a well-bonded track of known weight and resistance, the problem resolves itself into one of feeder design.

Since the problem is necessarily treated differently for inter-urban and urban roads, the former will be first considered.   The minimum permissible voltage at the car under the worst conditions must first be assumed.   While this voltage drops at times in interurban practice to 250 volts, a value of at least 350 volts should be used.   This allows a 250-volt drop in the distribution

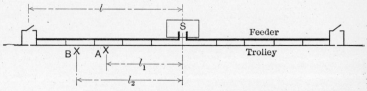

Fig. 42.—Continuous feeder distribution.

system under maximum traffic conditions.   Reference to the train schedule will determine this maximum condition, which usually involves two cars starting simultaneously and possibly others operating on the same section.   Assuming the simplest form of distribution (Fig. 42), with the feeder paralleling the trolley for the entire length of the section and tapping into it sufficiently often so that they may be considered as one wire of large section, the following solution may be outlined:

$e =$ permissible voltage drop.

$l =$ one-half length of section in feet.

$l_1 =$ distance of car (A) in feet.

$l_2 =$ distance of two cars at B in feet.

$I_A =$ current taken by one car at A.

$I_B =$ current taken by two cars at B.

$R_T =$ resistance per foot of track (two rails).

$R_{FT,} =$ combined resistance per foot of feeder and trolley.

$r =$ resistance of copper per mil-foot.

As in mechanics, the combined loads I_A and I_B, determined from the current-time curve, may be considered as acting through the equivalent distance l_g of the center of gravity of load from the substation where

$$l_g = \frac{I_A l_1 + I_B l_2}{I_A + I_B}.$$ (71)

Volts drop in track $e_{Tr} = l_g R_T (I_A + I_B)$. (72)

Allowable drop in feeder and trolley

$$e_{FT} = e - l_g R_T (I_A + I_B)$$ (73)

$$R_{FT} = \frac{e - l_g R_T (I_A + I_B)}{(I_A + I_B) l_g}.$$ (74)

Combined area of feeder and trolley in

$$\text{Circular mils} = \frac{r}{R_{FT}}.$$ (75)

Having determined the necessary combined area of feeder and trolley from Eq. (75), or from the wire tables, the known area of the trolley wire or wires may be subtracted and the necessary size of feeder remains.

Assume for illustration, two cars, whose current-time curves are represented in Fig. 29, starting 3 miles from the substation and a similar car running at full speed 2 miles from station. The trolley consists of two No. 4/0 B. & S. wires and the track is of 70-lb. rail with 9-in. bonds equivalent to one-half the rails in conductivity. The resistance of copper may be taken as 10.6 ohms per mil.-foot.

Armstrong gives the resistance of third rail and track with the above bonding in the following table:

TABLE XIII.—RESISTANCE OF THIRD RAIL AND TRACK

Wt. of rail per yard	40	50	60	70	80	90	100	110
Third rail resistance, ohms per mile........	0.093	0.074	0.062	0.053	0.046	0.042	0.038	0.034
Third track rails resistance, ohms per mile.................	0.066	0.053	0.044	0.038	0.033	0.029	0.027	0.024

I_A from Fig. 29 = 672 amp.

$$I_B = 160 \text{ amp.}$$

$$l_g = \frac{5,280(672 \times 3 + 160 \times 2)}{832} = 14,800 \text{ ft.} = 2.8 \text{ miles.}$$ (71)

Volts drop in track $= 832 \times 0.038 \times 2.8 = 88.5$ volts. (72)

Allowable drop in feeder and trolley = 161.5 volts.   (73)

$$R_{FT} = \frac{161.5}{832 \times 14{,}800} = 0.0000131, \text{ or } 0.0131 \text{ ohm per } 1{,}000 \text{ ft.}$$

Corresponding area from wire table = 800,000 cm.

Two 4/0 trolley wires = 423,200 cm.

Feeder section = 376,800 cm.

Either a standard 350,000- or 400,000-cm. cable might be chosen.

If, in place of isolated sections of trolley, the wires be continuous from terminal to terminal and the substations connected in parallel with one another between trolley and rail, such a problem as that assumed above would involve the determination of the portion of the current per car which was supplied from each of

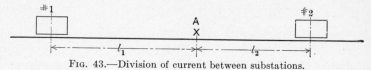

Fig. 43.—Division of current between substations.

the two adjacent stations. Here again the principles of mechanics may be applied as illustrated in Fig. 43, where A is a car at distances l_1 and l_2 from substations No. 1 and 2 respectively. If the car is drawing a current I_A it may be safely assumed that its current demand on substation No. 1 is

$$I_1 = \frac{I_2 I_A}{l_1 + l_2}, \tag{76}$$

while the current taken from No. 2 is

$$I_2 = \frac{l_1 I_A}{l_1 + l_2}. \tag{77}$$

With this understanding a problem in feeder calculation similar to the above offers no additional difficulties.

Each half of the section in Fig. 42 was considered independently of the other for the reason that the feeders and trolleys of the two halves of the section are in parallel and, therefore, the voltage drop in one does not affect the other. The solution of a problem with the substation located at the end of the section would, therefore, be treated in a similar manner.

In many cases, however, feeders are tapped into the trolley at infrequent points, thus forming a network whose calculation is slightly more involved. Such a condition is illustrated in Fig. 44. The feeder is tapped to the trolley at the two points a and

b at distances from the station of l and l_1, respectively. Two cars are starting at B at a distance l_2 from the station with total current I_B.

$$\text{Volts drop in track} = I_B R_T l_2. \qquad (78)$$

Allowable drop in feeder and trolley $e_{FT} = e - I_B R_T l_2.$ (79)

In any branched circuit problem such as this it is always most convenient to make use of Kirchhoff's laws, which may be stated as follows:

First, "At any point in a circuit, the sum of the currents directed toward the point is equal to the sum of those directed away from it."

Second, "In any closed circuit the algebraic sum of the IR drops is equal to that of the e.m.fs."

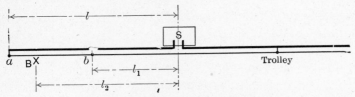

Fig. 44.—Feeders with infrequent taps.

While in this simple problem it is obvious without stating such a law that the current entering the cars at B is the sum of the two currents arriving at B by the two paths from a and b, respectively, and also that the drop in potential between B and b must be the same by either path, yet in complicated networks, especially in city streets, the statement of Kirchhoff's laws in this form is most acceptable.

The resistance from b to B direct is that of $(l_2 - l_1)$ ft. of trolley, or

$$R_{bB} = R_W(l_2 - l_1), \qquad (80)$$

if R_W represents the resistance of the trolley per foot. The corresponding resistance by path a is

$$R_{aB} = R_W(l - l_2) + R_F(l - l_1), \qquad (81)$$

with R_F representing resistance of feeder per foot. The currents in the two branches may now be calculated from the two equations

$$I_B = I_a + I_b \qquad (82)$$

$$\frac{I_a}{I_b} = \frac{R_{bB}}{R_{aB}}. \qquad (83)$$

With the current in each branch known, the fall of potential between point b and the car B may be determined from either of the equations

$$e_{aB} = I_a(R_{aB} + R_{ba}) \tag{84}$$

$$e_{bB} = I_b R_{bB}. \tag{85}$$

That these two drops in voltage are identical will be shown more conclusively by substituting in Eq. 84 the value of current I_a obtained from Eq. 83.

As the total current I_B is flowing through the feeder between b and S, the additional drop over this distance is

$$e_{bS} = I_B R_F l_1.$$

The total drop in the overhead conductors between substation and car is, therefore,

$$e_1 = I_B R_{bB} + I_B R_F l_1. \tag{86}$$

If the feeder had been tapped into the trolley at the substation S in addition to the other taps, a second network would have been added to the calculation, but the method of solution would not have been changed. In fact, any network may be readily solved with the use of Kirchhoff's laws, if taken step by step.

City Systems.—The principal difference between the calculation of urban and interurban feeder systems is that in the former it is necessary to consider a large number of cars per section, each drawing an average current, which may be readily determined from their relative current-time curves or from actual tests with meters on the car if the road is already in operation. Such sections may ordinarily be considered as uniformly loaded without serious error.

Such a section, represented by Fig. 45, may be treated as a uniformly loaded beam in mechanics, and in place of using the individual values of current taken by each car at a, b, c, etc., the total current of all cars on the section combined may be considered as being taken from the midpoint, distant $\frac{l}{2}$ ft. from the station. The correctness of this method may be readily proved by integrating the voltage drops $irdl$ between the limits of zero and the length of the line l, where i represents the current per foot and r the resistance per foot, respectively. Having now but the single equivalent current to consider, the problem may be solved as in the case of interurban systems previously described.

Although the limiting voltage drop is always the first consideration in railway feeders, it is well to check the safe carrying capacity of the cable selected by the above methods with the actual current which is flowing therein, the safe carrying capacities for open wiring being readily found in any electrical handbook.

Financial Considerations.—While the foregoing calculations will give the proper size of feeder to be installed for a given minimum potential at the car, it may be found that, because of too great an assumed distance between stations or for other reasons, the cost of the copper is prohibitive. Some consideration must, therefore, be given to the amount of power lost in the distribution system, and the relation of its annual cost to the interest and depreciation on the copper to be installed.

If the I^2R losses be summed up for each portion of the distribution section or if this same total loss be obtained from the

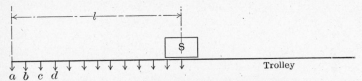

Fig. 45.—Uniformly loaded distribution section.

product of the squared current by the equivalent resistance of the overhead conductors and rail return, the efficiency of the distribution system and the annual cost of power lost in distribution may be determined from the following equations:

Efficiency distribution system =

$$\frac{\text{Power delivered to car}}{\text{Power delivered to car} + I^2R \text{ loss}}. \quad (87)$$

Annual cost of distribution loss $= \left(\dfrac{I^2R \text{ loss}}{1{,}000} \times \text{hours per year} \right) \times$
$\left\{ \begin{array}{l} \text{Cost of power} \\ \text{in cents per kilo-} \\ \text{watt hour at} \\ \text{direct-current} \\ \text{busses of substa-} \\ \text{tion.} \quad\quad (88) \end{array} \right.$

Kelvin's law states that the most economical size of feeder to install is that in which the annual cost of power loss is equal to the interest and depreciation figured on first cost of installation. As the annual cost of power loss for a given length of feeder and current transmitted will decrease, while the interest and the depreciation charges will increase as the size of the cable increases, curves of these costs plotted with the size of cable as abscissæ will intersect at the most economical size of wire to be installed. Such curves plotted for a current of 100 amp. in 1,000 ft. of feeder with interest taken at 6 per cent and deprecia-

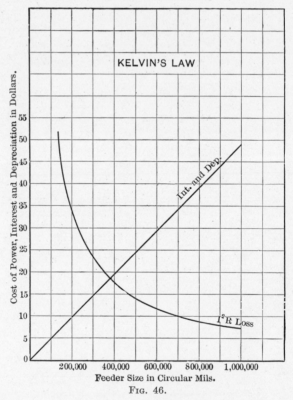

Feeder Size in Circular Mils.
Fig. 46.

tion at 2 per cent will be found from Fig. 46 to determine a feeder size of 375,000-cm. section, for which either the 350,000- or 400,000-cm. standard size might be selected. The calculations from which these curves were plotted involved a cost of power of 1 ct. per kilowatt-hour and a cost of copper installed of 20 cts. per pound.

Since any one of these feeder calculations taken by itself may give results which are unfavorable when all requirements of the

distribution system are considered, it is the duty of the engineer
to calculate the proper feeder sizes necessary for a satisfactory
line drop, to check these calculations for carrying capacity and by
Kelvin's law, and then to determine the relative weight to be
given to the considerations of fall of potential, carrying capacity,
and relative cost of power loss in the particular system in question.[1]

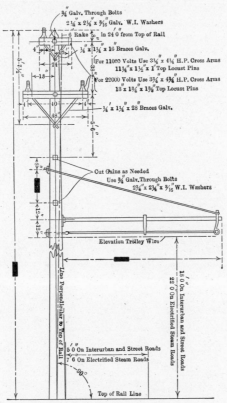

Fig. 47.—Typical bracket construction.

Types of Systems.—The various systems of electric railway
distribution of power may be classified with regard to structure
and working potential. Where structure is considered, it is
found that the systems group themselves into the simple over-

[1] See also CRECELIUS, L. P. and PHILLIPS, VICTOR B., "The Economics of
Direct-Current Railway Distribution, with Particular Reference to the
Automatic Substation," *Trans.* A. I. E E., vol. 41, p. 417, 1922.

head trolley with bracket or span construction, the third-rail, and the so-called catenary construction.

Bracket and Span Construction.—Typical forms of bracket and span construction are familiar to all because of their very general use in city and interurban installations.   Figure 47 indicates a satisfactory standard of bracket design, while Fig. 48 combines the span type of trolley suspension with a double-track roadway and duplicate three-phase transmission lines.

Hard-drawn grooved trolley wire of 2/0 or 4/0 B. & S. gage is now almost universally used with mechanical clamping ears.

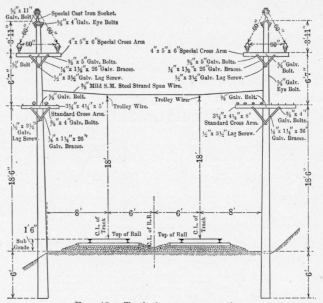

FIG. 48.—Typical span construction.

The latter are hung from the insulating hangers or cones and are made to grip the groove in the trolley wire by means of machine screws.   Much time and maintenance cost is saved with this mechanical construction as compared with the older soldered ears.   Double insulation is provided between pole and trolley wire by means of an insulating hanger and the strain insulator in series.   The latter insulators in span construction should be sufficiently near the trolley wire so that a broken "live" span cannot reach the ground, and yet they should be sufficiently distant therefrom that a trolley pole cannot make contact with the live trolley wire and the insulated span wire simultaneously.

Poles are usually spaced from 80 to 125 ft. apart, the lesser spacing being used on curves. Poles should be guyed on curves transversely with the line and anchors installed to take longitudinal strains at least every mile. With the present high cost of lumber it seems worth while to treat at least the butts of poles with preservative compound before installation, and it is often desirable to treat the entire pole. The poles should at least be kept well painted, even upon interurban lines. Iron and concrete poles have found a place in the city streets, principally because of their ornamental appearance. The corrosion of iron poles can be held in check by frequent painting and by setting butts in concrete. In fact, the latter method is often used for the protection of wooden poles even after they have begun to decay at the surface of the ground.

Detailed specifications applicable to the material used in the simpler types of overhead distribution systems may be secured from the "Manual of the American Electric Railway Association" or the *Transactions* of the National Electric Light Association.

The Third Rail.—The third rail presents one solution of the high-speed, heavy-current collection problem. The conductor in this case consists of rails well bonded together and supported on insulators. These insulators are placed on the ends of extra long ties spaced every sixth to tenth tie, so that the third rail is at one side and slightly above the running rail. At grade crossings there is necessarily a break in the third rail, but the conductor is made continuous by means of a copper cable laid in conduit under the crossing. The current is collected from the rail by contact shoes of iron, one or more of which are carried by each motor car. These shoes ordinarily are pressed down on the head of the rail by their own weight, but the protected rail is inverted and the contact shoe is held up against the rail head by means of springs.

The third rail is supplied with power at various points by means of feeders, as in ordinary trolley construction. The calculations for third-rail installations are the same as for the ordinary direct-current trolley distribution system, the resistance of the third rail, (Table XIII) being used in place of that of the trolley wire.

This system is used mainly in 600-volt, direct-current service, although there are several installations of 1,200-volt, third-rail in operation. Some companies have gone so far as to use the third rail as a direct-current potential of 2,400 and 3,000 volts on part of their systems. The danger of the third rail to human life restricts its use to private right-of-way on interurban lines and to elevated or tunnel installations in cities.

Catenary.—The catenary system of distribution was devised to eliminate the troubles that are necessarily attendant upon high-speed operation when the overhead trolley is used as a collector. The supports at the end of each span of the simple overhead trolley wire act as rigid points in the otherwise flexible

Fig. 49.—Rigid catenary construction, N. Y., N. H. & H. R. R.

conductor, thus resulting in a tendency of the trolley wheel to leave the wire at these points, particularly at high speeds.

For most successful high-speed operation the common rule for a railroad track may be applied to the track of the current collector. The track must be level and either uniformly rigid or uniformly flexible. Under these conditions a current collector will move smoothly upon the distributing conductor.

The catenary construction is a direct result of single-phase, alternating-current distribution development. The high voltages used in the single-phase system make a conductor so near the ground as a third rail undesirable and one as large as a third rail unnecessary for current-carrying capacity. The overhead trolley was, therefore, improved for use at high speeds, resulting in the so-called catenary construction. The New York, New Haven & Hartford system (Fig. 49) is an example of rigid catenary construction. Nearly all the other styles of catenary are of the uniformly flexible type and are much more simple and economical.

A simple form of catenary construction (Fig. 50) consists of a single messenger wire and a trolley wire, the messenger wire being supported with the proper amount of sag by insulators on the bracket arms of the poles, on cross-spans, or the horizontal members of the bridges at the end of each span. The trolley wire

Fig. 50.—Single catenary construction, N. Y., N. H. & H. R. R.

is supported in a level position from this messenger by means of hangers of varying lengths. Most installations use an 11-point suspension of the trolley in a span of 150 ft. This construction was considered by some engineers as of not sufficiently uniform flexibility on account of the larger weight of the longer hangers near the span supports. The design was, therefore, modified by the hanging of a third wire, the trolley, from the second wire. This wire is supported by equal-weight hangers, which are free to move vertically. The result is a level, uniformly flexible trolley, moving through the same vertical distance at any point in the span for a given pressure of the collector.   The collectors used on catenary construction are either the ordinary trolley wheel at the end of a trolley pole or a roller contactor mounted on a bow or pantograph.   These are described in a later chapter.

From the standpoint of working potential the classes of distribution systems are:

1. Low-voltage direct current.
2. High-voltage direct current.
3. Three-phase alternating current.
4. Single-phase alternating current.

Under the heading of low-voltage direct current (550 to 600 volts) are found practically all the city street-car lines, since city ordinances in this country, as a rule, prevent the use of higher voltages on public streets.   A good many interurban lines are also equipped with this system.   Ordinarily, trolley suspension or third-rail construction is used on these low voltages.

A few years ago high-voltage, direct-current railway systems were considered more or less of an experiment.   Since the 1,200-volt systems have proved their merit, 2,400- and 3,000-volt potentials have been installed and have already demonstrated their success.

The feature which has made this high-voltage direct-current supply possible is the commutating pole.   It has eliminated the commutator troubles of high-voltage, direct-current generators and synchronous converters and has made possible the successful operation of high-voltage motors.

Many roads in the United States have been equipped for 1,200-, 1,500-, 2,400-, or 3,000-volt, direct-current operation. By far the greater number of these use the catenary construction. Their distribution systems are not essentially different from those operating at a potential of 600 volts.   The potential is applied between trolley and rail and the trolley is paralleled with feeders whenever necessary.

Three-phase supply of alternating-current power to the electric locomotive has not been very popular in this country thus far, although wherever it has been used it has proved successful. Probably the most unfavorable feature is the use of at least two trolley wires and a motor of constant-speed characteristics. A good example of three-phase installation in the United States is furnished by the Great Northern electrification of the Cascade Tunnel. The power is furnished at high tension to the transformers on the locomotive through the agency of the two trolley wires and the track. One side of the track only is bonded and grounded. A double trolley pole equipped with collecting wheels is used. In place of trolley poles one Swiss railway makes use of a bow with roller collectors. The trolley wires are spaced farther apart than in the Great Northern installation and the two roller collectors, separated by insulating material, make contact with the wires.

Some of the more recent electrified steam railroads handling heavy through passenger and freight traffic have retained the advantages of high-voltage current distribution and collection with a single-phase overhead conductor and track return, together with the corresponding advantages of polyphase and direct-current motors, by installing either phase converters of alternating- to direct-current rotary converters or motor generators, respectively, upon the locomotives.

The Norfolk & Western phase-converter locomotives providing for single-phase trolley and two-phase drive and the very recent decision on the part of the New York, New Haven & Hartford R. R. to contract for locomotives with direct-current motors supplied by a motor generator and single-phase trolley represent notable examples of such installations. This rolling-stock equipment is described more in detail in a later chapter, but the point of importance here is the extent to which railroad engineers will go in order to take advantage of the economy and convenience of operation of high-voltage, single-wire trolley with track return circuit.

CHAPTER XIV

SUBSTATION LOCATION AND DESIGN

Probably no question which the engineer of a proposed electric-railway system has to decide is more dependent upon good engineering judgment and common sense than that of the location of substations and power stations. Many theoretical rules and formulas have been devised for calculating the most economical location of such a station and many of these must be given consideration and granted their proper weight in the final decision, but they are of little value when taken alone and often lead to serious errors when given too much prominence or when adopted with too little reference to local engineering and financial relations.

With this foreword a few of the most important of these theories will be discussed, their relative importance being decided in each case by local and particularly by financial conditions. If the distinction between the design of alternating-current substations for single-phase lines and substations supplying 600-volt direct current as subsequently outlined is kept in mind, the following considerations may readily be applied to either type of station.

Substation Location.—When considering a substation whose function it is to supply power to a network of lines in a limited district of a large city system, one of the important considerations, as in the case of the power station, is to locate the station as nearly as possible at the center of gravity of the load. This center of gravity may be conveniently determined graphically as in problems in mechanics as follows: Locate the principal centers of distribution in the district, such as prominent street crossings and points from which several feeders radiate, and determine the average load at these points as well as the distances between them. These may be graphically represented as in Fig. 51, with the loads considered as weights at the corners of the diagram which is drawn to a convenient scale of distance. The center of

130

gravity of the loads A and B would, obviously, be at E where $\dfrac{AE}{BE} = \dfrac{500}{200}$ and AB or $(AE + BE) = 1.5$ miles, while D and C might be combined into a single load of 1,650 kw. at F where

$$\frac{DF}{CF} = \frac{1,000}{650}.$$

The center of gravity of E and F with loads of 700 and 1,650, respectively, located at G will, therefore, be the center of gravity of the system, and from the standpoint alone of supplying the loads most economically this should be the location of the station.

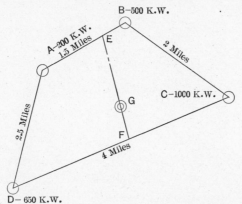

FIG. 51.—Center of gravity of power demands.

With the more common problem, however, of locating substations for interurban lines where the loads are usually located in a single straight line, the question to be decided is how far apart the stations should be placed in the single direction and therefore how many and what capacity stations are necessary. The maximum distance between stations is limited by the voltage of the distribution system and in the case of the more common 600-volt, direct-current distribution the distance between stations seldom exceeds 12 miles, each station feeding 6 miles in either direction. Whether this distance shall be diminished or slightly increased in each particular case depends largely upon the following considerations.

As the number of substations for a given road is increased and, therefore, the distance between them diminished, the governing factors will vary as outlined below.

The total cost of buildings and real estate will usually increase in direct proportion to the increase in the number of stations. This statement is, of course, subject to the qualification that such spacing of stations does not locate one or more of them in the centers of towns or cities, or in such other places as may increase their cost from the standpoint of high land values or expensive architectural effects.

The cost of attendance will increase directly with the number of stations as the increased capacity of the fewer stations would seldom, if ever, require more attendants than the small station unless the station were located in a congested city district where the high cost of real estate necessitated double decking the station.

The substation equipment will cost more with the increased number of stations, but not proportionately more. Whereas much of the equipment will have to be duplicated with each station that is added and although the cost of small units is greater per kilowatt capacity than that of large machines, yet if all the stations considered are of fairly large capacity the relay capacity necessary for overloads of long duration and for emergency use will not be as great with an increased number of stations. This may be illustrated by assuming a total average demand upon all substations of 2,000 kw. If two substations are decided upon, it would be good practice to install three 500-kw. units in each, or a total of 3,000 kw., thus leaving one 500-kw. machine in each station as a relay. If, however, four stations seem advisable of 500-kw. average demand each, it is probable that three 250-kw. units would be used in each station requiring the same total of 3,000 kw. While the switchboards, wiring, lightning protection, etc. would, therefore, cost double the amount for the four stations, the machines and transformers would be increased in cost only by the increase per kilowatt of small as compared with large units, which increase between units of 250 and 500 kw. is not great. Where the total demand on all stations is much less than that assumed in this case, however, the small station is at a disadvantage with respect to relay capacity and the increased cost of equipment may equal if not exceed the rate of increase in the number of stations.

The losses in substation machinery will increase slightly with increase in the number of stations because of the lower efficiency of smaller units and the increased no-load losses of the larger number of machines running light or idle for a portion of the time as is often the case in interurban stations.

The cost of distribution copper and the losses in the distribution system will decrease with the increase in the number of stations, as the length and therefore the cost and resistance of feeders will decrease as the stations are moved nearer together.

In order to reduce all of these quantities to common terms for comparison, an annual charge representing a certain predetermined percentage of the first costs involved must be combined with the annual cost of attendance, maintenance, and power losses. This percentage of the first cost which becomes an annual charge in all estimates of this nature is termed a "fixed charge" and involves interest on investment, taxes if any, insurance, and depreciation on the equipment. This charge may be accurately estimated in each instance, but is often assumed a total of 15 per cent of the first cost whenever local conditions are such as not to eliminate any of the above-mentioned items involved in its make-up. If, therefore, a curve be plotted between ordinates representing the sum of fixed charges, annual cost of power losses, and maintenance and abscissæ expressed in terms of number of substations, the total annual cost curve will result. Because of the fact that some of the factors are increasing and some decreasing with an increase in the number of stations, a minimum point on the curve will be found which will denote the proper number of substations to install and, therefore, the distance between stations, considered solely from the standpoint of the factors involved in the curve.

Such a method as that outlined above appears rather involved, requiring as it does at least a tentative station location, design of equipment, and feeder-loss calculation for each group of stations considered. Since the capacity alone and not the detailed plan of the station changes with an increased number of stations, and as the feeder losses in an interurban system will vary approximately in proportion to the length of the feeders, the number of calculations necessary for such a curve is not great and, as the cost variations when thus graphically plotted are easily studied and compared, the solution is well worthy of serious consideration. Chapter XIII on the Distribution System will aid materially in the construction of these curves.

It will be noted that nothing was said regarding the variation of transmission-line costs and losses in the above discussion. While these factors may occasionally enter the problem for city stations with underground high-tension lines, yet for inter-urban installations the transmission line usually parallels the road for nearly the entire distance, often looping through each of the substations *en route*. With such construction, it will be seen, the transmission-line first cost and annual losses will not vary appreciably with substation location, especially since in long lines with relatively small power requirements the transmission-line wire is much larger than that required for any electrical considerations because of the mechanical strength needed. Even in high-tension underground systems the substations are usually tied together by such a network of primary feeders, for the sake of reliability of service, that the first cost and annual losses in the primary system may be considered practically independent of the number of stations, provided the total output does not change.

Another important factor which should not be overlooked, especially when express and freight service is contemplated, is the question of combining the substation, waiting station, and freight or express depot into one building with a material saving in the item of substation attendance, since the substation operator can often attend to the other duties of the passenger station as well.

If the station is not operated throughout the 24 hours the question of living accommodations for station attendants must be given some attention, as the theoretical determination might locate the substations in localities where no attendants would be willing to live, even though the railway company provided living apartments in the substation building, as is often the case. With some of the shorter systems it is possible to connect the various sections of trolley and feeders through the substation switchboard to the 600-volt, direct-current supply of the power station and thereby enable the first car in the morning to run over the line before the substations are started. With such an arrangement the operators may live in the nearest town to the substation.

Substation Design.—Assuming the most common type of substation, whose function it is to transform energy supplied by a high-tension, alternating-current transmission line into direct current at approximately 600 volts, the principal factors entering into its design will be briefly discussed.

With a knowledge of the load-demand curve and the efficiency of the distribution system and with the number and location of substations determined, the average and maximum loads on the substation may be found as outlined in Chap. XII. To decide upon the proper capacity of units to be installed, however, is

FIG. 52.—Typical manually operated substation and crossing signal. (*Union Switch and Signal Co.*)

largely a matter of good judgment. The duration of the peak load must be studied as well as its magnitude. It must also be known whether or not there is a possibility of greater loads at any time during the year and also what the growth in power demand is likely to be within the next few years. With these facts in mind it is well to provide for the average power by the installation of two or more units, usually leaving one unit as a relay in case of emergency. This relay unit should ordinarily be as large as the other units in the station in order that it may take the place of another machine in case of breakdown. Units of less than 200 kw. are seldom installed and if the average load is less than this value, the 200-kw. machines are usually run at light load rather than install smaller units. This procedure involves relatively large idle relay capacity as well, but the smallest units are usually less reliable and offer little reserve capacity or inertia in case of sudden overloads.

In the problem taken for illustration in Chap. XII the average load is 69.3 kw., while the maximum demand is 655 kw. The low average value is due to the fact that during several rather long periods there is no car on the section and the unit is, therefore, running light. Further study of the curve will show that a load

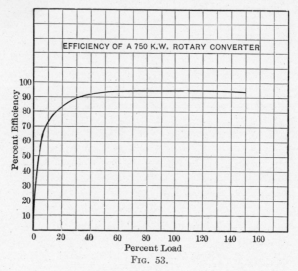

EFFICIENCY OF A 750 K.W. ROTARY CONVERTER

Fig. 53.

of 130 kw. is maintained for an hour at a time, while peaks of 260 kw. exist for 15 min. A 200-kw. machine would supply the average load and these latter peak loads, but would not be of sufficient capacity for the peaks of 655 kw. caused by the simultaneous starting of two cars. A 300-kw. unit would, therefore, be necessary for this station, as it could withstand the momentary overload of 100 per cent. This case is a good example of the necessity of taking the overloads and their duration into account in such determinations.

Synchronous Converter.—Most substations designed to supply direct current to a distribution system when receiving alternating-current power from a high-tension transmission line make use of the synchronous converter. This consists of a synchronous alternating-current motor and direct-current generator combined in a single unit with but one frame, one armature, and one field. It is really a direct-current generator with armature tapped to slip rings at symmetrical points, which rings are supplied with alternating current as in the synchronous motor.

Without detailed analysis of the theory of the synchronous converter it will be seen that there is a fixed ratio between the direct-current and alternating-current voltages for a given machine. For converters operating upon systems of different phases the ratios are different, as indicated in Table XIV. The series winding on the field of the converter cannot be made to vary the direct-current voltage with load variations as is so conveniently done with the compound railway generator. It is necessary,

TABLE XIV.—VOLTAGE RATIOS IN SYNCHRONOUS CONVERTERS

	No. of phases			
	1	2	3	6
D. c. volts...........	600	600	600	600
A. c. volts...........	424	300	367	212
Ratio...............	0.71	0.50	0.61	0.35

therefore, to provide some means of varying the alternating-current voltage impressed upon the converter as the load varies. This is generally done by means of series reactance, a synchronous booster, or induction regulator.

The use of series reactance for compounding a converter depends upon the fact that an overexcited synchronous converter or motor will draw a leading current. The increased current through the series-field winding of the converter with increased load merely changes the phase relation of alternating current to voltage but does not directly increase the voltage. If, now, inductive reactance be introduced between the step-down transformers and the converter, the inductive drop in potential through this reactance may be neutralized at heavy loads by the leading current drawn by the converter, and the voltage impressed upon the converter may thus be maintained constant or actually raised. While formerly these reactances were provided as separate units, it is now very common to introduce the reactance in the low-voltage winding of the transformer, thus economizing first cost and floor space. The voltage variation possible is limited to about 10 per cent in this method, but it has the advantage of being automatic.

The synchronous booster, as its name implies, is an alternating-current generator of the same number of phases and poles as the converter whose armature is connected phase by phase in series with the converter windings. The booster is mechanically direct connected to the converter, in fact, it is usually mounted inside the bearings and slip rings upon the converter shaft, while the frame adjoins that of the larger machine. The voltage is varied over a large range by controlling the booster-field excitation.

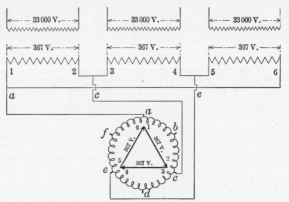

Fig. 54.—Three-phase delta transformer connections.

Induction regulators, which consist of automatically controlled, variable-ratio transformers, are often inserted between transformers and the converter in order that the alternating-current voltage may be varied, but this method is more common in substations supplying lighting and power loads than in railway installations.

Of the foregoing methods of voltage variation, the series reactance is cheapest but most limited in its range, the induction regulator fills a medium ground with respect to expense, requires considerable extra floor space and more complex circuits, while the booster converter may be considered the most expensive of the three, although covering a greater range of voltage and taking practically no extra floor space.

Although, as previously stated, there is in the ordinary design of synchronous converter a fixed ratio between the voltages upon the two sides of the machine, a special design known as the split-pole converter is an exception to the above statement. By dividing each pole into two or three radial sections, each provided with separately controlled windings, it is possible so to vary the flux distribution in the air gap as to produce a variable voltage ratio. This variation is confined within rather narrow limits, however, and for this reason, and also because of the greatly increased expense and complexity of control, it has been used more for lighting and power substations than in railway distribution.

Not to be confused with this, however, is the development of the commutating-pole or interpole converter. This design involves the use of an auxiliary pole halfway between main field poles with the winding of the former connected in series with the armature. By properly proportioning the ampere turns on the interpole so as to neutralize as nearly as possible the cross-magnetizing effect of the armature at all loads, the conditions for sparkless commutation are greatly improved. As the commutation of the converter usually limits its rating, the commutating-pole converter has a very high rating for a given size of frame. The use of these poles has also permitted commutation at much higher voltages, thus opening the way for the installation of the high-voltage, direct-current, railway distribution systems discussed elsewhere. One objectionable feature of the commutating-pole converter is the large short-circuit currents which exist under the brushes during the operation of starting. This difficulty has been overcome by providing a mechanical means of lifting the brushes from the commutator when the machine is being started.

Synchronous converters, because of the interaction of the direct and alternating currents in the armature, operate with higher efficiencies and less heating than either an alternating- or direct-current generator of the same size. The rating is, therefore, correspondingly higher when referred to a direct-current machine using the same frame as indicated in Table XV.

The advantages of a six-phase over a three-phase converter are apparent from this table, and since it is possible to supply six-phase power from a bank of transformers operating upon a three-phase transmission line, a large number of six-phase converters are now being installed.

TABLE XV.—COMPARATIVE RATINGS OF CONVERTERS

D. c. generator	Single-phase converter	Three-phase converter	Two-phase converter	Six-phase converter
1.00	0.85	1.32	1.62	1.92

In Fig. 53 will be found an efficiency curve for a 750-kw., three-phase synchronous converter from which it will be noted that, although the efficiency falls off with light loads as with all other electrical machines, it may be considered constant for all loads above 50 per cent of its rating.

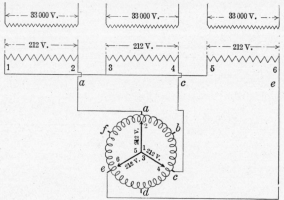

FIG. 55.—Three-phase "star" or "Y" transformer connections.

Methods of Starting Converters.—Three distinct methods of starting synchronous converters are available. In many cases provision for starting from either direct-current or alternating-current sources is made. If the direct-current method of starting is adopted, a starting rheostat must be provided, which, in turn, will be controlled by a multipoint switch, usually mounted on the switchboard. This switch starts the converter from the 600-volt feeder system as an ordinary direct-current motor, gradually cutting out resistance until the motor comes up to speed, when the main direct-current switch may be closed. The speed may then be varied by changing the field excitation until the alternating-current side is synchronized, by means of the synchroscope or synchronizing lamps, as in the synchronous motor or alternator.

With the variable-voltage, alternating-current method of starting, low-voltage taps are taken from the bank of transformers to

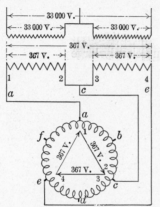

FIG. 56.—Three-phase "V" or "open delta" transformer connections.

a double-throw switch usually located on a separate panel near the converter. When the switch is thrown down a low voltage, usually about one-third rated voltage, is impressed on the arma-

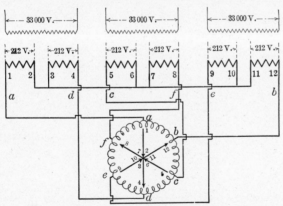

FIG. 57.—Six-phase "star" or "Y" transformer connections.

ture of the converter and the machine starts as an induction motor. As the converter approaches full speed the armature is supplied with full voltage by throwing the starting switch into the "up" position.

This method requires a rather large starting current at low power factor but it eliminates the necessity of synchronizing. It is necessary to open the shunt-field winding of the converter in several places in order that the excessive voltage otherwise induced in the many turns of the field by the large circulating currents in the armature may not puncture the field winding.

If the auxiliary-induction-motor method be used, a small induction motor, sufficiently large to start the converter with no load and bring it to slightly above synchronous speed, is mounted on the end of the converter shaft. This motor is usually operated by means of a three-pole starting switch on the switchboard which is supplied with power from auxiliary transformer connec-

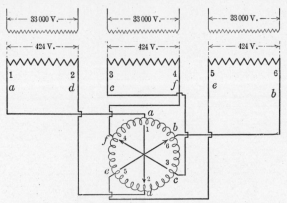

Fig. 58.—Six-phase "diametrical" transformer connections.

tions. As the converter reaches its proper speed it is synchronized with the transmission line as in the first case. The starting motor is then cut out of circuit.

Transformers.[1]—Since the supply voltage necessary for a converter bears a fixed ratio to the direct-current voltage, step-down transformers are usually necessary. The secondary voltages of the latter will depend upon the method of connection adopted for the converter. The connections available between the transformers and the converter are indicated in Figs. 54 to 60 inclusive. In all these figures a voltage of 600 has been assumed for the direct-current side of the converter. The voltages necessary between taps on the converter armature and those of the transformer coils are indicated in the figures.

[1] See also Chap. XVI.

The primary coils may be connected in either "Y" or "delta," the latter having the advantage of continuous operation with 86 per cent of rated capacity per transformer as the so-called "V" or "open delta," in case of trouble with one transformer of the bank, without change of connections. As it is

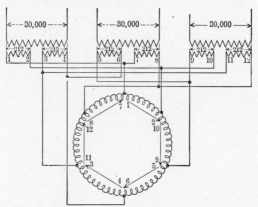

Fig. 59.—Six-phase ring transformer connections.

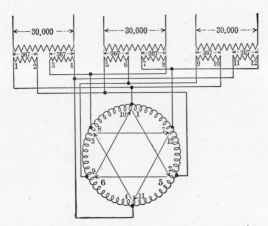

Fig. 60.—Six-phase double-delta transformer connections.

often found desirable to raise the transmission-line voltage at some later date, this may be very conveniently done by changing from "delta" to "Y" if the former connection is installed at first. This change is possible since the line voltage with the "Y" connection bears the ratio of 1.73 to the transformer coil voltage, while in the "delta" the coil and line voltages are identical.

In this country preference has been shown for single-phase transformers combined into banks, usually of three each, in place of three-phase transformers, largely because of the increased

Fig. 61.—Self-cooled oil-insulated transformers of the radiator type with respirator tanks. (*General Electric Company.*)

flexibility of the system with smaller units and the avoidance of crippling the transformers of all phases in case of damage to a single unit. The rating of each transformer will, therefore, be determined as follows:

$$\text{Transformer kilowatts} = \frac{\text{Converter kilowatts}}{3 \times \text{converter efficiency}}. \quad (89)$$

A bank of three transformers, each of the foregoing rating, should be installed for each converter or motor generator usually with switches in both high- and low-tension connections.

Transformers may be further classified with regard to their method of cooling as follows:

1. Self-cooled, oil-insulated.
2. Air-cooled.
3. Water-cooled.

Fig. 62.—Inertaire transformer showing deoxidizing device mounted on side of tanks. (*Westinghouse Elec. & Mfg. Co.*)

Transformers of the oil-cooled class depend for their cooling upon the natural circulation of a comparatively large body of oil within the transformer case or through radiators projecting from the case. The latter offer a greater cooling surface to the

oil from which the heat is radiated to the air.   This construction
is suitable for transformers of all potentials within a wide range of
capacities, particularly in the outdoor type.

In order that explosive gases, oil sludges, and other objectionable products resulting from contact between the transformer
oil and the oxygen of the air may be avoided, various "respirator"
tanks and "Inertaire" transformers have been supplied, particularly in the larger sizes.   Provision is made for dehydrating and
deoxidizing the air which is drawn into the transformer case
during the so-called "breathing" process which results from

Fig. 63.—Typical 7,500 kw. 13,000/600 volt substation.

temperature changes.   These two recent developments, which
have very greatly increased the available sizes of transformers of
the oil-cooled type during the last few years, are well illustrated
in Figs. 61 and 62.

Air-cooled transformers (Fig. 63) are cooled by means of an
air blast provided by a motor-driven blower and forced through
the air ducts of the transformer core.   This method of cooling
requires the construction of air ducts in the floor, usually of concrete, and involves the additional cost of blower outfits.   It is

suitable for all capacities, but is limited to potentials of 33,000 volts or less.

Transformers of the third class contain a series of pipe coils within the case, the insulating oil circulating around the coils while the latter are cooled by means of circulating water within. This type of transformer is used for most of the largest installations and is not limited as to capacity or voltage.

Motor Generator vs. Converter.—A motor-generator set may be installed in place of a synchronous converter. The motor may, of course, be of either the induction or the synchronous type mounted upon the same shaft with a direct-current generator. The advantages and the disadvantages of the two types of apparatus for converting from alternating to direct current are as follows:

In the motor generator the ratio between alternating-current and direct-current voltage is not fixed. For transmission voltages not exceeding 13,000 this set may, therefore, be operated without step-down transformers if the motor be wound for transmission-line voltage.

The direct-current voltage may be readily controlled by means of the generator field rheostat without affecting the alternating-current voltage or power factor.

The direct-current generator may be automatically compounded or overcompounded without auxiliary apparatus. The converter requires an external reactance in addition to the series field.

The motor generator is not as sensitive to commutation troubles, especially upon sudden overloads, as the converter.

"Hunting," or the periodic variations in speed on either side of an average value, with the usual accompaniments of poor commutation and "arcing over," are less marked in the synchronous motor-generator set because of its greater inertia, while they are entirely absent in the induction motor set.

The power factor of the synchronous motor-generator set is controlled quite as easily as with the converter. The induction motor set, of course, has the disadvantage of low uncontrollable power factor.

On the other hand, the converter has a higher efficiency.

Its rating for a given size of frame is much higher.

The floor area taken up is considerably less.

Its cost is less for a given capacity, although, where the adoption of the motor generator enables the transformers to be eliminated, the first cost of the converter with transformers is about the same as that of the motor generator alone.

Switchboard.—The typical substation switchboard consists of the following classes of panels:

1. High-tension line.
2. High-tension transformer.
3. Alternating-current converter or motor generator.
4. Direct-current converter or motor generator.
5. Totalizing.
6. Direct-current feeder.

The number of panels in each class is dependent upon the size of station and the number of converters it contains, but all panels of each class are usually grouped by themselves.

The two classes of high-tension panels are usually of the remote-control type. This is universally the case above 13,000 volts. With this construction the high-tension switches are mounted in fireproof compartments of concrete, tile, or brick and may, therefore, be located at some distance from the control board. No high-tension lines are connected with the control board, the switches being operated by means of auxiliary 125-volt, direct-current circuits and the meters connected with the secondary windings of current and potential transformers whose primary windings are in the high-tension circuits. Red and green lights on the switchboard panels indicate whether the main switches are closed or open, respectively.

The high-tension line switches control the connections between high-tension lines and the station bus bars, while each bank of transformers is connected to the high-tension buses by means of the switches controlled by the panels of the second group. These latter switches and often both groups of switches are provided with inverse time-limit relays which act as circuit breakers in case of overload, with the further provision that they may be adjusted to operate only after the overload has continued for a prearranged interval. The "inverse" type of relay is, in addition, so designed that the greater the overload the shorter will be the time in which it will open. With the transformer relays set for a very short interval, the high-tension line switches arranged so as to open a fraction of a second later if the overload still continues, and with the relays in the outgoing high-tension feeders at the power house adjusted for an interval of 1 or 2 sec., it will be seen that only those switches connecting apparatus or lines upon which there is trouble will be opened and the interference with other service reduced to a minimum.

The meters to be installed on the first two groups of panels often vary widely with the personal preference of the engineer in charge, an average equipment probably consisting of an ammeter in each phase, a power-factor meter, and a voltmeter on a swinging bracket at the end of the board.

The panels of group 3 contain all equipment necessary for the control of the alternating-current side of the converter or motor generator, as the case may be, and usually include a low-voltage, secondary, alternating-current switch for connecting converter to transformers, motor field rheostat in case of a synchronous motor-generator set, starting switch if starting motor be used, together with synchronizing and voltmeter plugs. The instruments usually consist of three ammeters and a power-factor meter. A field ammeter is added for large synchronous machines.

The direct-current panels perform the office of connecting the direct-current or output side of the converter or motor generator to the direct-current bus bars. For this function three single-pole switches are usually employed, one positive, one negative, and an equalizer switch. The negative and equalizer switches are often located on a pedestal or on the frame of the converter, thereby simplifying the switchboard connections. The field rheostat control of the converter or of the generator of the motor generator set is located on this panel together with a circuit breaker, a direct-current potential receptacle, and a starting switch in case it is planned to start the machine from the direct-current side. The meters are usually confined to a main ammeter and indicating wattmeter with a direct-current voltmeter on a swinging bracket. In large installations a field ammeter is often included on this panel.

The totalizing panel contains instruments only and these are so connected as to measure the total output of the station between the direct-current converter panels and the outgoing feeders. An ammeter or indicating wattmeter and an integrating wattmeter are usually installed. This panel is often entirely omitted and the latter instrument mounted on the sub-base of one of the other panels.

The outgoing feeder panels may be designed to control one or two feeders each. Single-pole (positive) switches and circuit breakers in series with ammeters make up the usual equipment for each feeder.

The entire board is usually of the standard size 90 in. in height, including a 28-in. sub-base with panels varying in width from 16 to 36 in. Blue Vermont marble forms the principal material of construction for high voltages, although low voltage and

Fig. 64.—Substation equipment of 1,500 volt, 300 kw., Chicago, Milwaukee and St. Paul Railroad.

remote-control boards are built of slate. The board should be spaced at least 4 ft. from the wall and the wiring at the back should be generously lighted. Where gallery boards of the remote-control type are installed from which the operator may view all the machines under his control, the "desk type" of board has been quite frequently specified.

Figure 63 represents a typical General Electric six-phase synchronous converter substation with remote-control switches and air-cooled, single-phase transformers. The high-voltage oil switches are seen at the extreme left, while the low-voltage alternating-current starting switches are placed upon small panels in front of the transformers.

Storage-battery Auxiliary.—While the storage battery is looked upon by many engineers and managers as an evil to be avoided, it certainly has its important place in the substation equipment of many roads. Its possible function is threefold, although it is often installed for the purpose of meeting but one of the following requirements:

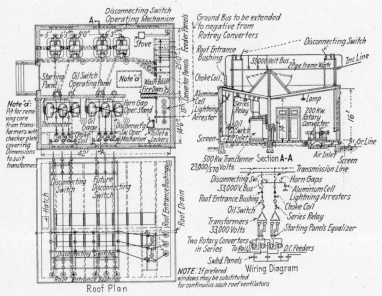

Fig. 65.—Synchronous converter railway substation.   (*General Electric Co.*)

1. To aid in maintaining constant potential.

2. To supply all peak loads above a certain predetermined average.

3. To assume the entire load of the substation for a short period of time.

When the second and third functions listed above are assumed by the battery, its capacity must be greatly increased, yet in many instances batteries of sufficient capacity to fill these three requisites are maintained in practically all substations of the road.

As the maintenance and the depreciation of a battery are relatively high, the local problem must be carefully studied before a decision can be reached.   Such a study should balance the fixed charges of the battery and accompanying control equipment combined with its maintenance against the fixed charges of the relay equipment and the extra line copper that would otherwise have to be installed, plus the rather intangible factors of irregular schedule due to variable voltage and total interruption to service.

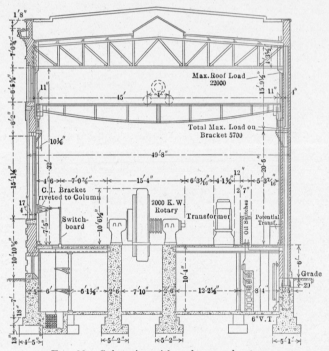

Fig. 66.—Substation with underground entrance.

As an example of the use of a battery in a substation of a large urban railway system the Plymouth Court station of the Chicago Surface Lines may be cited.   Two synchronous converters of 1,200-kw. capacity each are supplemented by a battery having a capacity of 8,610 amp. for 18 min., or 4,080 amp. for 1 hr.   It is housed on the two upper floors of the station over the converters.   It is regulated by a motor booster of 3,000-amp. capacity at 70 volts.   A most interesting feature of this installation is an electric recording hydrometer which records at a distant point the specific gravity of the electrolyte of each cell, from which an idea of the condition of the battery may be obtained. Whereas the battery might not pay for itself on the basis of increased load factor produced by the reduction of the peak load on the converters, yet when it is remembered that power is purchased in this case at a figure dependent upon the peak load supplied, the battery is of great value in smoothing out the load curve.

Arrangement of Apparatus.—There is little variation in the arrangement of apparatus in a railway substation except in the extreme cases where it is necessary to locate the equipment on two floors. The high-tension apparatus is usually confined to a separate room and is often located in fireproof vaults. The converters, reactances, and switchboard are usually located very close together in a single room with the wiring either in conduit embedded in the floor or of the open type supported from insulator racks on the basement ceiling. The principal features which tend materially to alter the design of a substation are the overhead or underground entrances of high-tension and direct-current feeder cables. Typical stations involving each type of construction are illustrated in Figs. 65 and 66.

Wiring.—The wiring of the station is usually figured from the standpoint of carrying capacity only, as the potential drop for the short distances involved is generally negligible. The resistances of the direct-current cables between converter and switchboard should, however, be carefully proportioned in order to divide the load properly between two or more machines operating in parallel. The low-tension wiring and the high-tension cables up to 13,000 volts are usually insulated with rubber, paper, or varnished cambric and are protected either with braid or a lead sheath. A simplified wiring diagram for a typical substation will be found in Figs. 65 and 67. Wiring above 13,000 volts, and often that at lower voltage, is carried on line-type insulators with no further insulation, these lines often being run in individual concrete or brick compartments with convenient chambers provided for sectionalizing or disconnecting switches and instrument transformers.

Lightning Protection.—The incoming high-tension lines and the outgoing railway feeders are each provided, just within the wall of the station, with a helix of wire of the same size as the

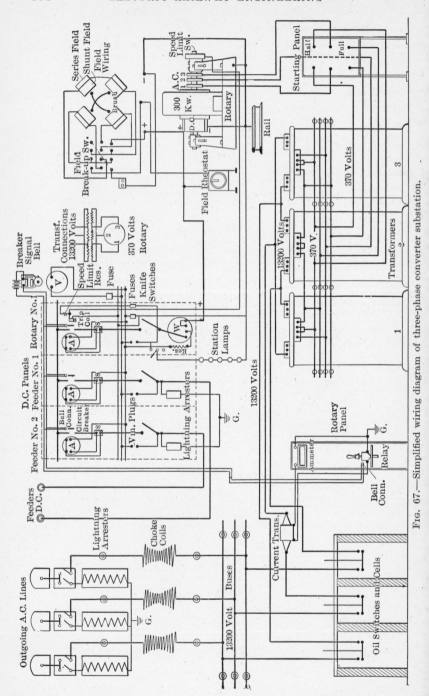

Fig. 67.—Simplified wiring diagram of three-phase converter substation.

line wire which acts as a "choke coil" to divert high-frequency surges to the lightning arresters connected between the coils and the outside lines.

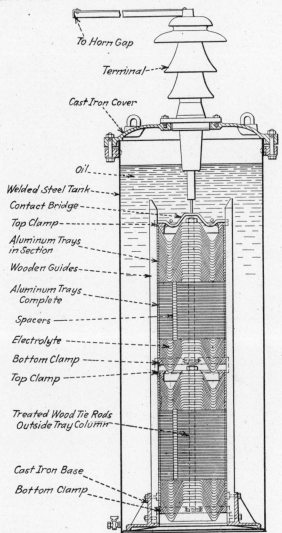

To Horn Gap

Terminal

Cast Iron Cover

Oil

Welded Steel Tank

Contact Bridge

Top Clamp

Aluminum Trays in Section

Wooden Guides

Aluminum Trays Complete

Spacers

Electrolyte

Bottom Clamp

Top Clamp

Treated Wood Tie Rods Outside Tray Column

Cast Iron Base

Bottom Clamp

FIG. 68.—Section of electrolytic lightning arrester. (*Westinghouse Elec. & Mfg. Co.*)

Arresters for use upon circuits of 2,200 volts and less are usually of the multigap type. Where serious consideration must be given to first cost this type may be extended to as high as 33,000-volt circuits.

The mutligap arrester, as its name implies, consists of a series of very small spark gaps formed by placing knurled cylinders of non-arcing metal near one another. A sufficient number of such

Fig. 69.—Installation of electrolytic lightning arrester. (*Westinghouse Elec. & Mfg. Co.*)

gaps are placed in series to prevent the line voltage arcing across. Another set of gaps, shunted with graphite resistance rods, is also included in the series. High-frequency surges will tend to arc over all the gaps in order to reach ground, whereas the generator current which follows will usually be diverted sufficiently through the resistance to cause the arcs over the shunted gaps and finally those on the series gaps to be quenched.

The electrolytic lightning arrester, although expensive, is now universally recognized as the best protection from lightning for high-voltage circuits. It consists of a series of aluminum trays separated slightly from one another by a space filled with an hydroxide solution. A thin film of aluminum hydroxide is formed on the plates which will offer a high resistance up to approximately 400 volts per tray. When this voltage is exceeded, a current is readily conducted through the various elements from line to ground. The group of trays is mounted in a steel tank filled with transformer oil for insulating and cooling purposes, as indicated in Fig. 68.

Since such a series of metal plates separated by a dielectric will act as a condenser on an alternating-current system, thereby drawing a rather objectionable charging current from the line, one or more horn gaps are usually introduced to break the circuit. These are adjusted to arc at critical voltages and relieve any abnormal potential which may exist on the line.

The disadvantages of this type of arrester, aside from its high first cost previously mentioned, are the regular charging necessary to maintain the insulating film on the aluminum trays and the tendency to freeze in exposed installations.

A still more recent arrester which is particularly adapted for exposed conditions takes the form of a condenser bushing. It consists essentially of a number of metal cups in series with a resistance mounted upon an insulating bushing, which, in turn, is supported upon a metal rod. Porcelain bushings insulate one cup from another. The upper cup of the series is connected to the line and the supporting metal rod is grounded. This apparatus may be considered, therefore, as a series of condensers between line and ground, while each is in itself a shunted condenser with respect to the ground. The breakdown of the upper condenser, due to abnormal potential, exerts excessive voltages upon the remainder of the series and the complete discharge takes place. The principle of operation is not unlike that of the electrolytic arrester, except that the insulating film is permanent. It has the disadvantage of not being self-healing in case the insulation is punctured.

The oxide film lightning arrester which is a more expensive but very effective piece of apparatus which has been developed recently, consists essentially of a number of cells connected in series with an air gap between line and ground. The cells are held together under slight pressure and are arranged in sections or stacks according to the voltage and kind of circuit. The complete installation for a three-phase line is shown in Fig. 70.

The cells are disk-shaped, made of two circular brass plates, crimped firmly to the edges of an annular piece of porcelain.

Fig. 70.—Oxide film lightning arrester. (*General Electric Co.*)

Lead peroxide powder, which has a very low resistance, completely fills the space between the metal plates. The inner surfaces of these plates are covered with an insulating varnish film. A sufficient number of cells are used in series to provide a voltage of approximately 300 volts per cell.

When a lightning discharge takes place over the air gap its high voltage is impressed upon the cells and the insulating coating of the plates is broken down, thereby allowing the discharge current to flow through the cells to ground, thus relieving the lightning pressure. This flow of current through the cells immediately causes a chemical change in the lead peroxide at the point of puncture. Red lead and litharge result which offer a very high resistance which is automatically introduced into the discharge path. This cuts off the generator current which would otherwise follow the lightning discharge and the arcs across the series air gaps are extinguished. This operation may be repeated at any future time when the voltage becomes excessive.

With subsequent discharges through the cells, the insulating film becomes thickened resulting in a corresponding higher breakdown voltage of the arrester. Tests and service records indicate that the life is a matter of many years, however, varying with service conditions.

Another important recent development in lightning protection is the autovalve arrester. This arrester consists of a stack of flat circular discs of material of comparatively high resistivity, separated by thin, insulating washers and connected through a series gap between line and ground. At normal voltage with no series gap a small leakage current would flow.

At voltages above a critical value, slightly in excess of line voltage, the short gaps between the discs break down. The resistivity of the discs does not permit the concentration of current in any small area but keeps the current flow between the discs in the form of a glow discharge, thus preventing excessive local heating. When the voltage falls to the critical value, the current becomes zero, and no dynamic current flows. As in the case of the electrolytic arrester, the critical voltage is proportioned to the line voltage by the use of the proper number of elements in series. The desired resistance of the structure is secured by the use of restricted disc area, holding the resistivity at the value necessary to keep the discharge distributed.

This arrester has given a very good record for one of moderate cost throughout the short period of its service.

Portable Substations.—On many roads traffic demands become excessive upon certain days or weeks of the year on different sections of the line. A means of meeting this local and temporary demand for power has been found in the "portable substation" (Figs. 71 and 72), which usually consists of a box car with a converter, transformers, switchboard, etc., complete and ready for connection to the high-tension lines at any point on the system and capable of operating in parallel with the permanent station on any desired trolley section. Such a portable station has proved a means not only of providing good service under extreme conditions, but has protected the regular equipment from damage due to serious overload as well.

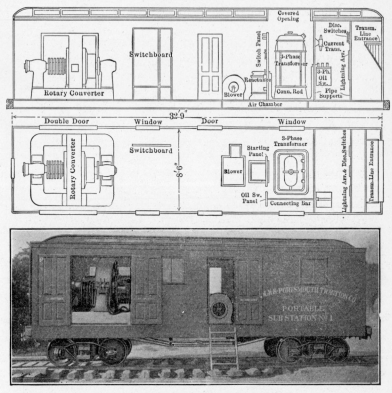

FIG. 71.—Portable substation.

Steel cars are now invariably used for such stations and are recommended in all cases. The important factors in the design of a portable substation are as follows:

1. It should be fireproof throughout.

2. The size of the car should be limited to the clearance dimensions of the local road and the steam roads which the car will traverse to its destination.

3. The car design should be in accordance with the Interstate Commerce Commission's rules and Master Car Builders' standards.

4. Good ventilation is essential for both the apparatus and the operator.

5. All apparatus should be securely anchored to the car floor and framing so that is will not shift or topple over unless it should meet with a destructive accident.

6. Converter and motor-generator sets should be arranged for leveling the shaft when the car is standing on a grade or uneven track.

FIG. 72.—Side view of a portable substation.

7. All doors, windows, hatches, etc., should be made effectively tight against all kinds of weather conditions.

High-voltage, Direct-current Substations.—Within the last few years the high-voltage, direct-current railway system has been developed and many interurban roads are now operating on from 1,200 to 3,000 volts. This increase of voltage decreases the first cost of installation, as it reduces the number of substations necessary as well as the amount of distribution copper required. A more detailed comparison of its cost and advantages will be found in a later chapter.

The substation design for such a system is not materially different from that outlined above, except in the case of the converting equipment. Two standard 600-, 1,200,- or 1,500-volt machines, connected in series, are usually installed for this service, the negative terminal of one unit being connected to the

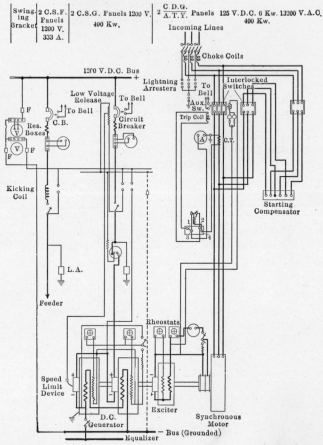

Fig. 73.—Wiring diagram of high voltage direct current substation.

rail while the positive lead from the second machine is carried to the switchboard bus bars and thence through feeder panels to the feeders and trolley. The wiring diagram for such a station will be found in Fig. 73. It should be noted that in this installation no transformers are used, although the synchronous motor of the motor-generator set operates at 13,200 volts.

Automatic Substations.—During the last five years a great deal of attention has been devoted to the automatic substation, particularly for interurban, surburban, and lightly loaded urban systems. The development and the experimental stage may now be said to have been satisfactorily passed, in so far as the dependable operation of automatic equipment is concerned. Further developments, resulting from experience with many automatic substations in operation at the present time, will probably be in the direction of simplification and reduction in number of protective devices.

The economic advantages, particularly in reduced operating expenses, are already apparent. The possibility of installing more such stations without additional operating expense for labor also provides better voltage regulation at lower cost and less potential difficulty from electrolysis.

Although several more years of service must be experienced before a correct appraisal of the depreciation and long-term maintenance and replacement costs can be made, the indications all point to a rapid and economical adoption of this type of substation upon a large number of electric railroads.

Savings through automatic operation may be classified as follows:

1. Savings in wages of attendants.

2. Savings in conversion and distribution losses because of more advantageous location of substations.

3. Mitigation of electrolysis due to the greater number of feeding points which may be economically employed.

4. More uniform and higher trolley voltages may be maintained, making possible increased schedule speeds, thus permitting either more frequent service with increased revenue, or a reduction in the number of cars required for a given schedule, with a resulting decrease in the platform expense. Within certain limits the higher voltage will result in reduced power consumption for a given schedule.

5. Higher voltages will permit more coasting.

6. Prompt restoration of service after an interruption to the power supply, simply by energizing the transmission lines.

7. Elimination of shutdowns due to the strikes of the operators.

The automatic substation, in simple language, consists of a synchronous converter, a bank of transformers, and three or more switchboard panels on which are mounted electrically operated switches, relays, and instruments. When the trolley voltage falls below a predetermined value the converter starts up, without human aid, reaches synchronism, and assumes its share of the total load on the line. If the load reaches a point dangerous to the converter the latter immediately shuts itself down and the line switches are all opened. If a converter bearing should overheat, the relay operates and shuts the converter down. If the load on the line decreases to a point where the converter is not required,

FIG. 74.—High-voltage synchronous motor-generator substation, Chicago, Milwaukee & St. Paul, 3,000 volt, direct-current electrification.

the converter automatically comes to rest. This cycle of starting and stopping will be repeated just as often as the line conditions make it necessary, it being possible to start up, close all switches, and stop the converter in a minimum time of 35 sec.

Substations, for the most part, function through the agency of some form of remote control. They are started automatically by means of a voltage relay, which closes its contacts at some predetermined value of the trolley voltage. The following scheme is used by the Westinghouse Electric & Manufacturing Co. for starting automatic substations. Circuits permit the control of transformers, automatically energized from the transmission line, in such a way as to close the main oil circuit breaker, the normal field switch, and the alternating-current starting switch. Synchronism and polarity are indicated by a polarized motor relay, which, in the case of reversed polarity, causes the polarity of the machine to be corrected by field reversal accomplished by normal and reverse field switches which open and close automatically. The control of the field switches consists of a small direct-current magnet switch driven in a counterclockwise direction by the polarized motor. The field of the polarized motor relay is fixed by means of a permanent magnet, while the polarity of the relay armature becomes that of the machine, because during starting, it is directly connected across the direct-current terminals of the converter. It is thus obvious that the relay armature will not rotate until the machine has pulled into step, since prior to synchronism it is receiving alternating current of a diminishing frequency, the value of which becomes zero at the instant the converter armature reaches synchronous speed.

In the General Electric Company's automatic substation system a motor-driven drum controller supplied with energy from a permanently energized transformer, is provided in order properly to time and fix the sequence of operation. The polarity of the machine is definitely and instantly fixed by means of a small exciter direct connected to the control transformer. The converter is cushioned to the line through load limiting resistances. These resistances are also used for overload protection. A motor mechanism is provided to raise and lower the brushes on interpole converters, as required. The brushes are lowered through interlocks closing in proper sequence, before the direct-current switches close. This latter operation connects the machine to load through current-limiting resistances. These are then shunted in sequence by switches closed by the functioning of current-limiting relays. The machine remains in operation until cut out of service by the light-load control.

Single-phase, Alternating-current Substations.—In systems where single-phase alternating current is supplied to the car in place of direct current there is, of course, no demand for the conversion of alternating current to direct current in the substation. On long lines, however, substations are still necessary to reduce the potential of the transmission line to that suitable for the trolley, the latter voltage usually being 6,600 or 13,000 volts. Such substations, involving only transformers, lightning protection, and switches, require no attendants and are therefore, very small and simple in design as compared with the stations previously considered. Automatic oil switches are usually installed in both primary and secondary circuits of the step-down transformers, although in this case the time element of the automatic relay is adjusted for a greater time interval than those at the power station in order that the latter switches will open first in case of trouble. This method, which is just the reverse of that in converter substations, is adopted to avoid frequent trips to the substation to close switches.

Outdoor Substations.—The successful operation of small outdoor substations for lighting service has encouraged larger

TABLE XVI.[1]—ESTIMATED COSTS OF SUBSTATIONS

	Indoor	Outdoor
Building..........................	$21,835	$7,480
Switchboard......................	20,000	20,200
Transformers.....................	15,000	16,000
Motor generator sets.............	48,000	48,000
Exciters.........................	4,500	4,500
	$109,335	$96,180

[1] A. I. E. E., Vol. XXVIII (Randall).

and higher voltage designs, especially in single-phase systems in which no converting apparatus is necessary. Even in the latter cases the high-tension bus bars, lightning arresters, and transformers may be installed outside the station, while the low voltage apparatus requiring supervision is placed under cover. The advantages of such construction are lower first cost, less space and building capacity, and less life and property hazard. Contrasted with these must be considered the greater difficulty of inspecting and repairing apparatus located out of doors and the greater danger of its being molested by trespassers.

Transformers and remote-controlled oil switches or circuit breakers must be specially designed and constructed to keep out all moisture and even the effects of condensation of moist air within their cases. Self-cooled, oil-insulated transformers may be operated with greater loads when located outdoors in most climates, especially if shaded from the sun in hot summer weather. When water cooled, care must be taken to avoid freezing of the circulating water in winter at light loads, although the oil itself will usually be sufficiently protected by the heat generated by the core losses alone.

With reference to first cost, the following estimate will indicate the gain to be experienced in a 3,000-kw. 600-volt, motor-generator station supplied from a 22,000-volt transmission line when the

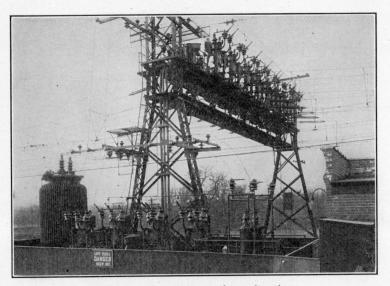

Fig. 75.—Single-phase outdoor substation.

high-tension equipment is placed outside the building. While such a station shows a gain of but 12 per cent, a similar change on a substation requiring no converting machinery may be accompanied by a saving as high as 30 per cent.

In Fig. 75 will be found a halftone of one of the outdoor substations of the New York, New Haven & Hartford R. R. which represents probably the largest railway outdoor substation yet installed. The 2,000-kw., 22,000/11,000-volt single-phase, water-cooled transformer with weatherproof insulating bushings is seen at the extreme left, while the oil circuit breakers and electrolytic lightning arresters provided with weatherproof

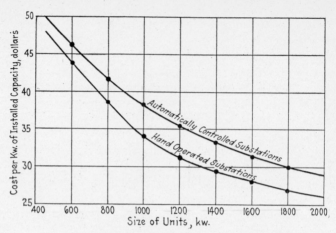

Fig. 76.—Costs of substations for electric railways.

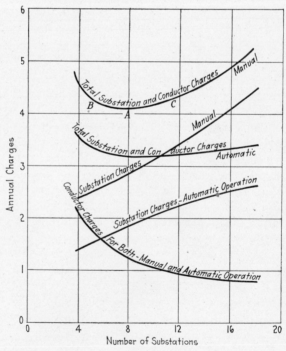

Fig. 77.—Relation of number of substations to annual charges for interurban line.

tanks are indicated in the central and right-hand portions of the figure, respectively.

Substation Costs.—The installation of automatic equipment on existing systems requires careful study. In general, it is not advisable merely to augment the manual installation with automatic features. The grade of service must first be considered. Then the cost of power, the cost of feeders, the investments in apparatus and real estate must be computed, and the interest charges must be allocated. Finally, the saving in operating charges must be reckoned.

Saving Affected by Automatic Equipment.—A comparison of the expense of purchasing and operating three 1,500-kw., 250-volt synchronous converters, manually operated, in a single station with the same capacity installed in three single-unit automatic stations follows:

The manually operated, three-unit station would require booster converters. The automatic single-unit station could use the less expensive field-controlled type. The three automatic stations complete would cost about $20,000 more than the single, manually operated substation. The manual station would require three shifts of two operators each. The average annual wage may be taken at $1,500, which gives an annual operating charge of $9,000 for the manual station. The automatic stations would have a combined operating expense of $750 per year for maintenance and inspection. To this is added 15 per cent investment charge on the additional cost of the automatic equipment. The equivalent operating charge of the automatic station thus is $3,750 per year. This is a saving of $5,250 per year in favor of the automatic station. Thus the automatic equipment shows a margin of over 25 per cent, or $5,250 per year on a $20,000 investment. To this must be added cost of feeder copper, losses, and real estate.[1]

The curves in Fig. 77 show the results of calculations on a typical interurban railway system. They are based on the data contained in the paper by H. F. Parshall presented to the (British) Institute of Civil Engineers (Vol. 199), and on the present-day (1921) prices of copper and electrical machinery and labor.

[1] From *Report* of the American Committee on Electrolysis.

CHAPTER XV

TRANSMISSION SYSTEM

The necessity for greatly detailed calculations in designing high-tension transmission lines for railway systems is often exaggerated. The fact that the careful predetermination of all characteristics of such a transmission line is unnecessary, when compared with the careful study required in connection with a line for the transmission of power for lighting or even for the very high-voltage, long-distance transmission of energy in large quantities from hydroelectric plants, will be made clear by the following outline of conditions generally pertaining to the railway system.

In the first place the close regulation of voltage is both unnecessary and impossible. The sudden variations of power demanded by cars, especially upon an interurban system, must inevitably mean variable voltage, and with such voltage variation on the distribution system there is little need of the closest possible regulation on the transmission line.

Nor is the service impaired by such voltage variations as would be suicidal to the lighting substation. The motorman or passengers upon an interurban car will hardly notice a 10 per cent voltage variation, while sudden variations of 2 or 3 per cent are to be avoided, if possible, with incandescent lighting, particularly as the intensity of light varies throughout a greater range than the voltage. The lighting of interurban cars is, of course, greatly impaired by poor voltage regulation and this is one of the features that is receiving a great deal of just criticism from the traveling public. Its remedy, however, lies in making the lighting independent of trolley voltage and not by attempting to regulate the latter more closely.

The regulation of transmission lines is greatly affected by low power factor. The addition of induction motors or arc lighting systems which operate at low power factors to long-distance

170

transmission lines involves very careful design and costly regulating apparatus if lighting loads are to be successfully supplied by the same line. In many such instances synchronous motors are installed, often without direct financial return to the company, in order that the power factor may be properly controlled. Such control is present in the railway substation in either the synchronous motor-generator set or converter, and with little practice the substation attendant can maintain very nearly unity power factor on the transmission line and thereby aid its regulation to a great extent.

Many of the limiting factors in high-tension line design, such as the pin type of insulator, corona losses, troubles involved by wide spacing and long spans, etc., are introduced only when the voltage becomes higher and the amounts of power become much greater than those involved in the major part of the interurban transmission. In fact, a census of transmission lines for railway purposes only would probably reveal the fact that an extremely small percentage of these lines are above 33,000 volts. At this voltage two parallel, three-phase circuits on pin-type insulators and wooden poles, carrying, in addition, the distribution feeders and trolley brackets, represent common practice. Such a line in the Middle West has for years been satisfactorily operating an interurban system 110 miles in length at 33,000 volts. In such design simple electrical and mechanical considerations are alone involved.

For the above reasons, therefore, and because of the very able treatises in complete volumes devoted to the details of this subject, an exhaustive study of transmission-line design will not be attempted in these pages.

The three-phase system of alternating-current transmission has been standardized almost exclusively for railway work. This is principally because polyphase apparatus is necessary for substation units in large sizes and, in addition, because the three-phase system requires but three-fourths the copper of the single phase installation. Other polyphase systems, although more economical in copper in some instances, have not found favor, largely because of the complication introduced by the greater number of wires. While six-phase substation apparatus was shown in the preceding chapter to be highly desirable, the possibility of its operation from a three-phase line has introduced no serious consideration of six-phase transmission. For these reasons, therefore, three-phase transmission only will be herein considered.

A summary, prepared by the *Electrical World*, of technical data of all transmission lines of 44,000 volts and above constructed prior to Jan. 1, 1925, indicates the following average practice:[1]

Each utility has designed and installed high-tension lines to meet local operating and economic conditions, and there is no such thing as standard practice in high-tension transmission

Conductors for transmission systems are made of several different materials, with copper, aluminium, and A.S.C.R. predominating. Stranded, solid and specially fabricated conductors are used on lines at the several voltages listed.

The majority of transmission lines in this country operate as grounded systems without ground resistance. Several recent installations use a low-resistance ground; one system has operated for years with a ground resistance of 1,000 ohms, and many systems operate without any ground.

Standards in sags, clearances, spans, and stringing tensions are not evident in existing systems, and great differences exist in practice.

Ground wires are used on the majority of exisiting systems, but the trend in more recent installations is toward the omission of the ground wire.

Arrestors of several types are used on existing systems in the majority of installations, but many lines are in operation at 60 kv. and above which are not equipped with arrestors.

The trend in all sections of the country is toward higher voltages, but an examination of recent installations shows that a very great range of voltages is used; for example, 44, 45, 60, 66, 88, 100, 110, 132, 166, and 220 kv. It would seem good practice, in view of future developments in interconnection, to omit several of these voltages from the list for future installations.

There exists little agreement in transmission-line design and installation in this country even in a geographic section, and work to bring closer agreement on many items would seem advisable.

Mechanical Strength.—Since calculations of the proper size of wire for transmission lines, based on Kelvin's law, voltage regulation, and carrying capacity, in most cases result in a wire too small to withstand the. mechanical stresses incurred by

[1] See *Electrical World*, Jan. 3, 1925.

ordinary line construction and weather conditions, the mechanical strength of the line may well be considered first and the size of wire checked in accordance with the electrical considerations later. No wires smaller than No. 4 B. & S. hard-drawn copper or its equivalent in tensile strength should be used, for mechanical reasons. If aluminum be used, it should be remembered that for the same size aluminum weighs about 30 per cent and has a resistance of 1.67 times that of hard-drawn copper. Aluminum costs considerably less than copper for the same conductivity and melts at a much lower temperature. It also has a greater coefficient of expansion, causing greater variation in sag with change of temperature. It is difficult to solder and has a tensile strength of approximately one-third that of copper, although with a steel core this difficulty is overcome. In spite of its disadvantages aluminum is used to a considerable extent for line construction, largely because of its low cost and light weight. Joints are made mechanically by overlapping the ends in an oval sleeve and twisting the sleeve and wire ends together without solder. On account of its large diameter for a given conductivity, the total wind pressure on a line is greater, and because of its low melting point it is more likely to melt apart than is copper, in the event of an arc forming between wires.

The question whether one or two parallel, three-phase lines shall be intalled, one for the purpose of acting as a relay for the other in case of breakdown, is an open one and is generally decided by the personal preference of the engineer in charge. If a single line only be installed, it is usually mechanically stronger and, therefore, better able to withstand abnormal strains. In this case the wires are spaced at the vertices of an equilateral triangle with one wire on the pole top and the two lower wires on a single cross-arm. If two circuits are employed, two arms are used and one circuit is installed on either side of the pole. Such construction permits repairs to be made on one of the lines with the other in operation when the voltage does not exceed 33,000 volts.

No particular specifications need be made for the poles, which are also used for the trolley span wires, feeders, and probably signal and telephone circuits as well, except that they must be sufficiently high to give sufficient clearance to the high-tension wires during the period of maximum sag and that they be at least

7 in. in diameter at the top.   The forces acting on the poles due to the presence of the high-tension line are:

Vertical downward force, due to weight of conductors with possible ice sheath and vertical component of wire tension.

Bending moment, due to angle in line or with one or more wires broken.

Bending moment, due to wind pressure on pole and ice-sheathed wires.

Although these forces may be readily calculated by means of the fundamental laws of mechanics, it is safe to assume that there is a sufficient factor of safety with a properly constructed pole line sufficiently heavy for the trolley and feeder installation, since the latter acts as a longitudinal anchor guy in case of a broken high-tension wire, and also since the possible strains on the high-tension line are generally small as compared with those incurred by the feeder and trolley construction.[1]

Electrical Considerations.—Considering the large number of railway high-tension lines using No. 4 B. & S. wire, and remembering that this should be a minimum for mechanical reasons, it will probably save time in calculation to assume this size at the start.   A convenient spacing for wires not exceeding 33,000 volts is 36 in.   With these dimensions in mind it will be remembered that in determining the regulation of an alternating-current line the impedance must be considered in place of the resistance which is used in direct-current calculations.   Impedance may be considered as the resultant of the resistance and the reactance of the line combined at right angles.   In other words,

$$Z = \sqrt{R^2 + X^2} \tag{90}$$

where $Z =$ impedance of line in ohms.
  $R =$ resistance of line in ohms.
  $X =$ reactance of line in ohms.

The reactance X of a transmission line is partly due to inductance L, which, in turn, is dependent upon the cutting by the wire of lines of force set up by the current in the wire, and the capacity C, which is the effect due to the wires acting as the plates of condensers with the air as a dielectric medium between.

---

[1] Standards of the A. E. R. A., N. E. L. A., and the National Bureau of Standards Safety Code should be consulted for mechanical specifications.

Since the formulas for these quantities given below show that the capacity is decreased and the inductance increased as the wires are moved apart and also as the size of wire is decreased, these two functions of reactance will be seen to be opposed to one another, one neutralizing the other to some extent. Since the capacity effect is relatively small, especially on the average short line of the interurban railway operating at moderate voltage, it will be neglected in the first determination of regulation and the error introduced by such a procedure pointed out later.

As the theoretical proof of the formulas for line inductance and capacity is beyond the scope of this book, and as their methods of derivation are included in most theoretical treatises on electrical engineering, they are listed below without proof.

$$C = \frac{0.0776\, l}{2 \log_{10} \dfrac{d}{r}}. \tag{91}$$

$$L = 0.000322\ (2.303 \log_{10}\!\left(\frac{d}{r}\right) + 0.25)l, \tag{92}$$

where L = self-inductance per wire in henries.

d = distance between wire centers in inches.

r = radius of wire in inches.

C = capacity between one wire and neutral point in microfarads.

l = lenth of circuit in miles.

Considering only the resistance and inductive reactance of the line at present, the latter may be found from the equation

$$X_L = 2\pi f L, \tag{93}$$

where X_L = reactance due to inductance in ohms.

f = frequency in cyles per second.

L = inductance from Eq. (92) in henries.

Tables giving such of the inductive reactance values and resistances as will be needed in railway transmission-line calculations are to be found on the following pages.

TABLE XVII.—INDUCTIVE REACTANCE OF SINGLE WIRE IN OHMS PER MILE[1]

Size wire	Spacing inches 25 cycles									
	24	36	48	60	72	84	96	108	120	150
350,000 cm.	.235	.255	.270	.280	.290	.298	.304	.310	.315	.327
300,000	.238	.258	.273	.285	.294	.301	.308	.314	.320	.330
250,000	.242	.263	.278	.289	.298	.305	.313	.319	.324	.335
4/0 B. & S.	.248	.268	.283	.294	.303	.310	.318	.325	.329	.340
3/0	.254	.274	.289	.300	.309	.317	.324	.330	.335	.346
2/0	.259	.280	.294	.306	.315	.323	.329	.335	.341	.352
0	.265	.286	.300	.311	.321	.329	.335	.341	.347	.358
1	.271	.292	.306	.318	.327	.334	.341	.347	.352	.364
2	.277	.297	.312	.323	.332	.340	.347	.353	.358	.370
3	.283	.303	.318	.329	.338	.345	.352	.359	.364	.375
4	.289	.309	.324	.335	.344	.352	.359	.365	.370	.381
6	.300	.321	.335	.347	.356	.363	.370	.376	.381	.393

TABLE XVIII.—RESISTANCE OF COPPER AND ALUMINUM AT 70°F.[1]

Size wire	Ohms per mile	
	Copper	Aluminum
500,000 cm.	0.109	0.176
450,000	0.121	0.196
400,000	0.137	0.221
350,000	0.156	0.252
300,000	0.182	0.294
250,000	0.219	0.353
4/0 B. & S.	0.258	0.417
3/0	0.326	0.526
2/0	0.411	0.664
0	0.518	0.837
1	0.653	1.055
2	0.824	1.330
3	1.039	1.678
4	1.309	2.116
6	2.082	3.309

[1] "Standard Handbook," sec. 11, p. 40.

Since the power factor at the substation may be maintained at approximately 100 per cent by control of the field of the synchronous converter or motor generator, such a power factor may be safely assumed in line calculation. In fact, it would not introduce a serious error to neglect reactance of the line entirely and solve the problem as if for a direct-current system, since even the effect of line reactance may be overcome by careful regulation of the substation apparatus as explained on page 171.

Voltage Determination.—The voltage and the current per wire must now be determined. They are principally dependent upon the substation input and distance of transmission.

In deciding upon the proper voltage for the transmission line as well as in selecting electrical equipment it is necessary to take into consideration the standards established by the manufacturers. Primary substation voltages have been standardized as follows: 11, 19.1, 33, 66, 110, 120, 132, 166, and 220 kv. The two lower potentials are most often used with delta connections, while voltages of 33 and 66 kv. are usually obtained with star-connected transformers. It should be noted that the three lower voltages bear the ratio of $\sqrt{3}$ to one another, thus permitting the next higher standard voltage to be obtained by changing connections of transformers from delta to star. For a rough selection of the voltage to be first used for calculation, 1,000 volts per mile of transmission are often used. As local conditions enter into the problem to a marked degree, and since it is almost impossible to express intelligently in equation form all the factors entering into the selection of the proper voltage from the standpoint of regulation, first cost, and economical operation, it seems advisable to select two of the nearest standard voltages by the above rule and compare the resulting calculated data of the two cases before finally determining upon the best operating voltage.

Regulation.—The transmission-line calculations are usually based upon the combined substation inputs supplied by a single line at full rated load, although, if the number of substations be large, it may be found from a study of their load curves that their maximum loads do not occur simultaneously and that the total demand on the transmission line may be considerably below the summation of the substation ratings. The rated output of the substation transformers was found in Chap. XIV (Eq. 89). The input to the station may be obtained from the above by dividing the output of all transformers by the transformer efficiency, which may be safely assumed for large transformers at full load as 98 per cent.

The current per wire on the transmission line is, therefore,

$$I_W = \frac{Kw \times 1,000}{\sqrt{3}E \cos \phi},$$ (94)

where I_W = current per wire in amperes.

Kw = substation input in kilowatts.

E = voltage between wires at substation.

$\cos \phi$ = power factor of load at substation.

For this calculation $\cos \phi$ is taken as unity, as explained above.

The impedance of the transmission line may now be found from Eq. (90) if values of reactance and resistance from Tables XVII and XVIII for No. 4 B. & S. wires spaced 36 in. apart be substituted. The voltage drop on the line is

$$e = I_W Z.$$ (95)

These relations, including the generator voltage E_g, are shown in Fig. 78, from which the value of E_g may be derived.

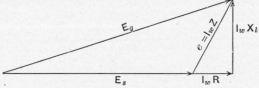

FIG. 78.—Vector diagram for transmission line regulation unity power factor.

$$E_g = \sqrt{(E_s + I_W R)^2 + (I_W X_L)^2},$$ (96)

where E_s represents substation voltage between wire and neutral, or $\dfrac{E}{\sqrt{3}}$

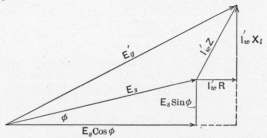

FIG. 79.—Vector diagram for transmission line regulation lagging power factor.

$$Regulation = \frac{E_g - E_s}{E_s}.$$ (97)

If less than unity lagging power factor be assumed, as in an induction motor-generator set for example, other conditions remaining the same, a larger current I_W' would have resulted from Eq. (94) and the voltage diagram would appear as in Fig. 79, the resulting generator voltage being

$$E'_g = \sqrt{(E_s \cos \phi + I'_W R)^2 + (E_s \sin \phi + I'_W X_L)^2}. \quad (98)$$

As before, the percentage regulation may be obtained from the equation

$$Regulation = \frac{E_g' - E_s}{E_s}. \quad (99)$$

If the regulation from either Eq. (97) or (99) is unreasonably high, a suitable value, say 10 per cent, may be substituted back into the equation and corresponding values of E_g or E'_g found, from which the correct value of R may be calculated by means of Eq. (96) or (98) and the proper size of wire obtained from the wire table.

As a concrete illustration of these two approximate methods of obtaining regulation, assume the following conditions:

$$\begin{aligned}
\text{Substation input} &= 1{,}500 \text{ kw.} \\
\text{Power factor} &= 100 \text{ per cent.} \\
\text{Length of line} &= 50 \text{ miles.}
\end{aligned}$$

Using No. 4 wire and a substation voltage of 33 kv., there results:

$$\begin{aligned}
R &= 1.309 \times 50 = 65.4 \text{ ohms.} \\
X_L &= 0.31 \ \times 50 = 15.5 \text{ ohms.}
\end{aligned}$$

$$E_s \text{ per terminal} = \frac{33{,}000}{\sqrt{3}} = 19.1 \text{ kv.}$$

$$Z = \sqrt{(65.4)^2 + (15.5)^2} = 67 \text{ ohms.}$$

$$I_W = \frac{1{,}500{,}000}{33{,}000. \sqrt{3}} = 26.2 \text{ amp.}$$

$$E_g = \sqrt{(19{,}100 + 26.2 \times 65.4)^2 + (26.2 \times 15.5)^2} = 20{,}820. \quad (96)$$

$$Regulation = \frac{20{,}820 - 19{,}100}{19{,}100} = 9 \text{ per cent.} \quad (97)$$

Now suppose the power factor to be lowered to 85 per cent by low field excitation of synchronous apparatus or the operation of an induction motor-generator set.

$$I'_W = \frac{1{,}500{,}000}{33{,}000\sqrt{3} \times 0.85} = 30.9 \text{ amp.} \quad (94)$$

$$E'_g = \sqrt{(19{,}100 \times 0.85 + 30.9 \times 65.4)^2 + (19{,}100 \times 0.527 + 30.9 \times 15.5)^2} = 20{,}900 \quad (98)$$

$$Regulation = \frac{20,900 - 19,100}{19,100} = 9.43 \text{ per cent.} \qquad (99)$$

Both the regulation for 85 per cent power factor and unity power factor are sufficiently small for railway service and the conditions of size of wire, voltage, spacing, etc. may be tentatively decided upon and checked further with regard to Kelvin's law, carrying capacity, etc., as explained under Distribution System.

Capacity Effect.—Since, however, the capacity has been entirely neglected in the above calculations, the error introduced by such omission should at least be pointed out.

As previously explained, the line wires act as plates of a condenser and thus draw a leading "charging" current from the power house, just as an infinite number of small condensers would do if connected in parallel across the line wires throughout their entire length. As such a uniform distribution of capacity involves a constantly changing charging current, power factor, and voltage throughout the entire length of the line, which condition can be represented only by a rather involved mathematical equation, it has been shown by Steinmetz[1] that this capacity effect may be represented sufficiently accurately by locating one-sixth of the total capacity at either end and two-thirds in the middle of the line. In fact, little error is introduced if the entire capacity is considered in parallel with the line at either the generator or receiver end. Adopting the latter assumption, the equations below show the method of derivation of the values in Table XVII and the calculation of charging current for any assumed length of line, voltage, and wire spacing.

The values of charging current in Table XIX which are dependent upon a voltage between the line wires and the neutral point of 100 kv. for a single mile of line at 25 cycles frequency and a given spacing are obtained by substitution in Eq. (91).

For example, assuming the conditions of the transmission problem above,

$$C = \frac{0.0776}{2 \log_{10}\left(\dfrac{36}{0.102}\right)} = 0.0153 \text{ mf.} \qquad (92)$$

between 1 mile of No. 4 wire and neutral with 36-in. spacing

$$I_c = \frac{2\pi f C E}{10^6}. \qquad (100)$$

[1] STEINMETZ, DR. C. P., "Alternating Current Phenomena."

If $I_c =$ charging current in amperes per mile at 100 kv.,

$f =$ frequency in cycles per second,

$C =$ capacity in microfarads per mile,

$E = 100,000$ volts,

$$I_c = \frac{2\pi \times 25 \times 0.0153 \times 100,000}{10^6} = 0.239 \text{ amp.} \quad (100)$$

TABLE XIX.—CHARGING CURRENT OF SINGLE WIRE IN AMPERES PER MILE PER 100 KV., 25 CYCLES

Size wire stranded	Spacing in inches									
	24	36	48	60	72	84	96	108	120	150
350,000 cm.	.329	.300	.283	.270	.261	.254	.248	.243	.239	.230
300,000	.323	.295	.278	.267	.258	.250	.245	.240	.236	.227
250,000	.316	.290	.274	.262	.253	.246	.241	.236	.232	.224
Solid 4/0 B. & S.	.301	.278	.262	.253	.243	.239	.232	.228	.224	.210
3/0	.295	.272	.257	.245	.239	.234	.228	.224	.220	.212
2/0	.287	.265	.251	.242	.232	.228	.224	.220	.217	.209
0	.279	.261	.246	.237	.229	.225	.220	.217	.212	.206
1	.275	.251	.242	.229	.223	.220	.217	.212	.209	.203
2	.268	.250	.237	.226	.221	.217	.212	.209	.206	.199
3	.264	.246	.229	.225	.217	.212	.209	.206	.203	.196
4	.255	.239	.226	.220	.214	.209	.206	.203	.200	.193
6	.245	.231	.220	.212	.204	.201	.198	.195	.191	.189

This value will be found in Table XIX opposite No. 4 wire with 36-in. spacing.

The charging current for any other voltage E' between wire and neutral and for any other length of line l is, of course,

$$I'_c = \frac{2\pi f C E' l}{100,000 \times 10^6}, \quad (101)$$

or

$$I'_c = \frac{\text{Table value} \times l \times E'}{100,000}. \quad (102)$$

Again, considering the concrete illustrative problem at unity power factor, the charging current for the line is

$$I'_c = \frac{0.239 \times 50 \times 19,100}{100,000} = 2.28 \text{ amp.} \quad (102)$$

It will be seen, therefore, that the charging current with this particular load and design of line is quite an appreciable percentage (8.7 per cent) of the full-load unity-power-factor current.

The charging current might be decreased somewhat by separating the wires. As this current is independent of load, its percentage will decrease, of course, as the load increases.

In refiguring the regulation, this time taking the charging current into account, it must be remembered that this current leads the voltage at the substation E_s by 90 deg. The vector diagram of voltages is, therefore, represented by Fig. 80 where the direction of the charging-current vector, and, therefore, of the vector of resistance drop due to charging current $I_c R$, is vertical and the reactance drop due to charging current $I_c X_L$ horizontal, since E_s is horizontal. The generator voltage $E''g$ may be seen from the geometry of the diagram to be

$$E''_g = \sqrt{(E_s + I_W R - I_c X_L)^2 + (I_W X_L + I_c R)^2}, \qquad (103)$$

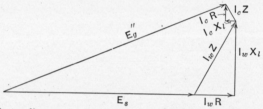

Fig. 80.—Vector diagram for transmission line regulation with charging current.

which is obviously less than E_g (Eq. (96)), since the charging current tends to neutralize the effect of line inductive reactance, thereby reducing the regulation to the value

$$Regulation = \frac{E''_g - E_s}{E_s}. \qquad (104)$$

Substituting the numerical data of the above problem,

$$E''_g = \sqrt{(19{,}100 + 26.2 \times 65.4 - 2.28 \times 15.5)^2 + (26.2 \times 15.5 + 2.28 \times 65.4)^2} = 20.76 \text{ kv.} \qquad (103)$$

$$Regulation = \frac{20{,}760 - 19{,}100}{19{,}100} = 8.7 \text{ per cent.} \qquad (104)$$

A similar diagram might be drawn and the regulation calculated showing the effect of charging current with low initial lagging power factor by adding the triangle of charging-current fall of potential to the diagram (Fig. 79) with the vector $I_c R$ leading E_s by 90 deg.

Comparing the regulation found by taking charging current into account (Eq. (104)) with that which neglected that particular effect (Eq. 97), the error will be seen to be

$$\text{Error} = \frac{9 - 8.7}{8.7} = 3.5 \text{ per cent,}$$

which may safely be neglected in most railway work, especially as the approximate method gives the highest and, therefore, the most conservative estimate of the regulation.

It is believed that the above considerations, together with some of the suggestions regarding high-tension line protection and wiring considered in Chap. XIV, cover the more important factors involved in the design of high-tension lines for railway service. For further details of construction and for theoretical consideration of the limiting factors which enter into exceptionally high-voltage installations, reference should be made to the many complete works on these subjects.

Estimates of construction costs on both distribution and transmission systems have been purposely omitted, since the cost of copper is the dominating factor in these portions of the railway system and such cost is so variable a quantity that estimates or costs of previous installations have to be used with great caution when applying them to proposed systems.

CHAPTER XVI

SOURCES OF ELECTRICAL ENERGY

The electric power station, designed and constructed solely for the purpose of generating electrical energy for railroad use, is a thing of the past. The advantages of low cost, greater continuity of service, and high load factor, resulting from the supply of several classes of electrical energy from large centralized power stations are now recognized to be so great that the consideration of sources of contracted energy must necessarily take the place of Power Station Location and Design.

The majority of electric railway power demands, particularly those of city street railways, electrified city terminals of steam railroads, heavy surburban passenger service, and power-regenerating systems on trunk lines, are especially suitable types of load to superimpose upon large efficient central stations having lighting and industrial power characteristics. The reasons for this were outlined in Chap. XII.

As the result of the recognition of these advantages and the greater generating economy of the larger and more favorably located power stations, the purchase of electrical energy by the railroads from central-station corporations operating greatly enlarged generating stations or interconnected superpower systems must take the place of the smaller isolated power stations.

Although types of electric rate schedules are almost as numerous as the central-station corporations themselves, yet the fundamental principles upon which the charges for wholesale lots of electrical energy are based have been well established, so that power contracts differ only with respect to details of more or less local interest. One such contract, in which have been carefully considered the most important phases of the legal, economic, and engineering requirements associated with the purchase of electrical energy for electrified surburban and terminal service from one of the largest and most efficient central station networks in the country, is, therefore, quoted in full.

184

Electric Service Agreement between Commonwealth Edison Company and Illinois Central Railroad Company, Oct. 1, 1924

Agreement, Made this first day of October, A. D. 1924, by and between Commonwealth Edison Company, a corporation organized under the laws of the State of Illinois (hereinafter commonly referred to as the "Edison Company"), and Illinois Central Railroad Company, likewise a corporation organized under the laws of the State of Illinois (hereinafter commonly referred to as the "Railroad Company"),

Witnesseth:

Whereas, the Railroad Company, in compliance with the **Preamble.** provisions of an ordinance of the City of Chicago, Illinois,

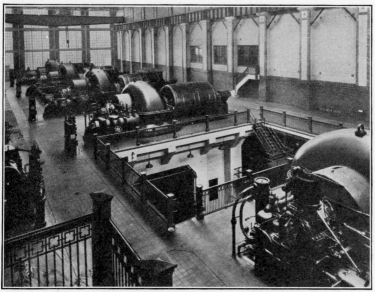

Fig. 81.—Interior Lakeside Station, T.M.E.R. & L. Co.

passed July 21, 1919, effective February 20, 1920, is now engaged in the electrification of portions of its railway system situated within its Chicago Terminal District (as hereinafter in Article X defined) in and in the vicinity of the City of Chicago, Illinois, and has found it advisable to take from the Edison Company during the term hereof, and during any extension or extensions of such term under the provisions hereof, electrical energy to the extent and in the manner hereinafter in this agreement provided, and the Edison Company desires to furnish such electrical energy to the Railroad Company;

Now, THEREFORE, in consideration of the premises and of One Dollar ($1) and other valuable considerations each to the other in hand paid, the receipt of which is hereby mutually acknowledged, and in consideration of the mutual covenants and conditions hereinafter set forth and the benefits expected to result herefrom, the parties hereto do hereby agree with each other as follows:

ARTICLE I

TERM OF CONTRACT

Original term.

SECTION 1. For and during the term of ten (10) years, commencing on January 1, 1927, or on such earlier or later date (but not later than January 1, 1928) as may be designated by the Railroad Company, in compliance with the provisions of said ordinance and in accordance with the provisions of this section, as the date of the commencement of the term, and for and during any extension or extensions of said term under the provisions hereof, the Edison Company shall supply and at all times stand ready to supply all the electrical energy which the Railroad Company shall require from the Edison Company in the Chicago Terminal District of the Railroad Company under and in accordance with and subject to the terms and provisions hereinafter set forth. In case the Railroad Company shall desire to have the term commence on a date prior to January 1, 1927, it shall give to the Edison Company not less than twelve (12) months' written notice of the date upon which it desires the term to commence. In case the Railroad Company shall desire to have the term commence on a date subsequent to January 1, 1927, it shall give to the Edison Company, not later than January 1, 1926, written notice that the Railroad Company does not desire that the term shall commence on January 1, 1927, and shall thereafter and prior to January 1, 1927, give to the Edison Company not less than twelve (12) months' written notice of the date (not later than January 1, 1928) upon which it desires the term to commence. If on the day specified in any such notice as the date of the commencement of the term the Railroad Company shall not be ready to commence complete, or substantially complete, operation hereunder, it shall pay to the Edison Company for each month during which it shall not be so ready an amount of money equivalent to one-half ($\frac{1}{2}$) of one per cent (1%) of the cost of the unused portion of substation buildings, machinery, apparatus, transmission lines and other equipment theretofore installed by the Edison Company for the purposes of the operation contemplated to be commenced on the said day specified and necessary therefor. Such electrical energy (herein-

Date of commencement of term.

The energy

after commonly referred to as "energy") shall be in the form of direct current and alternating current as hereinafter in Section 1 of Article IV provided, and shall be used by the Railroad Company only in connection with the operation, construction and maintenance of its railway system and appurtenances within its Chicago Terminal District as hereinafter in Article X provided.

SECTION 2.   The Railroad Company shall have the privilege of extending the original term hereof for a period of five (5) years by giving to the Edison Company, not later than one year prior to the expiration of the original term, written notice of its election to make such extension.   If such extension be made the Railroad Company shall have the right to three (3) further extensions for periods of five (5) years each by giving to the Edison Company in each case, not later than one year prior to the date of the expiration of the then current five (5) year period, written notice of its election to make such extension; *provided, however,* that if any such extension shall run later than May 31, 1947, the term hereof shall nevertheless terminate on that date unless prior to that date the ordinance of the City of Chicago under which the Edison Company is now operating shall have been extended, or a new ordinance obtained, or legislation enacted, authorizing the Edison Company to continue to operate in at least as ample or broad manner as at the time of the execution hereof.   Unless otherwise indicated by the context the word "term" as used in this contract shall include not only the original term of the contract but also any and every period of extension effected by election of the Railroad Company under the provisions of this section; and during any extension of the term all of the obligations of each of the parties hereto shall continue and remain in force.

SECTION 3.   The period of time commencing at the date of this contract and extending to the first day of the term determined in the manner provided in Section 1 of this Article will hereinafter in this contract be referred to as the "Preliminary Period" of the contract.

Marginal notes:

Extension of term.

Definition of "term."

Preliminary period defined.

ARTICLE II

DEMAND

SECTION 1.   As soon as practicable after the end of each calendar month in the term the Railroad Company's maximum demand in kilowatts for such month shall be ascertained as hereinafter stated in this section.   The Edison Company shall select from such month the three (3) hours (one to be taken from each of three (3) different days) in which the aggregate output of energy supplied hereunder by the Edison Company shall be greater than the aggregate output of energy

Marginal note:

Determination of maximum demand.

supplied hereunder by the Edison Company in any other three
(3) hours in such month (one to be taken from each of three (3)
different days), and one-third ($\frac{1}{3}$) of the aggregate number of
kilowatt hours drawn and consumed by the Railroad Company
during the three (3) hours selected as aforesaid from such
month shall be deemed and considered as the number of kilowatts constituting the Railroad Company's maximum demand
of energy supplied hereunder during such month; *provided,*
however, that in ascertaining the maximum demand hereunder
for any month the Edison Company shall not select any hour or
hours of abnormal demand (as defined below), except as hereinafter in this section specified, but *provided, further,* that if in any
month every hour shall be an hour of abnormal demand the
maximum demand for such month shall be the number of
kilowatts constituting the maximum demand for the last preceding month in which the maximum demand was ascertained
in the manner hereinabove in this section stated.

The term "maximum demand," as used in this contract,
shall be considered to mean the maximum demand of the
Railroad Company hereunder, ascertained and determined in
the manner aforesaid. The term "hour," as used in this
contract, shall be considered to mean the sixty (60) minute
period between any two (2) consecutive even clock hours, as
for example: between one o'clock and two o'clock. The term
"abnormal period," as used in this contract, shall be considered to mean any interval of time during which there shall be
abnormally heavy railroad traffic or abnormally low temperature or other abnormally severe weather conditions. The
term "abnormally heavy railroad traffic," as used in this contract, shall be considered to mean traffic caused by failure of
other transportation line or lines to furnish its or their normal
service, traffic arising from extraordinary assemblages, such as
fairs, race meets, ball games, conventions, and the like; congestion of traffic arising from a railroad accident, derangement
of power supply or other emergency condition or other excessive
traffic beyond that usually carried by the Railroad Company
and due to some unusual circumstance or condition; *provided,*
however, that, in the event that such "abnormally heavy railroad traffic," due to failure of other transportation lines to
furnish their normal service or due to extraordinary assemblages, shall continue beyond ten (10) consecutive days in any
month, the Edison Company in ascertaining the maximum
demand for such month may select, in accordance with the
provisions of the first paragraph of this section, any hour or
hours (whether of abnormal demand or not, provided such
abnormal demand is due to said last mentioned two causes)
occurring in such months after such ten (10) days, but any
monthly maximum demand resulting from the selection of

any hour or hours of abnormal demand shall not be used in determining the load factor for such month under the provisions of Section 4 of Article III, nor in determining the primary charge for any subsequent month under the provisions of Section 1 of Article III. The term "abnormally low temperature," as used in this contract, shall be considered to mean a temperature of five degrees (5°) Fahrenheit, above zero, or any lower temperature, as officially determined and recorded by the United States Weather Bureau at Chicago. But it is agreed that no period shall be considered as abnormal because of "abnormally heavy railroad traffic" unless notice of such abnormally heavy traffic shall be given by the Railroad Company, as required under the provisions of Section 1 of Article XII hereof. The term "hour of abnormal demand," as used in this contract, shall be considered to mean an hour during all or some part of which an abnormal period exists.

"abnormally low temperature;"

"hour of abnormal demand."

It is agreed that if the total usable surplus generating, transmitting and converting capacity of the Edison Company shall at any time be insufficient or unavailable to enable it to supply to the Railroad Company a portion of the excess energy in an abnormal period, due to abnormally heavy railroad traffic, as in this section provided, the Railroad Company shall, upon notice by telephone, or otherwise, from the Edison Company, refrain or immediately cease from drawing and consuming such portion of the excess energy until notified by the Edison Company that surplus generating, transmitting and converting capacity is available for supplying such portion of the excess energy; but in such case if the Edison Company shall have surplus capacity which is then unavailable it shall make such capacity available as promptly as possible. Nothing in this paragraph contained shall be construed as allowing or permitting the Edison Company to discriminate in any way against the Railroad Company in supplying the necessary energy hereunder.

Provision in case of lack of surplus capacity.

SECTION 2. During the term hereof, the Edison Company shall be able and ready to supply and shall supply to the Railroad Company, as required by it, and the Railroad Company shall take, in accordance with the provisions hereof, all the electrical energy which the Railroad Company shall require in such of its operations within its Chicago Terminal District as are required to be electrically performed, from time to time, by the said ordinance of the City of Chicago, Illinois, effective February 20, 1920; and, in consideration of the foregoing, the Edison Company further agrees that it will supply to the Railroad Company, as required, such additional or further electrical energy as the Railroad Company may from time to time desire it to furnish during said term in any other of its operations within said Chicago Terminal District, or in the

General obligations as to supply.

operations of any other company or companies within the provisions of Article X hereof; *provided*, that twelve (12) months' notice in writing shall be given to the Edison Company of any such additional supply of electrical energy desired by the Railroad Company in accordance with the provisions of Sections 4 and 5 of Article IV. The Edison Company shall furnish all such electrical energy and the Railroad Company shall pay therefor on the basis and at the rates in this contract provided.

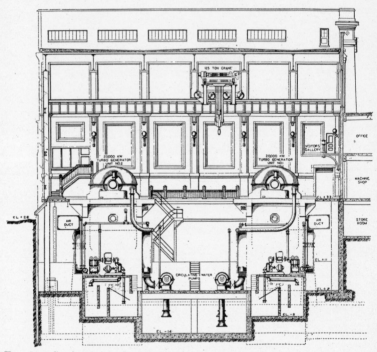

FIG. 82.—Sectional elevation, turbine room, Lakeside Station, T.M.E.R. & L. Co.

Supply of energy during preliminary period. SECTION 3. The Edison Company shall also supply to the Railroad Company during the Preliminary Period of the contract all such alternating current energy at the points specified in Section 2 of Article IV hereof for delivery of alternating current energy as the Railroad Company may from time to time desire to draw and use hereunder (such energy in any case to be supplied as promptly as possible) and also all such direct current energy as the Railroad Company may from time to time desire to draw and use hereunder if and so far as the Edison Company shall have such direct current energy available. Such energy shall be measured as to kilowatt hours consumed in like manner as other energy supplied during the term of this contract is metered. For all energy so supplied during the Preliminary Period the Railroad Company shall pay at the total rate of one and six-tenths cents (1.6c) per kilowatt hour.

Rate during preliminary period.

ARTICLE III

RATES

SECTION 1. For each calendar month of the term of this contract the Railroad Company shall pay to the Edison Company (subject, however, to reductions, if any, under the provisions of Article VI) a primary charge per kilowatt, reckoned upon the maximum demand hereunder (ascertained in accordance with the provisions of, and as defined in, Section 1 of Article II) for such month, or upon an amount of energy equal to seventy per centum (70%) of the highest one of the several maximum demands (so ascertained and defined) established for the last preceding twelve (12) months, whichever is greater, such primary charge to be in accordance with the following schedule:

Basis of primary (demand) charges.

SCHEDULE OF PRIMARY CHARGES

$1.85 per month per kilowatt up to and including 5,000 kilowatts;

$1.70 per month per kilowatt for the excess over 5,000 kilowatts and up to and including 10,000 kilowatts;

$1.60 per month per kilowatt for the excess over 10,000 kilowatts and up to and including 15,000 kilowatts;

$1.50 per month per kilowatt for the excess over 15,000 kilowatts.

Scale of same.

SECTION 2. In addition to the primary charge to be paid by the Railroad Company for each month as aforesaid the Railroad Company shall also pay to the Edison Company a secondary charge for each month based upon the number of kilowatt hours drawn and used by the Railroad Company under this contract during such month, which secondary charge, except as otherwise provided in Section 3 of this Article, shall be in accordance with the following schedule:

Basis of secondary (energy) charges.

SCHEDULE OF SECONDARY CHARGES

6.5 mills per kilowatt hour for consumption in such month up to and including 5,000,000 kilowatt hours;

6.45 mills per kilowatt hour for the excess over 5,000,000 kilowatt hours and up to and including 7,500,000 kilowatt hours;

6.4 mills per kilowatt hour for the excess over 7,500,000 kilowatt hours.

Scale of same.

SECTION 3. It is understood that the schedule of secondary charges established by Section 2 of this Article is based in part on the cost of coal used by the Edison Company in generating electrical energy at its several generating stations at the time of the execution of this contract, and it is the intent of the parties hereto that the secondary charges for energy supplied hereunder by the Edison Company to the Railroad Company shall vary from time to time with the variation in the cost to the Edison Company and the heat content of coal used by it in generating such electrical energy. The

fuel consumed by the Edison Company during the three years next preceding the date of this contract consisted of coal taken from mines in Illinois, Indiana, and Kentucky, having a weighted average heating value of ten thousand five hundred (10,500) B. T. U. per pound. The secondary charges provided for in Section 2 of this Article are based upon a cost to the Edison Company of Four Dollars ($4.00) per ton of coal of ten thousand five hundred (10,500) B. T. U. per pound and shall be subject to an increase or decrease per kilowatt hour, depending upon the average cost and heating value of the coal used from month to month by the Edison Company in the production of energy.

For any month in which the average cost of coal during the last preceding twelve (12) months shall have been more or less than Four Dollars ($4.00), or in which the average heat units per pound of coal used by the Edison Company during the last preceding twelve (12) months shall have been more than 11,000 B. T. U. or less than 10,000 B. T. U. per pound, or in which both of the above described conditions shall have existed, the secondary charge for such month shall be determined in accordance with the following formulae:

$$\frac{\text{Cost} \times 10,500}{\text{heat units}} + 2.5 =$$ mills per kilowatt hour for consumption in such month up to and including 5,000,000 kilowatt hours.

$$\frac{\text{Cost} \times 10,500}{\text{heat units}} + 2.45 =$$ mills per kilowatt hour for the excess over 5,000,000 kilowatt hours and up to and including 7,500,000 kilowatt hours.

$$\frac{\text{Cost} \times 10,500}{\text{heat units}} + 2.4 =$$ mills per kilowatt hour for the excess over 7,500,000 kilowatt hours.

The term "ton" as used in this contract shall be considered to mean a ton of two thousand (2,000) pounds. The term "cost" as used in the foregoing formulae and as applying to any given month shall be the weighted average of the cost (in dollars and hundredths thereof) per ton to the Edison Company of all coal delivered to it for the uses aforesaid during the last preceding twelve (12) months, including all freight, switching and car service charges paid by it in connection with such coal so delivered and including the cost of storing and handling the coal whenever the Edison Company shall store surplus coal for emergency purposes. While, as above stated, the secondary charges stated in Section 2 of this Article are based in part on the cost of coal to the Edison Company and are to vary from time to time with the variation in such cost, it is distinctly understood and agreed that no increase in such secondary charges, either as specifically set out in said Section 2 or as may at any time be established under the provisions of this section, shall at any time become effective when such increase is due to any arbitrary price, wage, charge, act, practice or rule of the Edison Company nor unless such increase be consistent with a contemporaneous general change, if any, in the cost of mining coal in the States of Illinois, Indiana and Kentucky and in the cost of transportation of such coal to Chicago and in the cost of labor used in the handling thereof. It is further understood that in computing such coal cost the actual cost of such coal and the charges directly relating thereto shall only be considered, and such computation shall be made without inclusion of any overhead or other like charges and expense.

Upon request of the Railroad Company at any time or times made, the Edison Company shall freely make available to the Railroad Company, for examination, all records of the Edison Company which may be required to establish the cost and heat content of coal, including all the items of cost above enumerated, for the purposes of this section.

The term "heat units" as used in said formulae and as applying to any given month shall be the weighted average number of B. T. U. per pound of coal used by the Edison Company during the last preceding twelve (12) months; *provided, however*, that if such weighted average number is not more than eleven thousand (11,000) nor less than ten thousand (10,000), then the number of heat units to be used in said formulae shall be ten thousand five hundred (10,500). "heat units."

SECTION 4. The Railroad Company agrees and guarantees that during each month of the term of this contract its total consumption of energy in kilowatt hours shall not fall below thirty per centum (30%) of the equivalent of its maximum demand for such month used continuously throughout the month for twenty-four (24) hours each day, and that its total aggregate payments for kilowatt hours consumed in such month shall not be less than such a load factor would require, subject, however, to the provisions of Section 1 of Article II and the provisions of Article VI hereof. Minimum load factor (30 per cent)

The deficiency, if any, between the amount of energy actually consumed during any month and the amount which the Railroad Deficiency in load factor.

Company has under this section guaranteed to consume in such month and to pay for, shall be considered as additional energy supplied hereunder by the Edison Company in such month, and in making up its bill hereunder for such month the Edison Company shall include the charge for such deficiency so considered at the rate for which the amount of energy represented by such deficiency would have been billed under the provisions of Sections 2 and 3 of this Article, if such energy had been actually consumed.

Billing.   SECTION 5.   As soon as practicable after the end of each month, except as otherwise specifically provided herein, the Edison Company shall render to the Railroad Company a bill or bills for all amounts due for such month under any and all provisions of this contract (including in such bill or bills any credit or credits to which the Railroad Company may be entitled for such month under any of the provisions of this contract), and the Railroad Company shall pay each such bill within **Bills payable in 30 days.** thirty (30) days after the receipt thereof.   If it shall be found that any such bill is erroneous in any respect, the Edison Company shall forthwith, and in any event with thirty (30) days, render to the Railroad Company a supplementary bill for any additional amount due from, or a credit memorandum for any amount to be credited to, the Railroad Company to correct such error.   The Railroad Company shall pay any such supplementary bill within thirty (30) days after the receipt thereof.

ARTICLE IV

FACILITIES AND OPERATION

Forms of energy to be supplied.   SECTION 1.   The energy to be supplied hereunder shall be in the form of (*a*) direct current at a nominal voltage of fifteen hundred (1,500) volts, and (*b*) sixty (60) cycle alternating current, three (3) phase, four (4) wire, at a nominal voltage of four thousand (4,000) volts between the phases and at a nominal voltage of twenty-three hundred (2,300) volts from each phase to neutral, and (*c*) sixty (60) cycle alternating current at such other voltages and number of phases as may be mutually agreed upon.

Points of delivery of energy.   SECTION 2.   The energy to be supplied hereunder shall be delivered by the Edison Company to the Railroad Company on the outgoing feeders from substations which substations shall be constructed and equipped by the Edison Company either upon property owned or leased by it or upon the right of way or property of the Railroad Company, which latter locations shall be approved by the Railroad Company, and which shall be located initially at or near the points specified in the table below; and such energy shall be delivered in the form of direct current (D. C.) at a nominal voltage of fifteen hundred (1,500) volts and alternating current (A. C.) at a nominal voltage of four thousand (4,000) volts between phases and twenty-three hundred (2,300) volts from each phase to neutral, as indicated in the following table by the symbols "D. C." and "A. C." respectively:

Points of Delivery	Kind of Energy	
South Water St., Chicago................		A. C.
12th Street (Central Station), Chicago......		A. C.
16th Street, Chicago.....................	D. C.	A. C.
69th Street, Chicago.....................	D. C.	A. C.
79th Street (Cheltenham), Chicago.........	D. C.	A. C.
95th Street (Burnside Shops), Chicago......		A. C.
115th Street, Chicago.....................	D. C.	A. C.
156th Street, Harvey, Illinois..............	D. C.	A. C.
Vollmer Road, Illinois....................	D. C.	A. C.
A point between Ashland Ave. and Vermont St., Blue Island, Illinois................	D. C.	A. C.

It is understood and agreed that no direct current fifteen hundred (1,500) volt converting apparatus will initially be provided by the Edison Company at the points of delivery for which no supply of direct current energy is indicated in the foregoing table. It is further understood and agreed that the Railroad Company shall provide suitable substation space within its own buildings for the installation of alternating current apparatus for the supply of alternating current at the points of delivery above mentioned from which no direct current is to be supplied. The Edison Company will provide feeder pressure regulators in any case where the length of the A. C. circuit or character of the A. C. service requires close pressure regulation.

SECTION 3. The Edison Company agrees to provide by purchase or lease such real estate as may be necessary for substation purposes hereunder, except such real estate as may be furnished by the Railroad Company under the provisions of this Article. The Edison Company further agrees to provide and maintain upon such real estate (whether provided by it or by the Railroad Company) at or near each of the points of delivery mentioned in Section 2 of this Article, except as otherwise specifically provided in said Section 2, and at or near any location specified in a request for an additional substation under the provisions of Section 4 of this Article, a suitable substation building, and to install therein and thereafter to maintain and operate such machinery, apparatus and other equipment as may be required for the constant and adequate supply of energy hereunder.

Marginal notes:

Railroad Co. to supply space for **A. C. substation** apparatus.

Feeder pressure regulators.

Facilities for supply of energy.

Provision of substations.

Adequacy of equipment.

The design and arrangement of each such substation, the type and capacity of the machinery, apparatus and other equipment installed therein, the construction work in connection therewith, the spare unit or reserve capacity to be provided and maintained, and the operation thereof, shall be in accordance with the most approved engineering practice and adequate for the service requirements of the Railroad Company as in this contract specified.

Initial capacities of D. C. substations.

In the several substations there shall be installed initially for the traction service of the Railroad Company units of not less than the following number and continuous capacity:

16th Street	3	3,000	Kw. Units
69th "	3	3,000	" "
115th "	2	3,000	" "
Harvey	2	3,000	" "
Vollmer Road	2	1,500	" "
Cheltenham	2	3,000	" "
Blue Island	1	1,500	" "

Spare capacity in traction substations.

The Edison Company agrees that there shall at all times be installed in the several substations from which the Edison Company is required to supply energy hereunder to the Railroad Company sufficient spare or reserve capacity to supply the traction power requirements of the Railroad Company as specified herein and in accordance with the provisions of this contract and especially of Section 8 of this Article whenever one unit of any particular kind of apparatus is out of service in any substation except initially at Blue Island substation.

D. C. substation and feeder facilities.

In any substation from which the Edison Company is required to supply energy in the form of direct current hereunder, the Edison Company shall install, maintain and operate in accordance with the most approved engineering practice, the necessary conversion apparatus, with suitable control and switching equipment, and the necessary feeder equipment. The number and kind of such feeders shall be such as are specified by the Railroad Company, in order to properly and safely control and sectionalize all main line tracks, yard tracks, and gap sections within interlocking limits near substations, and all such feeders shall be equipped with adequate protective apparatus for the electrical disconnection at the substation of the distribution lines which they serve.

A. C. substation and feeder facilities.

In any substation from which the Edison Company is required to supply energy hereunder in the form of alternating current, the Edison Company shall install, maintain and operate, in accordance with the most approved engineering practice, three (3) phase four (4) wire feeders with approximately four thousand (4,000) volts between phases and approximately twenty-three

hundred (2,300) volts from each phase to neutral, twenty-three
hundred (2,300) volt single phase feeders, and feeders at
such other voltages and phase as may be agreed upon under
the provisions of Section 1 of this Article; the number and
kind of feeders in each case to be such as are required by the
Railroad Company; and the Edison Company shall install,
maintain, and operate in each such substation suitable switching and protective equipment. Said feeders, so far as practicable and necessary, and as provided in Section 2 of this Article,
shall be equipped with automatic induction feeder regulators.
The energy supplied to said feeders shall be such that feeders
from adjacent points of supply hereunder (mentioned in Section
2 of this Article) located along the right of way of the Railroad
Company may be interconnected by the Railroad Company
through its distribution lines.

In case any substation from which energy is supplied here- *Feeders to R.
R. right of
under is not located on or immediately adjacent to the right way.*
of way of the Railroad Company the Edison Company shall
install, maintain and operate the necessary feeders connecting such feeder equipment in such substation with the Railroad Company's feeders at a point on the Railroad Company's
right of way line most readily reached from such substation
and which shall be satisfactory to the Railroad Company.

SECTION 4. If at any time for any reason the Railroad *Provisions
for additional
Company shall require additional fifteen hundred (1,500) volt substations.*
direct current energy at any point along its right of way in
the portion of its Chicago Terminal District located within
the State of Illinois to which such energy may not be economically transmitted from any then existing substation hereunder,
and shall request the Edison Company in writing to provide
an additional substation hereunder, specifying in such request
the approximate location of the proposed additional substation,
the estimated amount of additional energy to be supplied at
such additional substation and the approximate date of first
delivery, which date shall be not less than twelve (12) months
after the making of such request, then the Edison Company
shall install at or near such location an additional substation
(within the limits of said Chicago Terminal District within the
State of Illinois) at which energy shall be delivered hereunder,
and shall from and after the date so specified and during the
balance of the term, supply hereunder to the Railroad Company
at such additional substation the amount of energy in the form
requested, *provided, however,* that the amount of additional
energy to be so supplied in the vicinity of any such additional
substation shall not be less than three thousand (3,000) kilowatts, and *provided, further,* that the Railroad Company shall
provide and lease to the Edison Company under the provisions
of Section 9 of this Article the necessary ground space for any

such additional substation unless the Edison Company already possesses space suitable and available for such additional substation, and *provided, further*, that if such additional substation shall be located outside of the limits of the City of Chicago, the Edison Company shall be able to obtain from the authorities of the municipality in which such additional substation is to be located the necessary consent to extend its transmission lines from said city limits over and across public thoroughfares in such municipality to such additional substation.

Provisions for increase of load.

SECTION 5.   The Edison Company agrees that it will provide and at all times maintain sufficient generating, transmitting and converting equipment to furnish to the Railroad Company in accordance with the provisions hereof such energy as the Railroad Company shall require to meet its traffic and business. The Railroad Company agrees, however, to give to the Edison Company at least twelve (12) months' written notice of an expected substantial increase in the Railroad Company's traffic or business which may require the installation on the part of the Edison Company of additional generating, transmitting or converting equipment.

Easement for Edison Co. transmission lines.

SECTION 6.   The Railroad Company agrees that the Edison Company may construct in the right of way of the Railroad Company underground conduits and may install therein wires and cables for the transmission of energy, *provided*, that the location and details of such construction and installation shall be satisfactory to the Railroad Company, and, *provided, further*, that such conduits, wires and cables are installed primarily to supply energy hereunder to the Railroad Company. Detailed plans of any such construction and installation shall be submitted by the Edison Company to the Railroad Company for approval, and be approved by it before any such work is done.

Type and number of transmission lines.

All transmission lines extending from any generating station of the Edison Company to any substation from which energy is delivered hereunder shall be installed underground except such transmission lines or portions of such lines as shall be required outside the city limits of the City of Chicago, and any such transmission lines or portion thereof installed outside said city limits may, at the election of the Edison Company, be installed and maintained either overhead or underground. The number, capacity and distribution of such transmission lines in connection with each substation shall be such that the cutting out of any one of such lines will not prevent the delivery of the required amount of energy to the Railroad Company at such substation in accordance with the provisions of Section 8 of this Article.

Source of energy.

SECTION 7.   All or any part of the energy supplied hereunder to the Railroad Company may be generated by the

Edison Company at its own stations or may be procured by it from any other equally reliable source.

SECTION 8. Energy furnished hereunder in the form of direct current shall have a normal voltage of fifteen hundred (1,500) volts at the point of delivery at the Railroad Company's

Voltage regulation of D. C. energy.

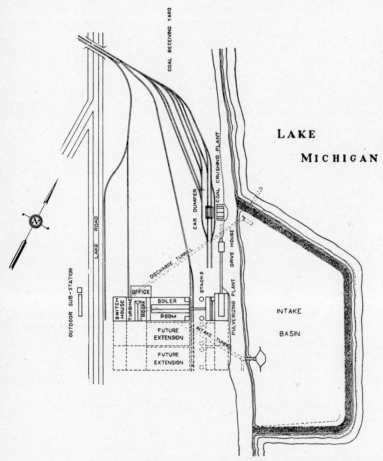

FIG. 83.—Plan of power station and coal pulverizing equipment of Lakeside Station, T.M.E.R. & L. Co.

right of way, and under normal and regular conditions of railroad traffic this voltage shall not be higher than fifteen hundred fifty (1,550) volts nor lower than fourteen hundred (1,400) volts.

Under normal and regular conditions of use the frequency and voltage of energy supplied hereunder in the form of alternating current shall not vary more than five per centum (5%) above or below normal.

In general, the Edison Company will approximately compensate for voltage drop in its transmission lines by carrying its power plant voltage higher at times of peak load than at times of light load. The voltage characteristics of the conversion apparatus installed in the substations of the Edison Company for the purposes of this contract shall be in accordance with the most approved engineering practice for railway service and satisfactory to the Railroad Company.

R. R. prop-
erty for
Edison Co.
substations.

Lease of
same.
SECTION 9. If the Railroad Company shall at any time own property that is available and suitable for a substation from which energy is to be supplied to it hereunder, the Railroad Company agrees to lease such property to the Edison Company for substation purposes during the term of this contract. So long as any substation located upon property of the Railroad Company shall be used primarily and to the extent of at least eighty per centum (80%) thereof for supplying energy hereunder to the Railroad Company, the rental which the Edison

Company shall pay to the Railroad Company for the use of such property shall be a nominal rental of One Dollar ($1.00) per year for each piece of property upon which a substation is erected. The Edison Company may distribute energy from any such substation to other customers as well as to the Railroad Company, but if in any year the amount of energy distributed from any such substation to customers of the Edison Company other than the Railroad Company shall exceed twenty per centum (20%) of the entire output of such substation in such year, the Edison Company shall pay to the Railroad Company as rental for the use of the property upon which such substation is located, a rental for such year ascertained as follows: The value of such property at the beginning of such year shall be determined by agreement of the parties, or if they are unable to agree, by arbitration under the provisions of Article VIII of this contract, and the rental which the Edison Company shall pay for such year shall be such proportion of six per centum (6%) of such value as the number of kilowatt hours distributed by the Edison Company in such year from such substation to its customers other than the Railroad Company shall bear to the total number of kilowatt hours distributed by the Edison Company from such substation in such year. The Edison Com-

pany may install and maintain upon or across the right of way of the Railroad Company the necessary underground transmission and distribution lines to connect such substation with the premises of any other customer, *provided*, that such installation and maintenance shall be satisfactory to the Railroad

Company. Detailed plans of any such installation shall be submitted by the Edison Company to the Railroad Company for approval, and shall be approved by it before any work is done or installation made under the provisions of this Section.

It is further understood and agreed that wherever in this contract permission or authority is given to the Edison Company to install or maintain upon or across the right of way or lands of the Railroad Company any lines, conduits, wires, or other equipment, property or structures, other than such as are required for the performance of this contract by the Edison Company, it shall be and is upon the express condition that no such use, installation, construction or maintenance shall be made without the specific approval of the Railroad Company in each particular instance, and that whenever the Railroad Company shall desire the removal of any such installation, construction or maintenance or the discontinuance of any such use, such removal and discontinuance shall be promptly made by the Edison Company upon notice from the Railroad Company, and upon failure of the Edison Company so to do such removal may be made by the Railroad Company at the expense of the Edison Company, and such use may be prevented.

SECTION 10. The Edison Company shall, in conformance with the request of the Railroad Company, operate from its substations certain remote-controlled auxiliary switching equipment for paralleling and sectionalizing the distribution lines of the Railroad Company along its right of way. But in the event that any auxiliary switching equipment required to be installed in the original construction of any substation shall have been completed, and the Railroad Company shall desire to increase this equipment in any substation to the extent of requiring a larger building, the Railroad Company shall pay for such extension of substation building and any other expense involved in the installation of such apparatus.

Edison Co. operation of R. R. tie-stations.

SECTION 11. The Railroad Company may, at its option, maintain and operate a suitable system of apparatus and wiring for the purpose of enabling it to communicate or indicate at any time to its Power Director the operating conditions of all machinery, equipment and feeders serving the Railroad Company's distribution lines hereunder. Any such apparatus and wiring may be installed in any substation of the Edison Company from which energy is supplied to the Railroad Company hereunder, in conjunction with equipment owned and operated by the Edison Company, *provided*, that in the judgment of the Edison Company such installation will not interfere with the safe and satisfactory operation of the Edison Company's apparatus. The Edison Company shall co-operate in

Railroad Co. indicating system in Edison Co. substations.

all reasonable degree with the Railroad Company in the installation and operation of such apparatus and wiring.

Installation of apparatus under Secs. 10 and 11. SECTION 12.   All equipment and apparatus and the wiring in connection therewith installed under the provisions of Sections 10 or 11 of this Article in or upon the right of way or property of the Railroad Company shall be installed by and at the expense of the Railroad Company except as may be otherwise agreed upon by the parties hereto.   All such equipment, apparatus and wiring installed in any substation of the Edison Company or installed elsewhere than in or upon the right of way or property of the Railroad Company shall be installed by and to the satisfaction of the Edison Company, under the direction and at the expense of the Railroad Company.   As

Apportionment of cost and bills therefor. soon as practicable after the completion of any such installation by the Edison Company, it shall render to the Railroad Company a bill or bills for the expense thereof, and such bill or bills in so far as they relate to any equipment, apparatus, or wiring installed for the benefit of both parties hereto shall be based on an equitable apportionment of the cost of labor and material; and the Railroad Company shall pay such bill or bills within thirty (30) days after the receipt thereof or within thirty (30) days after the approval and/or acceptance of such installation by the Railroad Company.

Determination of expense of work done by either party for other. SECTION 13.   When any work is performed by the Railroad Company for the Edison Company or by the Edison Company for the Railroad Company, including work as mentioned under Sections 10 and 11 of this Article, the expense, except as may otherwise be agreed upon by the parties hereto, shall consist of the actual cost of materials and supplies furnished, including transportation charges at the established rates, all plus fifteen per cent (15 %), and the actual cost of labor involved below the rank of general foreman, plus ten per cent (10 %).

Operation of R. R. feeders. SECTION 14.   All direct current and alternating current feeder switches and circuit breakers in and controlled from the substations of the Edison Company hereunder and serving distribution lines of the Railroad Company shall be operated by operators employed by the Edison Company under direct orders from the Railroad Company's Power Director, and in accordance with rules to be agreed upon and issued by the Railroad Company and the Edison Company

ARTICLE V

METERS AND METERING

Edison Co. to furnish meters. The energy to be supplied hereunder shall be measured, both as to maximum demand and as to kilowatt hours, by meters to be installed by the Edison Company at its expense for the measurement of the energy supplied to the Railroad

Company. Except as may be otherwise agreed upon by the parties hereto, such meters shall be installed, maintained and operated in the manner and under the conditions hereinafter in this contract set forth. Such meters shall be installed in each substation from which energy is supplied. In any case where any such substation is located upon or immediately adjacent to the right of way of the Railroad Company, energy shall be considered as delivered hereunder to the Railroad Company in such substation. In any case where such substation is not located upon or immediately adjacent to the right

Points of delivery; location of meters.

FIG. 84.—Dresser Power Plant of Central Indiana Power Co., near Terre Haute, Indiana.

of way of the Railroad Company, energy shall be considered as delivered hereunder to the Railroad Company at the point where the feeders leading from such substation intersect the Railroad Company's right of way line, and in such case the readings of the meter or meters in such substation shall be reduced by an appropriate factor to compensate for energy losses between the point of metering and the point of delivery, such factor in each case to be mutually agreed upon by the parties hereto.

Meter readings to be adjusted to points of delivery.

The meters for measuring energy supplied under this contract in the form of direct current shall be installed on the fifteen hundred (1,500) volt bus bars supplying the outgoing feeders to the Railroad Company's system. One watt hour meter or several watt hour meters in multiple, as shall be

D. C. meters.

required according to good engineering practice, shall be installed on each such bus bar, and such meter or meters shall be read on the last day of each calendar month at midnight for the purpose of ascertaining the kilowatt hours drawn and used during the month.

A. C. meters. The meters for measuring energy supplied under this contract in the form of alternating current shall be installed on the low tension side of the three (3) phase step-down transformer or set of transformers used for transforming energy supplied hereunder in any substation, one (1) three (3) phase watt hour meter being installed on each three (3) phase transformer or set of transformers; or in case any such energy is supplied at a pressure of twelve thousand (12,000) volts in such substation, then a three (3) phase watt hour meter or meters shall be installed directly on the outgoing feeder or feeders supplying such energy. All such watt hour meters shall be read on the last day of each calendar month at midnight for the purpose of ascertaining the kilowatt hours drawn and used during the month.

Demand meters. For the purpose of obtaining data for the ascertainment of the maximum demand a demand meter shall be installed in connection with each watt hour meter (whether used for measuring energy in the form of direct or of alternating current), and such demand meter shall record automatically hourly, from the commencement of each hour, the kilowatt hours drawn and used during such hour.

Testing of meters. The following provisions of this Article shall be applicable to any kind of meter that shall be used. The Railroad Company shall have the right to have representatives present at any or all of said readings, and all payments other than the guaranteed minimum payments representing the primary charge shall be based thereon. All watt hour meters shall be tested and calibrated monthly in the presence of duly appointed representatives of both parties, and if as a result of any test a meter shall be found incorrect or inaccurate it shall be restored to an accurate condition or a new meter shall be substituted. In case either the Edison Company or the Railroad Company shall at any time believe that any meter so installed registers incorrectly, the party holding such belief shall have a right to require that a test be made of such meter. The party desiring such test shall make a request therefor in writing upon the other party and thereupon such meter shall be tested and calibrated in the presence of duly appointed representatives of both parties, and if as a result of such test the meter shall be found incorrect or inaccurate it shall be restored to an accurate condition or a new meter shall be substituted. Any meter tested and found to be not more than one per centum (1 %) from normal shall be considered correct and accurate as to the registration of the number of kilowatt hours drawn and used. If as a result of any such test any meter shall be found to register in excess of one per centum (1 %), either above or below normal, then the readings of such meter previously taken for the purpose of ascertaining the number of kilowatt hours drawn and consumed, or for the purpose of ascertaining the maximum demand, shall be corrected according to the percentage of inaccuracy so found; but no such correction either in respect to maximum demand or kilowatt hours drawn and consumed shall extend back beyond thirty (30) days previous to the day on which such inaccuracy shall be discovered by such test, and if during such previous thirty (30) days one or more prior tests shall have been made under the provisions hereof, then no such correction shall extend back beyond the date of the last of such prior tests. If any test of any meter shall be made at the request of the Railroad Company with the result that such meter shall be found to register correctly or within two per centum (2 %) of normal, the Railroad Company shall bear the expense of such test. The expense of all other tests shall be borne by the Edison Company. All meters shall be kept under the seals of both Companies.

ARTICLE VI

INTERRUPTION AND DEFAULT

SECTION 1. If at any time in any month the Edison Company shall be unable to supply energy to the Railroad Company, in whole or in part, as required to be supplied by it under the provisions of this contract, the primary charge for such month, as determined under the provisions of Section 1 of Article III, shall be proportionately and equitably reduced, and if any such inability to supply energy shall cause the Railroad Company's load factor in such month to fall below the guaranteed amount specified in Section 4 of Article III hereof, the Railroad Company shall be relieved of such guaranty for such month or months, and the average secondary charge per kilowatt hour for energy consumed in such month shall not be at a higher rate, due to smaller consumption, than the average secondary charge per kilowatt hour for the consumption in the next preceding normal month. Any such reduction or abatement shall be made as soon as practicable after the end of the month in which the failure of delivery occurs by agreement of the parties, or, if the parties cannot agree, then by arbitration under the provisions of Article VIII hereof.

Reduction of charges in case of failure of supply.

It is agreed that nothing in this section shall be construed to discharge or relieve the Edison Company from its obligation to furnish energy hereunder as required by Section 2 of Article II hereof, but it is agreed that if the Edison Company

Failure due to strikes, fire, riot, action of elements, etc.

shall fail so to do at any time and such failure is caused by strikes not due to collusion of the Edison Company or caused by fire, civil or military authority, insurrection or riot, the action of the elements or by any other cause beyond its control, the concessions above in this Article made to the Railroad Company shall be accepted by it as full satisfaction of the Edison Company's liability to the Railroad Company for its loss or damage due to the Edison Company's failure so caused.

Minimum load factor in case of suspension of R. R. service.

SECTION 2.   If on any day or days in any month the Railroad Company shall be prevented from operating its regular train service, either in whole or in part, by strike, fire or explosion, civil or military authority, insurrection or riot, abnormal weather condition, or by any other cause reasonably beyond its control, and if such prevention shall cause the Railroad Company's load factor in such month to fall below the guaranteed amount specified in Section 4 of Article III hereof, then and in that case the provisions of said Section 4 of Article III shall not be effective for such day or days and the minimum load factor of thirty per centum (30 %) specified in said Section 4 shall apply only during those days in such month in which the Railroad Company shall not have been so prevented from operating its regular train service; *provided*, that the Railroad Company shall give to the Edison Company notice of any such prevention as required under the provisions of Section 1 of Article XII hereof.

Cancellation of contract by Railroad Co.

SECTION 3.   It is recognized that the Railroad Company must receive regular and uninterrupted service from the Edison Company in order to make this contract of value to it, and if for any reason interruption of service to be supplied under this contract shall be so frequent or of such duration as to interfere materially with the Railroad Company's operation of its lines, or if the character of service supplied hereunder shall not be in accordance with the provisions of this contract, then the Railroad Company may in writing notify the Edison Company thereof, specifying the reasons for complaint, and the Edison Company shall forthwith promptly correct its service so as to remedy the trouble so specified.   If the trouble so specified is not promptly remedied and in every event within not to exceed ninety (90) days from the date of such notice, the Railroad Company may elect to cancel this contract by giving to the Edison Company not less than thirty (30) days' notice in writing of its intention to cancel the contract, stating in such notice the date of proposed termination. If such notice shall be given, the contract shall terminate upon the date of cancellation specified in the notice or at any earlier date upon which the Railroad Company may be able to obtain elsewhere the necessary energy required for the operation of its lines and shall notify the Edison Company of such fact; and until such date of termination the Edison Company shall continue to supply energy hereunder to the Railroad Company in accordance with the terms and conditions of this contract, but no such notice or termination of this contract shall relieve the Edison Company from its liability under this contract with respect to any matters arising prior to such date of termination. If prior to such date of termination the Edison Company should at any time or times fail to supply to the Railroad Company any portion of the energy which the Edison Company is required to supply under the provisions of this contract, the Railroad Company shall have the right during the period of any such failure to secure the supply of such portion from some other source for the account of the Edison Company.

SECTION 4. Should the Railroad Company fail to pay when due in accordance with the terms hereof, any bill rendered hereunder, and such bill shall remain unpaid for a period of sixty (60) days after the same became due and payable, the Edison Company shall be entitled to receive, and the Railroad Company shall pay, interest upon the amount of such bill at the rate of six per centum (6 %) per annum from the date upon which such bill became due and payable. <small>Interest on defaulted bills.</small>

ARTICLE VII

PROTECTION AGAINST CLAIMS FOR DAMAGES

The Railroad Company shall indemnify and save harmless the Edison Company from and against any and all claims for damages in favor of any person, persons or corporation founded upon or arising from improper or negligent insulation, maintenance or operation of the electric wires, conductors and equipment of the Railroad Company during the life of this contract, and shall pay and reimburse the Edison Company for all costs, expenses and reasonable attorneys' fees which the Edison Company may be put to or incur in defending any suit or suits brought against it for such damages, *provided*, the Edison Company shall not have been responsible for such defective condition of the electric wires, conductors and equipment of the Railroad Company and the said condition shall not have been caused by its acts or negligence. The Edison Company shall indemnify and save harmless the Railroad Company from and against any and all claims for damages in favor of any person, persons or corporation founded upon or arising in whole or in part from improper or negligent insulation, maintenance or operation of the electric wires, conductors and equipment of the Edison Company during the life of this contract, and from and against all other claims for damages due to its acts or negligence and not above assumed by the Railroad Company, and shall pay and reimburse the Railroad Company for all <small>Railroad Co. to indemnify Edison Co.</small> <small>Edison Co. to indemnify Railroad Co.</small>

costs, expenses and reasonable attorneys' fees which the Railroad Company may be put to or incur in defending any suit or suits brought against it for such damages. It is agreed, however, that the respective party shall have prompt notice of any such claim, demand or suit, and shall be given an opportunity to defend the same.

Edison Co. liable for improperly closed switch.　If the Edison Company, at the request of the Railroad Company, shall have opened any switch supplying electrical energy to the Railroad Company under this contract, the Edison Company shall be liable for any damage resulting in case the Edison Company shall close such switch without first receiving from the Railroad Company or one of its duly authorized employees an order to close such switch.

Article VIII

ARBITRATION

Selection of arbitrators.　If at any time a difference of opinion shall arise between the parties hereto in regard to their respective rights, duties and obligations under this contract and within its terms and provisions or in respect of any payments to be made by virtue of this contract, the question in dispute shall be referred to a Board of Arbitrators consisting of three (3) competent disinterested persons experienced in the particular matter which is the subject of dispute. One (1) of said arbitrators shall be chosen by each of the parties hereto and the two (2) so chosen shall select the third arbitrator. The party desiring such arbitration shall give written notice of the same to the other party, setting forth definitely therein the point in dispute, and naming the person selected by such party to act as arbitrator. If the party on whom such notice is served shall for twenty (20) days thereafter neglect to name by notice to the other party a person to act as its arbitrator, then the party giving such notice shall name the second arbitrator, and the two (2) thus chosen shall select the third arbitrator. If the two (2) arbitrators chosen as provided in this Article shall be unable to agree upon a third arbitrator within twenty (20) days after their appointment (or if they were appointed on different days then within twenty (20) days after the appointment of the one last appointed), then such third arbitrator shall be named and selected by the person who at the time shall be the senior Judge, in point of service, of the United States District Court for the Eastern Division of the Northern District of Illinois, and application may be made upon two (2) days' notice in writing to the parties hereto by either or both arbitrators to such Judge for such purpose. The Board of Arbitrators so chosen shall immediately proceed to hear and **Proceedings before arbitrators.**　determine all matters submitted to them after giving to each party hereto not less than five (5) days' notice of the time and place of meeting; and at the time and place appointed they shall proceed summarily to hear and dispose of the matters in dispute unless in their judgment the hearing shall be adjourned to a later day or days, of which adjournment like notice shall be given unless such notice is waived by both parties, in which case the hearing may proceed at an earlier day.

The determination of such Board of Arbitrators, or a majority of them, as to any matter so submitted to them shall be final and conclusive upon the parties hereto and said parties shall abide by such decision and perform the conditions thereof as if the same were made a part of this contract. In case the Railroad Company shall dispute and shall desire to submit to arbitration, as aforesaid, any of the bills rendered by the Edison Company hereunder the Railroad Company shall nevertheless pay such bills promptly within thirty (30) days after such rendition, without prejudice, however, to its right to receive or recover back any sum which the decision of the arbitrators shall find to be overpayment, with interest thereon at the rate of six per centum (6%) per annum from the time when such overpayment was made until the date of refund. Reasonable compensation shall be paid to said arbitrators, which compensation shall be paid in equal parts by the parties hereto. Other expenses of said arbitration shall be borne by the party making the expense, unless otherwise agreed or unless otherwise determined by said Board of Arbitrators or a majority of them.

Conditions to attend and result from arbitration.

ARTICLE IX

DISCRIMINATION IN RATES

If at any time during the life of this contract the Edison Company shall supply energy to any other consumer for traction or transportation service at a lower rate than that hereinabove given to the Railroad Company hereunder, and such lower rate shall not be justified by different conditions of service, making the cost of production and distribution to such other consumer relatively less than to the Railroad Company (and the burden of proving such different conditions of service justifying the lower rate shall be upon the Edison Company), then and in that event and so long as such lower rate shall be given to such other consumer while this contract is in force the Railroad Company shall be entitled to a reduction in its said rate equal to so much of the amount of the difference between such lower rate and the Railroad Company's said rate as shall not be so justified.

Reduction of rates, if lower rates to other traction customers.

ARTICLE X

SCOPE OF CONTRACT

Definition of railway system.

The railway system and appurtenances of the Railroad Company for the operation, construction and maintenance of which energy is to be supplied by the Edison Company when and as provided in this contract shall, for the purposes of this contract, include any railway lines within the Chicago Terminal District of the Railroad Company which shall be electrified in compliance with the provisions of the aforesaid ordinance of the City of Chicago and which are now operated by the Railroad Company or which shall hereafter be constructed or acquired by lease, purchase, stock ownership, or operating agreement to be operated by it and shall also include any terminal company operating the Chicago terminal station of the Railroad Company when and as requested by the Railroad

"Chicago Terminal District."

Company. The term "Chicago Terminal District," as used in this contract, shall be considered to include the territory within the City of Chicago and also all territory within fifteen (15) miles of the present city limits of said City of Chicago. The

Tenants of Railroad Co. included.

Michigan Central Railroad Company, which is at present a tenant of the Railroad Company, and any other railway company or companies now using or that may hereafter use the Railroad Company's Chicago terminal or the Railroad Company's right of way within the Chicago Terminal District of the Railroad Company, are to be recognized and considered as part of the Railroad Company's railway system and for which energy is to be furnished under this contract to the extent and as and upon such limitations as the Railroad Company may from time to time request and direct. All electric service required to be furnished hereunder shall be deemed to be furnished to and shall be paid for by the Railroad Company.

Limitations on use of energy hereunder.

The energy furnished hereunder shall be used only for traction and other railway purposes within the Chicago Terminal District of the Railroad Company, including the operation of trains and signals, and the construction, operation and lighting of stations, shops and other buildings owned, used or operated for railroad purposes by the Railroad Company or by the other railway companies or the terminal company hereinabove in this Article referred to.

Provision for termination of existing contracts.

All other contracts under which the Edison Company shall be supplying energy to any company entitled to use any energy furnished under this contract which shall be in force at the date of this contract or which may hereafter be entered into shall continue in force unaffected by the terms hereof, *provided, however,* that any such company may at any time after the date hereof terminate any such contract with it by giving to the Edison Company, not less than sixty (60) days prior to the date of desired termination, notice in writing of its election to terminate such contract, specifying therein the date of desired termination, and, if such notice be given, such contract shall terminate on the date so specified, and the energy theretofore required to be supplied under any contract so terminated shall thereafter be a part of the energy to be supplied hereunder by the Edison Company, *provided, further,* that such termination of such contracts, respectively, and the supply of energy under this contract in lieu thereof be approved by the Railroad Company.

ARTICLE XI

PURCHASE OF SUBSTATION EQUIPMENT BY RAILROAD COMPANY

SECTION 1. If at the expiration of the original term of this contract or at the expiration of the first five (5) year extension of the term herein authorized, the Railroad Company shall not have effected a further extension under the provisions of Section 2 of Article I, it shall purchase from the Edison Company all the apparatus which the Edison Company shall have installed in any substation for the purpose of supplying direct current energy hereunder for traction service, including high tension switches, transformers, conversion apparatus, low tension switches, connections and switches to fifteen hundred (1,500) volt feeders, and all other auxiliary equipment installed in any substation for the purpose aforesaid, except such of said apparatus as the Edison Company shall elect to use for other purposes. If the term hereof shall be extended by the election of the Railroad Company under the provisions of Section 2 of Article I for more than one five (5) year period, the Railroad Company shall purchase at the expiration of the term so much of the apparatus just described as shall at such expiration have been in service for fifteen (15) years, or less, and as the Edison Company shall not elect to use for other purposes. The Railroad Company may, at its option, however, at the expiration or termination of this contract, purchase any or all of such substation equipment as the Edison Company may have installed in any substation erected upon the right of way or property of the Railroad Company and required for the service of the Railroad Company. After such expiration or termination the Edison Company shall, within sixty (60) days after receipt from the Railroad Company of a request so to do, remove at the expense of the Edison Company all substation apparatus and equipment not purchased by the Railroad Company. The Railroad Company shall also purchase at the expiration or termination of this contract all substation buildings which the Edison Company shall have erected under the provisions of Sections 3 and 4 of Article IV upon the right of way or other

Conditions of purchase.

property owned by the Railroad Company. It is agreed, however, that nothing in this section contained shall require the Railroad Company to purchase any of the equipment or apparatus above mentioned that shall have become defective or obsolete to such extent as to be unserviceable or not useful to the present system of traction of the Railroad Company.

Determination of purchase price.

SECTION 2. The purchase price to be paid by the Railroad Company for any substation building or for any equipment or apparatus purchased under the provisions of Section 1 of this Article shall be determined on an equitable basis by agreement between the parties, giving due consideration to the matters of replacement cost, obsolescence, normal depreciation and condition with respect to repair and serviceability of building or equipment or apparatus and all other matters affecting the then value of such building, equipment or apparatus. If the parties are unable to agree upon such purchase price in any instance the same shall be determined by arbitration under the provisions of Article VIII hereof.

ARTICLE XII

OPERATING RELATIONS

Notice of abnormal period or of suspension of train service.

SECTION 1. In case of any railroad accident or of any abnormally heavy railroad traffic resulting, or which may result, in any substantial increase of the Railroad Company's load of energy supplied hereunder, or in case of any suspension by the Railroad Company of its regular train service, either in whole or in part, under any of the conditions specified in Section 2 of Article VI hereof, the Railroad Company shall give to the Edison Company immediate notice thereof by telephone or otherwise, confirmed within forty-eight (48) hours by letter. In either case, unless such notice shall have been given and so confirmed, an abnormal period because of "abnormally heavy railroad traffic," as defined in Section 1 of Article II, or a suspension of train service under the provisions of Section 2 of Article VI, as the case may be, shall not be considered to have come into existence. Whenever an abnormal period as defined in Section 1 of Article II or a suspension of train service shall come into existence and notice thereof shall be given when required as above provided, the parties hereto, as soon as practicable after such abnormal period or such suspension of train service shall have terminated, shall agree, if possible, upon the duration of such abnormal period or such suspension of train service, as the case may be, or if they are unable to agree upon such duration within ten (10) days after such termination the same shall be determined by arbitration under the provisions of Article VIII of this contract; and when so agreed upon or so determined a memorandum of such dura-

Determination of duration of same.

tion shall be made in duplicate and signed by a duly authorized representative of each party hereto, and one copy of such memorandum shall be retained by each party. Any notice under the provisions of this section shall be given to the Load Dispatcher of the Edison Company on duty at the time of the giving of such notice.

SECTION 2. The Railroad Company shall have the privilege at any time or at all times during the life of this contract of keeping an employee of the Railroad Company in the Load Dispatcher's office of the Edison Company, and such employee shall have the right to observe and to keep records of the load dispatching operations of the Edison Company so far as they relate to service to be supplied to the Railroad Company, but in no event shall such records be given to any employee of the Railroad Company except for the Railroad Company's private use.

Railroad Co. representatives in Edison Co. Load Dispatching office.

SECTION 3. Each party shall allow properly authorized employees of the other party to have access to its premises, books, records and accounting for any purpose necessary for or incidental to the carrying out of this contract.

Access to premises and records.

SECTION 4. Whenever either party shall install any conduit, cable, wire or other apparatus or equipment in or upon the premises of the other party, under any provision hereof, the party owning the same shall have the right, upon giving due notice to the other party, to repair or remove such apparatus at any and all reasonable times, *provided* such repair or removal shall not interfere with the carrying out of this contract; and upon the termination of this contract, by lapse of time or otherwise, such party shall remove permanently any and all property owned by it upon the premises of the other party not required to be purchased by such other party under any other provisions of this contract, or which such other party shall not elect to purchase where the right of such election is given to it.

Access to apparatus for repair of removal.

SECTION 5. Any notice, request or demand which may be given to, or made upon, either party by the other under any of the provisions of this contract shall, unless otherwise specifically provided, be given or made by serving the same personally in writing upon, or by sending the same by registered mail addressed to, the President, Vice President or General Manager in charge of operation for the time being of such party.

Serving of notices by either party.

SECTION 6. All rights and privileges granted by either party to the other under the terms of this contract shall terminate at the termination of the contract, by lapse of time or otherwise; *provided, however,* that upon such termination each party shall have the right to remove with reasonable promptness from the premises of the other party any property which

Termination of privileges.

it is authorized to remove therefrom under the foregoing provisions of this contract.

Waivers not to affect subsequent rights. SECTION 7. Any waiver or any number of successive waivers of any of the rights that may accrue to either party hereto through the default of the other in keeping and performing any of the terms or obligations of this contract shall not estop the party so waiving the default from having the benefit in accordance with the terms of this contract of any other or subsequent defaults, but at any time during the life of this contract either party shall have the benefits herein provided in case of default by the other, without regard to any prior waivers or the number or time of such antecedent waivers.

Contract in duplicate, successor and assigns. SECTION 8. This contract is executed in duplicate and shall inure to and be binding upon the successors and assigns of the respective parties hereto.

Approval by Illinois Commission. SECTION 9. It is understood and agreed that this contract is made subject to the approval of the Illinois Commerce Commission.

IN WITNESS WHEREOF, the parties hereto have caused this electric service agreement to be executed in duplicate by their duly authorized officers, and to be sealed with their respective corporate seals, attested by their respective Secretaries or Assistant Secretaries, the day and year first above written.

COMMONWEALTH EDISON COMPANY,
By SAMUEL INSULL,
President.

(CORPORATE SEAL)

Attest:

    JOHN W. EVERS, JR.
        Secretary.

ILLINOIS CENTRAL RAILROAD COMPANY,
By C. H. MARKHAM,
President.

(CORPORATE SEAL)

Attest:

    BURT A. BECK,
        Assistant Secretary.

Approved as to Engineering:
    D. J. BRUMLEY,
        Chief Engineer Chicago Terminal
        Improvement.

Approved as to form:
    W. S. HORTON,
        General Counsel.

Approved as to Accounting:
    G. J. BUNTING,
        Vice President.

CHAPTER XVII

BONDS AND BONDING

The circuit which supplies current from the substation to the car has already been outlined. The return portion of this circuit is made up of the track rails, being augmented by return copper feeders in parallel with the track only in cases of heaviest service. As rail lengths of either 30 or 60 ft. are used, a single rail will have 88 or 176 joints per mile, at which the electrical resistance of the connection between rails made by means of corroded fish plates would normally be very high. With this high resistance directly in series with the return circuit, any reasonable addition to the copper in the positive feeders is of little value. It was quickly found, therefore, in the operation of the early railway systems that the ends of rails must be connected electrically by conductors of lower resistance than the fish plates. These conductors have been designated as "bonds."

In the first installations bare copper, negative return wires were laid along the ties between the rails and connected with the center of each length of rail with a copper wire. This method, however, proved very expensive and was abandoned, although it has been reinstated recently of necessity in similar form where traffic is very heavy, particularly in city systems. Later the ends of rails were bonded by means of No. 6 galvanized-wire bonds clamped under the heads of track bolts. Such bonds were not only soon destroyed by galvanic action in the earth but were found to be of such high resistance as to be of little use. A slight decrease in the contact resistance of these bonds was later affected by forcing the bond wires into holes drilled in the heads of the bolts. The inability to reduce the track resistance sufficiently by any of the above means led to the introduction of the solid copper bond, which, in turn, developed into the laminated strip copper and stranded copper bonds which are preferable because of their flexibility.

215

Several distinctive types of the latter bonds have now come into very general use and a brief description of each will, therefore, be found below.

Compressed Terminal Bonds.—This type of terminal has been applied to various designs of copper bonds. It consists of a cylindrical head varying from $5/8$ to 1 in. in diameter and slightly longer than the thickness of the web of the rail. This head is forced into a recently reamed hole in the web of the rail by means of a heavy screw clamp provided with a conical contact which engages the center of the bond head and causes it to expand and flow under the pressure applied so that it makes intimate contact with the inner surface of the hole and heads over, rivet like, so as to prevent easy loosening or removal. Some compressed terminal bonds have their heads drilled with an axial hole through which a tapered steel pin is driven in order to expand the copper head well into the hole in the web.

Compressed terminal bonds may be installed so as to surround the fish plate or they may be of the "protected" type, installed before the fishplates are put on and later covered by the latter plates, thus protecting the bond from mechanical injury or theft. When installing this bond great care must be exercised not to drill the holes much before the bonds are inserted and, in drilling holes, to use a lubricant which will not produce an insulating film on the inside surface of the hole. Clear water or a solution of bicarbonate of soda and water may be used, but oil and soapy water should not be tolerated as lubricants.

Soldered or Brazed Bonds.—Bonds similar to the above but with flat tinned heads are sometimes soldered or brazed to the side of the rail head or under the rail flange by means of a gasoline or oxyhydrogen blowtorch after the rail has been brightened at the point of contact. These bonds have not proved entirely satisfactory, however, as they are quite likely to work loose and are also quite easily stolen.

Arc-weld Rail Bonds.—The extended use of electric arc welding on the track of electric railways has resulted in the development of rail bonds which can be applied with the electric arc in one form or another. An arc-weld bond terminal has been developed which has a direct weld between the copper and the steel. The steel contact surface is in shell form, about $1/8$ in. thick throughout, and a large area of copper is provided as a backing for the steel welding surfaces.

Arc-welding Dynamotor Bonding Machines.—Dynamotors, as the name indicates, consist of two separate armature windings on the common core which revolve in a common magnetic field. The motor windings are designed for 200 to 300, 400 to 600, 600 to 750, or 1,200 to 1,500 volts, depending upon the supply

FIG. 85.—Arc-welding dynamotor in use, Rail Welding & Bonding Co., Cleveland, Ohio.

voltage. The generator windings are designed to give 60 volts (open circuit). The shunt field is connected directly across the 60-volt generator, while the cumulative series field is in the motor circuit. The main advantages of the dynamotor over the motor-generator type of welder are lightness and increased efficiency. The lightness makes possible a portable machine, a necessity for track work and desirable for other work for which it is necessary to take the welder to the job.

The machine is designed for bonding with either carbon or metal arc, and the usual steel-electrode welding. Certain other machines are modified by having an arc adjuster.

Such bonding consists of a direct copper-to-steel weld obtained through the copper alloy. This gives a direct path of copper from rail to rail, producing the maximum electrical conductivity and full bonding value. The resulting mass is a solid, homogeneous, and ductile metal, which has a shearing strength of about 25,000 lb. per square inch.

Fig. 86.—Arc welding dynamotor.

Flame-weld Bonds.—Flame-weld bonds are designed for application to the rail, with the oxyacetylene flame. A special copper-alloy flux wire is used, as pure copper oxidizes too rapidly in the flame for satisfactory results. It has very low electrical resistance and requires less skill to apply than the arc-weld bond.

Socket Terminals.—These terminals can be used where it would be inconvenient to order special lengths of bonds. The various types of terminal shanks are provided with deep sockets into which the conductors, cut to proper lengths, may be soldered by the purchaser.

Amalgam Bonds.—Bonds consisting of semiplastic amalgam forced between the brightened surfaces of rail web and fish plate are occasionally found, although not in common use.

Aside from the above, several methods of making continuous rail joints of high electrical conductivity may well be classified under the heading of Bonds.   Such methods in common use are as follows:

Cast-welded Joint.—In making this joint, melted iron of special composition and high conductivity is poured around the rail ends, with the exception of the heads, while they are enclosed in a sand or iron mold of such shape as to leave a heavy lug of cast iron about the ends of the rail.   While it is rather difficult with this process to raise the temperature of the rail quickly enough to insure molecular adhesion between the rail and the molten metal, yet very satisfactory results have been obtained in many instances from both the standpoints of electrical conductivity and mechanical rigidity.

Thermit-welded Joint.—A combined joint and bond may be produced by the "thermit" process.   As in the previous method, a mold of sand is made about the rail ends, but in this case only sufficient thermit for one joint is melted at a time.   This melting is accomplished by making use of the well-known fact that finely divided aluminum when oxidized develops a great amount of heat.   This reaction has been brought under control so that a small amount of powdered aluminum mixed with iron oxide, if ignited with a small amount of ignition mixture, will react as above explained, with sufficient heat to melt the iron, which, in turn, is poured about the rail ends.   This produces a joint sim'lar to the cast weld with less metal but with apparently quite as good electrical and mechanical characteristics.

Electric-welded Joint.—In contrast to the electric-welded bond mentioned above there may be found in the city tracks of many railway companies the electric-welded rail joint.   This, a rigid rail joint produced by electrically welding heavy iron bars on either side of the webs of adjacent rail ends, should be carefully differentiated from the electric-welded bond, although the process of welding is almost identical with that outlined above, except that iron only is used and the size of weld and corresponding power used are much greater.   In this latter type of joint, iron filler blocks are inserted between the rail ends and ground to the form of the rail head so that the joint is entirely closed and the operation of cars over rail joints is made so much the smoother.   This joint has given very satisfactory service both electrically as a bond, for its conductivity is practically equal to that of the rail, and mechanically as a rail joint, the breakages not exceeding 1 per cent of the total joints welded after several years of service in at least one installation and averaging very close to this record on several other roads.

When considering any of these three methods of making combination rail joints and bonds where the joint is necessarily mechanically rigid, it should be borne in mind that the track will expand in hot weather sufficiently to throw it noticeably out of gage if it is not rigidly held in place by street paving. None of these methods are, therefore, suitable for anything but paved city streets, unless an exception be made of the few cases where they have been tried with expansion joints every few hundred feet. At these joints, of course, some other type of bond must necessarily be installed.

Bond Testing.—The bond resistance of a well-bonded track using 4/0 B. & S. bonds will range from 5 to 7 per cent of the resistance of the track return. With a few missing bonds or

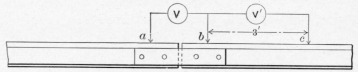

FIG. 87.—Connections of bond testing meters.

with poor contacts between bonds and rails this resistance may be increased many times. While the maximum allowable voltage drop in the return circuit is often very rigidly fixed in the city systems by municipal ordinance, it is for the interest of the operating company to keep this resistance at a minimum value, since the voltage at the car varies inversely and the losses vary directly with the resistance. It has been customary, therefore, to make frequent tests for the resistance of rail bonds and the standard has been rather arbitrarily set that the resistance of a bond shall be less than that of 3 ft. of rail.

The comparison of the resistance of the bond with that of 3 ft. of rail may be very readily made by making use of the current flowing in the rail. Two contacts a and b (Fig. 87), consisting of hardened-steel knife edges or points connected to a millivoltmeter V, are applied to the head of the rail at a distance

apart corresponding to the length of the bond. A third contact
c is permanently spaced 3 ft. distant from one of the former
contacts b. If another millivoltmeter V' be connected between b
and c and read simultaneously with the meter connected to a
and b, the readings are proportional to the resistance of a 3-ft.
section of rail and that of the bond, respectively. The bond
may be pronounced in satisfactory condition if

$$V < V', \tag{105}$$

while if V be too great its departure from the required value
may be recorded as

$$\frac{100(V - V')}{V'} \text{ per cent.} \tag{106}$$

Care must be exercised in making these tests not to damage
the millivoltmeter by attempting to measure an open bond.
It is always well to try the bond on a meter with a 15-volt scale
first and if the drop in potential is found to be within the range
of the millivoltmeter to make the final reading with the latter
instrument.

As this process is a rather slow and tedious one where there
are a large number of bonds to be tested, various methods have
been devised for making the tests on a car as the latter is traveling
over the road. Usually this is necessarily done when the regular
cars are off the line at night or with very little varying current in
the rails. The current sufficient to determine the voltage drop
in rail sections and bonds is fed through the local rail section by
means of specially designed trucks, the current being controlled
by a rheostat on the test car.

If it be desired to learn only the total resistance of the track
return, this may be determined after the cars are off a section of
line by passing a measured current through the rails by means of
a feeder to the distant end of the line and a rheostat at that point
in series therewith. A second feeder may be disconnected from
the generator temporarily and used as a potential lead so that the
fall in potential in the track may be read upon a voltmeter in the
power station.

Cross-bonding.—Thus far the bonding of rail ends alone has
been considered. It is sometimes necessary to provide against
the greatly increased resistance of the return circuit due to a
possible open bond by connecting the rails together electrically

by means of cross-bonds spaced several hundred feet apart. These usually consist of bare copper wire of approximately the size of the bonds soldered to the bonds on opposite rails or to special single-headed bond terminals forced into the rail web. Thus if a bond be open, the return current on that particular rail would follow the nearest cross-bond to the other rail and find its way back to the original rail at the next cross-bond nearest the power station.

As the bonding of all joints in special track work, such as switches, cross-overs, and frogs, would often involve a large number of bonds, a heavy cable is often laid around such portions of the track and thoroughly bonded to the sections of track on either side thereof.

Cost.—The cost of bonding is extremely variable, depending upon the type and size of the bond, cost of labor, etc. The following cost data should, therefore, be used with caution.

TABLE XX.—COST OF BONDING[1]

	Cost per joint		
	Labor	Material	Total
(a) 2—500,000-C.M. bonds soldered to head of third rail..........................	$0.66	$1.23	$1.89
(b) 2—500,000-C.M. pin-expanded concealed bonds applied to track rail..............	0.69	2.05	2.74
(c) 2—400,000-C.M. compressed terminal concealed bonds applied to track rail....	....	....	1.90
(d) 2—000 bonds of same type as (c)........	0.50	1.00	1.50

[1] "Handbook for Electrical Engineers," 2nd ed.

CHAPTER XVIII

ELECTROLYSIS

The subject of the electrolysis of underground pipe systems is closely allied to that of bonding. Beginning with the rather general introduction of the direct-current, street-railway systems in the early nineties, with their track return and relatively poor bonding, and extending through the rapid development and improvement of such systems, the question of electrolysis, its cause and prevention, has maintained an important place in the discussions of the engineers of gas- and water-works corporations as well as the telephone and street-railway interests.

It has, of course, been known for a long time that if a direct current be allowed to flow from a metal electrode, through an electrolyte to a second metal electrode, a chemical reaction takes place at the expense of the positive plate, *i.e.*, this plate is actually eaten away, the metal removed therefrom forming a salt with some of the acid radicals of the electrolyte. During these reactions which take place similarly when moist earth is the electrolyte it was noticed that hydrogen was given off at the cathode or negative terminal while oxygen was liberated at the anode. It was supposed for some time that those free gases were formed from the decomposition of the water in the earth. When it was later found, however, that this action often took place with potentials between terminals of the order of hundredths and even thousandths of a volt, which are not sufficient to decompose water and free these gases at their respective electrodes, a further study of the problem was undertaken.

Experiments carried on at the University of Wisconsin and recorded in the discussion of a very able paper upon this subject presented before the A. I. E. E. by the late Isaiah H. Farnham in 1894 demonstrated the fact that with iron electrodes embedded in moist earth electrochemical action is substantially as follows: Most earths contain salts of alkaline metals. Merely a directive e.m.f. of the order of 0.001 volt will cause the acid radical of these

salts to be isolated.   This radical then attacks the anode.   Suppose
sodium sulphate (NaSO$_4$) be present in the earth; this is broken
up by the current into Na and SO$_4$.   The SO$_4$ forms with the positive iron electrode FeSO$_4$ while the hydroxide of sodium (NaOH)
is formed at the cathode.   When the earth in the neighborhood
of the terminals becomes saturated with these compounds they
diffuse toward one another and finally meet in the earth at
a point easily detected by the formation of a green precipitate
of ferrous hydroxide and the original salt.   This reaction causes
a local rise in temperature at the point where the precipitate
forms.   The reactions mentioned above, which take place at
the electrodes, release oxygen gas at the anode and hydrogen at

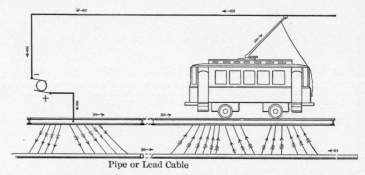

Pipe or Lead Cable

FIG. 88.—Direction of current with negative trolley.

the cathode, the former resulting from an excess of SO$_4$, forming
an acid with the hydrogen of the water and setting oxygen free.
The latter is the result of the formation of the hydroxide of
sodium with water, the free atom of hydrogen from the water
being liberated.

The one point of practical interest in this series of reactions is
the fact that iron is removed from the positive electrode to make
ferrous sulphate and later ferrous hydroxide, and the size and
weight of this plate are reduced thereby.   This loss of metal
from the buried plate is proportional to the current flowing therefrom.   Now if the track return circuit be of high resistance, a portion of the return current will flow back toward the power station
on underground pipes and cable sheaths, leaving these conductors
at points near the power station to complete the circuit through
the earth or on the rails and negative cables to the switchboard.

Since the above chemical reactions take place in the case of electric-railway currents leaving water and gas mains and the sheaths of telephone cables and entering the earth with values ranging from an infinitesimal leakage up to several hundred amperes in extreme cases, the importance of the study of the magnitude of troubles from electrolysis and the remedies to be applied is at once apparent.

In the early days of electric traction the bonding of the track and the proper installation of a low-resistance return circuit were seriously neglected, as has been explained in the previous chapter.

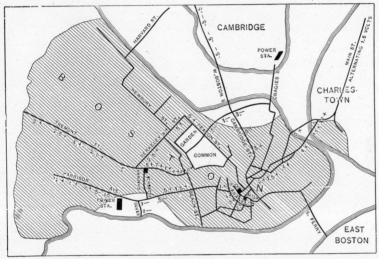

Fig. 89.—Early map of electrolysis in Boston.

It was also customary at first to connect the negative terminal of the generator with the trolley and the positive with the rail in many installations, this being just the reverse of the present method. These two conditions tended, first, to force a relatively large proportion of the current to follow the pipe and cable systems in place of the track, and, second, to make such pipe and cable systems positive to the rail over a wide area of territory in the average city.

This condition is clearly shown in the accompanying Fig. 88, which shows the direction of earth currents, and Fig. 89, representing the conditions in Boston, Mass., when the question of danger from electrolysis was first seriously considered. At the time this map was plotted from a large number of tests made of the voltage between pipe systems and rails, the trolley was negative and the rails positive. The shaded area designated as the "danger area" represents the territory in which the pipe systems are positive to the rails and, therefore, in which electrolysis might be expected to take place. The large extent of this danger area implies a great amount of possible trouble from electrolysis and a considerable expenditure of time and money for the proper maintenance of tests and the location of serious leakages of current.

A marked advance was soon made, however, in this problem when the trolley was connected with the positive terminal of the

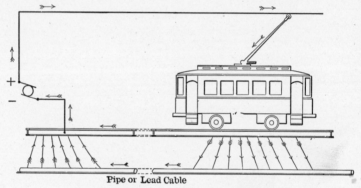

Pipe or Lead Cable

FIG. 90.—Direction of current with positive trolley.

generator and the rails with the negative terminal as in Fig. 90. This change would naturally limit the danger zone to a comparatively small area near the power station where the current which returned on the various pipe lines would leave these conductors and pass through the earth to the rails or return conductors and thence to the negative terminal of the generator. The effect of such a reversal of trolley polarity is obvious in Fig. 91, which represents a potential map of the territory included in Fig. 89 taken after the trolley of the West End system of Boston was made positive. This limitation of the area in which electrolysis may take place would usually increase the current leaving the pipes at any one place.

In this connection it might be of interest to note some of the results of electrolysis with currents of different magnitudes.

Experiments have proved that 1 amp. flowing steadily from an iron surface will remove appproximately 20 lb. of iron in 1 year, while the same current flowing continuously from a lead cable sheath or pipe will eat away 75 lb. of lead in the same time. A 48-in. iron water main in Boston was pitted in various places to a depth of $\frac{9}{16}$ in. in from 4 to 5 years, the average potential between pipe and rails being 8 volts with a current flowing in the pipe ranging from 5 to 95 amp. In this case the pipe was about $2\frac{1}{2}$ ft. below the rails of the street-railway company.

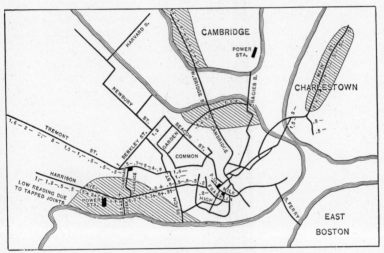

Fig. 91.—Later map of electrolysis in Boston.

Nor is the trouble confined alone to the points where the current leaves the pipe for other conductors. The joints in pipe lines often have relatively high resistance as compared with the pipe itself and even when compared with the surrounding earth in some instances. This is particularly true of the so-called bell and spigot pipe which is so commonly used for large water mains. At these high-resistance joints the current or a portion thereof passes in a shunt path through the earth around the joint. This causes an eating away of the iron on one side of the joint only, if the current flow is always in one direction.

Four general schemes are now in use for the mitigation of electrolytic effects in metal pipes, cable sheaths, and underground structures.

The first of these schemes provides for an insulated return conductor. This is the most reliable method, because it eliminates any leakage of current from street-car circuit to ground. There are objections, however, to this scheme, including high first cost, high maintenance cost, difficulties in insulation, and complication at crossings and in car equipment. Under this classification of insulated-return-conductor systems are the double-trolley system found at present in Cincinnati, Ohio, Key West, Fla., and Havana, Cuba, and the underground-conduit system as used in Washington, D. C., and New York City. In this connection it might be mentioned that tests made on long lines of well-bonded tracks having no intersections to cause complications and having the roadbed well drained show that the leakage from the rails to earth is almost entirely eliminated because of the high resistance of the leakage path.

Another of the schemes for reducing electrolysis has for its basic principle the reducing of current flow in pipes by surface insulation of the pipes or by means of insulating or resistance joints. Surface insulation of pipes is not very common at present. It is open to the objection that, in a positive area, any slight failure in the insulation leads to excessive electrolysis at one point and consequent pitting of the pipe. No paint, treated textile, or tarred paper is absolutely impervious to moisture. Once moisture has penetrated to the pipe, electrolysis is set up and a failure in the insulating covering results, due to the pressure of the gas formed by electrolysis. The use, however, of such insulating coverings in negative areas is of decided value.

The use of insulating joints at frequent intervals in a pipe line is to be considered as very good practice for reducing current therein. On the other hand, from an economic standpoint, on account of the high cost of such joints, especially in old pipe lines, it may not be deemed advisable to depend entirely on this scheme for protection. As an auxiliary protection, however, insulating joints judiciously used are very valuable.

In mitigating electrolysis by "pipe drainage" no attempt is made to reduce the current in the pipes, but rather to provide a metallic path for the current passing out of the pipes. The metallic path being of lower resistance than the ground path from the pipe, little electrolysis will result where such bonding is installed. The ordinary method of "pipe drainage" consists of electrically connecting the pipes and tracks together by metallic bonds at places where the pipes are positive to the rails. Another form of "pipe drainage" consists of negative feeders running direct from the bus bars to different points of the pipe system.

The chief objections to "pipe drainage" are, first, that the system is wrong in that its use involves an increase in the current in the pipes and a corresponding increase in electrolysis at high-resistance joints in obscure and unlooked for places; second, that unconnected pipes will be at a higher potential than the bonded pipes, thus causing leakage of current between them as indicated in Fig. 92; third, that the application of this scheme requires

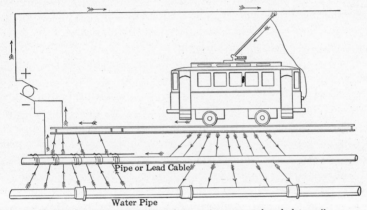

Fig. 92.—Current with portion of pipe system bonded to rail.

that the pipes be electrically continuous for the entire length through which current flows; fourth, and lastly, that the remedy when applied is not permanent and requires continual attention, as the street-railway load may change materially or the pipe system may undergo changes which will markedly affect the current flow in the pipes.

"Track drainage" possesses an advantage over "pipe drainage" in that it seeks to remove the cause of the trouble, *i.e.*, it eliminates stray currents in place of directing the existing stray currents in such paths that they may do no harm. The use of uninsulated negative feeders for track drainage has found wide application in this country. This scheme amounts to reducing the resistance of the return circuit. The advantages resulting from this scheme are: first, the reduction in potential drop in the rails, and a corresponding reduction in electrolysis troubles; second, the saving in power; and, third, the maintenance of a more uniform voltage on cars.

In the insulated negative feeder system, instead of connecting the track rails directly to the negative bus bars and thus depending on the conductance of the rails and whatever copper may be in parallel for conducting the current back to the power station, this connection at the power station is either eliminated or made through a suitable resistance. Insulated return conductors are installed at various points on the track system from the negative bus bar or from a negative booster, the other terminal of which is connected to the negative bus. Two important results are attained by this scheme: First, as the current is drawn from the rail at various points, high current densities in the rails are avoided. Consequently, the potential gradient in the rail is much reduced. Second, by properly designing the negative feeders the potential drop in each of the feeders can be made nearly the same, or by placing negative boosters in each group of feeders the potentials of the rails at the points where the feeders are tied may be made nearly the same. In either case the flow of current in the track can be subdivided so that the direction of flow will be frequently reversed, thus eliminating the possibility of an accumulation of large potential differences between widely separated points on the track.

The need of regulation of this phase of electric-railway operation is receiving increasing attention from the legislative bodies of the various municipalities. Chicago has had an electrolysis ordinance for a number of years. The ordinance was recently revised. Originally it specified a maximum possible rail drop of 25 volts in the city. It now provides for the division of the city into three zones. All uninsulated, electric return circuits are to be so arranged that between any two points on any uninsulated portion of the circuit the sustained maximum difference of potential shall not exceed 10 volts in the inner zone, 15 volts in the middle zone, and 20 volts in the outer zone.

Two tests are employed in locating electrolysis trouble, the current survey and the potential survey. The current survey involves the measuring with a millivoltmeter of the potential drop in definite lengths of the pipe under test, and, from these data, pipe data, and an application of Ohm's law, determining the current flowing in the conductor. The potential survey consists of finding the difference of potential existing between the metallic

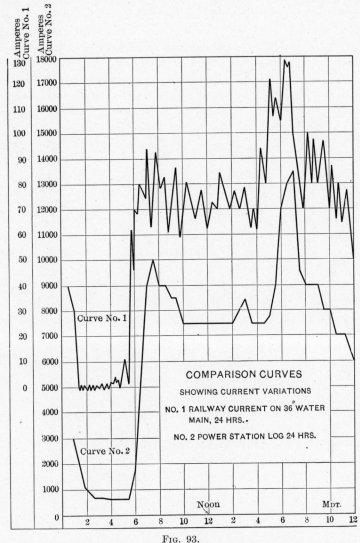

FIG. 93.

grounded conductor under test and adjacent rail or other grounded metallic conductors. The purpose of this survey is to show where, along the line, it is possible for current to flow from one conductor to another.

As a result of tests made by representatives of the National Bureau of Standards it was found that the average potential gradient expressed in volts per 1,000 ft. was 0.47 for the insulated feeder system and 0.91 for the uninsulated system. The following tests indicate very closely the advantages of the insulated system and the reduction in current in pipe lines which may be secured by its use.

	Total current returned by pipe lines in amperes
Uninsulated feeders, pipes drained..............	847.4
Uninsulated feeders, pipes undrained...........	275.7
Insulated feeders, pipes drained................	86.1
Insulated feeders, pipes undrained.............	48.4

In some cases, question has arisen whether all the current flow in pipes and cables and the damage resulting therefrom could be attributed to leakage from a railway system. Graphs of tests taken simultaneously with station-load curves, similar to those of Fig. 93, show conclusively by coincidence of peaks whether or not the cause may be charged to any particular system or station.

That the problem of electrolysis and its remedy is no small engineering task has been proved by the fact that no complete relief has been found after many years of study, although very recently much has been done to mitigate this evil. That the economic problem involved, especially in the large cities, is one of great moment is indicated by the fact that estimates of cost of meeting the new municipal ordinance in Chicago range from $3,000,000 to $4,000,000.

Report of the American Committee on Electrolysis.—The most authentic work upon the subject of electrolysis and its mitigation resulted from the activities of the American Committee on Electrolysis, the personnel of which included representatives appointed from all the national engineering and public utility associations directly interested in the problem of electrolysis acting in cooperation with the Bureau of Standards.

A preliminary report was made public in 1916, followed by a more comprehensive progress report in 1921, from which the following authoritative conclusions have been abstracted:

Potential Profile of Railway System.—If the cars are uniformly distributed along an electric-railway line, and if the track is of uniform resistance throughout its length, the voltage profile along the track will be as shown in Fig. 94. The curve is a parabola with a vertical axis and its apex at the end of the line. The slope of this curve is the measure of the potential gradient. If the resistance of the track is known, the potential gradient at any point serves as a measure of the amount of the current flowing in the rails at that point.

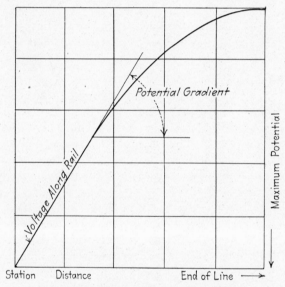

Fig. 94.—Potential profile of railway system.

Potential Profile Showing Rails and Pipes without Connections between Pipes and Railway Return Circuits.—If there are no metallic connections between the rails and the pipes, the potential profile of the pipes will be as shown in Fig. 95.

In the regions remote from the supply station the pipes are negative, and near the station they are positive to the rails. Ordinarily, the positive area extends from 30 to 40 per cent of the distance from the supply station to the end of the line. At neutral points where no potential difference exists between the pipes and the earth, the stray current in the earth and underground structure is a maximum.

Effect of Feeding Distance on Stray Currents.—The effects of the reduction of the feeding distances on stray currents and over-all potential drops are illustrated in Fig. 95 and 96. The stray-current curves are calculated from the formulas found in *Technologic Paper* 63 of the Bureau of Standards, entitled "Leakage Currents from Electric Railways." The various constants of the line are shown on the charts.

Calculations of stray currents have been made for both the insulated bus and the grounded bus conditions. The latter

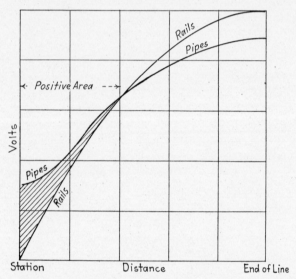

Fig. 95.—Potential profile showing rails and pipes without connections between pipes and railway return circuit.

occurs only when all of the stray current returns to the negative bus without reentering the track system, a condition which does not ordinarily occur in practice. An approach to a grounded bus would be a system where extensive pipe drainage existed with a larger portion of the current returning to the bus from the underground piping and cable systems. Railway stations generating direct current are often located in low grounds or on rivers where condensing water is available, and unless special precautions are taken to insulate negative cables entering such stations they are likely to pick up a considerable current from the earth, thereby establishing a condition of the semigrounded bus.

Figure 96 shows the total current returning to a single supply station located at the end of the line. The stray current at any point is also shown for the cases of the bus grounded and the bus not grounded. By insulating the bus the maximum value of the stray current is reduced to 147 amp. from 417 amp. and by putting the supply station at the middle of the line instead of at the end, and thereby reducing the feeding distance to one-half, the maximum value of the stray current with the insulated bus is reduced from 147 to about 24 amp.

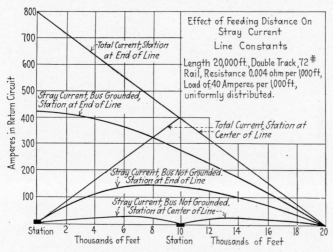

Fig. 96.—Stray currents in track return.

Figure 97 shows the overall-voltage curves for the same line fed from the end, from the center, and also from two stations located at one-fourth and three-fourths of the distance to the end of the line respectively. Shortening the feeding distance to one-half reduces the overall voltage to one-fourth of the original value and cutting the feeding distance to one-fourth reduces the overall voltage to one-sixteenth of the original value. Thus overall voltage varies as the square of the feeding distance. The curves in Fig. 97 are based on the theoretical conditions that with no stray currents the actual overall voltages will be somewhat

less because part of the current is in the earth.   The dotted lines
in the Fig. 97 illustrate in a general way the potential of the
earth and of the pipes under the several conditions of feeding.

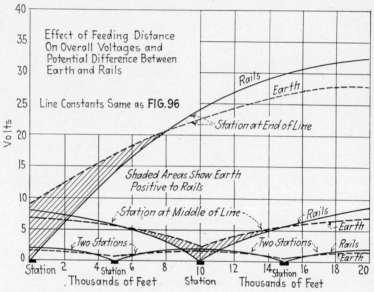

FIG. 97.—Effect of feeding distance on overall voltages and potential difference
between earth and rails.

The shaded portions represent the areas where the earth and
the pipes are positive to the rails.

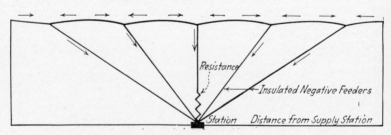

FIG. 98.—Equi-potential insulated negative feeder system.

Insulated Negative-feeder Systems.—Two arrangements approaching equipotential systems are shown in Figs. 98 and 99,
where four feeders are connected to the track at important

intersections and connections are made to the track near the
station through a resistance. One of the feeders is shown con-

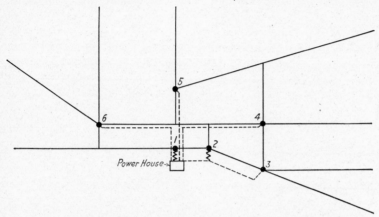

Fig. 99.—Insulated negative feeder applied to city network of tracks.

nected to the track at two points, a resistance being inserted at
the point nearest the station.

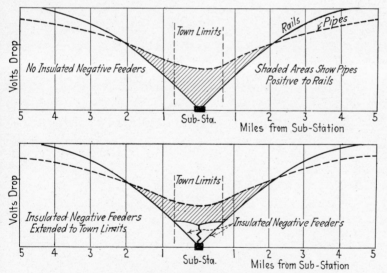

Fig. 100.—Insulated negative feeders applied to interurban line.

The effect of installing insulated negative feeders within the
limits of a small town through which an interurban line passes

is shown in Fig. 99. Without the use of negative feeders, that part of the piping system within the city limits is shown to be positive to the tracks, a condition which is often found in practice, although not a reliable criterion as to the degree of hazard to underground structures, as pipes are sometimes positive to the rails and negative to the adjacent earth. In some instances where insulated feeders have been applied on interurban lines, the positive area has actually been extended and no material improvement in the general conditions effected.

PART III
EQUIPMENT

CHAPTER XIX

SIGNALS AND DISPATCHING SYSTEMS

The problem of dispatching cars and of protecting one car from another on the same section of the track is largely confined to the interurban systems, for in the city railways speeds are low, the headway is small, and double tracks are commonly used. Cars are, therefore, usually operated as closely as possible on a predetermined schedule by the car crews and considerable responsibility is placed upon them for regaining the schedule time in case of delay. In many cities branch-line dispatching is done by a starter stationed in the city square or at the junction point of branch line and the main tracks. For these reasons, therefore, this chapter will be principally devoted to interurban systems, although the possible application of a number of signal systems to urban car operation will be obvious.

A complete system of train dispatching by a single dispatcher for the entire road does away to a large extent with the necessity of signals, other than those under the control of the dispatcher, installed for the purpose of attracting the attention of a train crew for special orders while *en route*, or for stopping a car in case an error in orders is discovered after the last communication with the crew. Most of the signal systems are, therefore, operated in conjunction with a dispatching system, to act as a check thereupon. Some of the more complete systems, however, are operated with little attention from the dispatcher, and the complete automatic block-signal system may be practically independent of dispatcher's orders.

Where a dispatching system is adopted, those signals commonly used in steam railroads are occasionally found on electric lines, involving the manually operated signals and telegraphic orders to way-station agents. Even the "staff" system which is used extensively in England may occasionally be found. This is really a combined signal and dispatching system, consisting of two electrically interconnected mechanisms, one at either end

241

of a block, which permit a staff to be removed therefrom if there be no train in the block ahead. A second staff cannot be removed from either of the terminal stations until the missing staff has been replaced at the farther end of the line. This system not only protects the block but also gives the train crew tangible evidence that they have the right-of-way in the block.

The dispatching system most common to electric railways uses the telephone for communication between the dispatcher and the train crew. Either telephone booths are provided at sidings or a portable telephone is carried on each car, which may be readily connected with the telephone circuit paralleling the track by means of a flexible cable and a two-pole plug switch. It is customary to require the motorman to receive the orders and write them on an order blank, thus furnishing a carbon copy for the conductor. The order is checked by the conductor reading from the carbon copy to the dispatcher over the telephone. This check message is either O. K.'d or corrected by the dispatcher. Although many modifications of this method are in use, the telephone is very generally adopted and has proved very satisfactory. In fact, a large number of steam-railroad trunk lines have adopted the telephone in place of the telegraph for train dispatching.

Such telephone lines should be constructed for dispatching only, the business to be transacted between other officials or departments of the road being provided for by another line. This duplicate line is fully warranted in the interests of safety and the avoidance of train delays. Care should be taken also to insist upon the repetition of orders, for serious wrecks have occurred when the train crews have received but a portion of the order, or have mistaken an order given to a crew at the dispatcher's office when the telephone receiver was off the hook for an order intended for them.

Signal Systems.—The present signal systems, which usually augment but may replace the dispatching system, have been a gradual growth from the single incandescent, five-lamp series circuit between trolley and ground to the more elaborate automatic block signals similar to those used on steam roads, and which are now being rapidly adopted by the large interurban railroads.

For protection against accidents, and in order that the schedule may be maintained, it is desirable that the train crew should know upon entering a block or certain section of the road:

1. Whether there is another car in the block.
2. How many cars there are in the block.
3. What direction the cars are going.

The last requirement is, of course, applicable to single-track roads only. As a matter of fact, nearly all signals are confined to the first class only or the first and the third classes, but very few in general use answer the second question. In order to do this automatically, complex circuits, which involve difficulties and excessive expense in their maintenance, are required. Signals displayed on cars are often used to signify that there is another car in the same block.

As to the method of the signal control, commercial signaling systems may be divided into four classes: namely, manual, dispatcher's, intermittent, and continuous track circuit. The distinctive features and the application of these systems will now be discussed.

Block Signals.—A "block," as defined by the American Railway Association, is "a length of track of defined limits, the use of which by trains is controlled by block signals." If but one train is permitted in a block at a time, the system is known as an "absolute" block system. Where two or more trains, going in the same direction, are permitted in a block at the same time, the system is called a "permissive-following" block system, and it must be so arranged that the "following" trains will receive a "caution" signal at the block entrance. Permissive systems are often used where the traffic is fairly dense and trains operate at low or medium speeds. In order to insure safety, the absolute system should be used where the trains are operated at high speeds.

The length of block used varies greatly and depends on local and traffic conditions. For heavy, high-speed service, blocks vary in length from 2,000 ft. to 2 miles. For interurban service they may extend from siding to siding. In general, they must be sufficiently long to enable a heavy, high-speed train to stop within their limits and yet short enough to permit the smallest headway between trains to be used.

At the entrance of each block a signal must indicate, both by day and night, whether or not there is a train in the block.   Such a signal is termed the "home" signal.   In addition, it has been

FIG. 101.—Block signal effect of train movements.

found adivsable, if high-speed trains are to operate smoothly without frequent periods of slow-down, to install an additional signal, upon the same standard as the home signal, to indicate the condition of the next block ahead. This signal is termed the "distant" signal.

These indications are often given in daylight by means of a semaphore and at night with colored lights, although many of the signal systems recently developed for use on electric roads use light indications for both day and night. In order to make the lamps visible in daytime the lamp cases are deeply hooded.

The use of light lowers the first cost and maintenance expense of a signal system and has been a great factor in the development of automatic block systems for electric railways. The lamps may be lighted from the signal power circuits and where the continuous-track-circuit system of control is used, if desired the connections can be so arranged that the lamps are lighted only when the signal is being approached by a train, thus cutting down the expense for the power and lamp deterioration. As considerable trouble has been experienced from the use of colored "bull's-eyes" or signal "roundels" at night upon roads using the very powerful headlights, owing to reflections from unlighted roundels appearing as signals, it is believed that if the more powerful headlight is adopted the semaphore or "position" signal will be ultimately very generally used as a night signal as well in the more expensive types of signal systems, as they are sufficiently well illuminated by the headlights to permit the accurate reading of signal aspects.[1]

Fig. 102.—Semaphore arm signal. (*Electric Railway Signal Company.*)

The Chapman automatic signal is strictly a "semaphore" signal, in that the indications are given by the position of a red arm rather than by lights. The arm and its background are illuminated by light thrown from electric lamps in the top of the hood. Electric lamps form no part of the indication and are not a part of the operating circuit, nor in series with the line.

[1] HARDING, C. F., and TOPPING, A. N., "Headlight Tests," Trans. A. I. E. E., vol. 29.

In some types of semaphore signals three angular positions are used, a 45-deg. position indicating "caution" and a vertical position "proceed" or "clear," aside from the horizontal or "danger" indication. The corresponding signals at night are usually red for "danger," green for "clear," and yellow for "caution," although the latter two colors vary somewhat for the

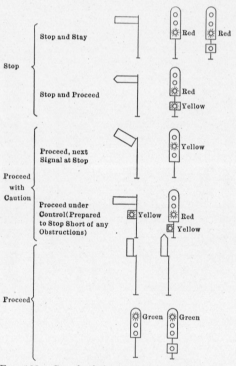

FIG. 103.—Standard three-position signal aspects.

different roads. While in steam-road signaling one of the right-hand quadrants is usually used, the overhead distribution system of the electric railway practically compels the use of one of the left-hand quadrants where semaphore signals are used. The A. E. R. A.[1] has adopted as standard a three-position signal operated in the upper left-hand quadrant with signal aspects as shown in Fig. 103.

Figure 104 illustrates a semaphore signal manufactured by the Union Switch & Signal Co. In two-position signaling,

[1] *Proc.* A. E. R. A., 1912.

the semaphore when in horizontal position indicates "stop," while the "proceed" or "clear" signal is usually indicated by a 60-deg. angle from the horizontal.

As the train arrives at the entrance of a block the home signal denotes the condition of the first block and the distant signal that of the second block ahead. With both at "stop," the two blocks ahead are occupied and the train stops. With the home signal at "clear" and the distant signal at "stop," the first block is clear and the second occupied. The train may enter the block under control. With both signals at "clear" the engineer

Fig. 104.—Semaphore signals, proceed and stop positions. (*Union Switch and Signal Company.*)

knows that two blocks ahead at least are clear and he many enter the block at full speed. The distant signal at the first block and the home signal of the second block are so interlocked that the former cannot move to "clear" until the latter has attained a similar position. Upon the entering of the first block under control with the distant signal at "stop" it is expected that the next home signal will be at "stop." Since, however, the signal may have changed before the train reaches the second block, it is often advisable to install a second distant signal within safe stopping distance of the second block. This is especially true if the second block signal is not readily seen at some distance, since it avoids slowing down if the second block has been cleared in the meantime.

While it is unnecessary to describe in detail the operation of the semaphores and colored roundels in their various forms, it may be said that their movement is accomplished by means of mechanical levers and bell cranks. These levers are operated either electrically by means of solenoids or series motors, or through the agency of gas or air pressure in the base of the signal. The control of the local apparatus at the signal by means of electric relay circuits is, however, of greatest importance and will be explained in detail later.

Manual-control Block System.—Probably the most simple arrangement used as a signal, and one to which several roads have returned after trying the more nearly automatic types, is that

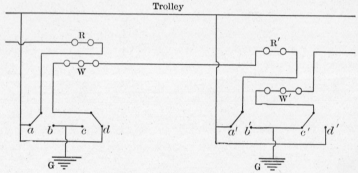

FIG. 105.—Simple lamp signal.

shown in Fig. 105. This consists of a series of five incandescent lamps connected as shown by means of a double-throw switch between trolley and ground, two of each group being located at one end of the block and three at the other. The group of three lamps is placed behind a white or green lens and the two-lamp group provided with a red lens. Upon entering the block the circuit is closed by means of the switch, which lights a red light at the opposite end and a white or green light at the entering end. Upon arrival at the other end of the block the lights may be switched out and the circuits are such that the lights may then be lighted from either end. An extra circuit duplicating that of Fig. 105 should be provided, however, for operation in both directions. The advantages of this signal are its simplicity and the necessity of one of the crew leaving the car, when stopped, to operate the signal switch. Its disadvantages are that the signal lights may be extinguished and the signal reversed from either end with a car still in the block, and if the switch be accidentally left in the "off" position the signal cannot be operated from the other end. This system is, of course, suitable for use only on roads on which the cars are operated at low speeds and where the traffic is relatively light.

Another type which has been used in the past to a considerable extent on steam roads and which has been installed on a few electric roads makes use of block sections, at the end of which are located block-control stations or "cabins." An operator stationed in one of the cabins receives information concerning the condition of a given block by means of the telephone or telegraph from the operator at the other end of the block and sets the signals accordingly. As the safety of operation depends upon the accuracy of the human element in the system, it is being rapidly displaced by other systems. Also, it is very costly to operate. When the operators receive instructions direct from the train dispatcher, this system becomes a type of dispatcher's control system.

Controlled Manual Block.—This system is, in general, similar to the manual system just described, except that the signals are electrically interlocked, so that if the signal at one end of the block indicates danger the signal at the other end cannot be made to indicate "clear." The "staff" system described on page 241 is another form of controlled manual block.

Dispatcher's Control System.—The common form of this system employs signals located at sidings, stations, and other points along the line at which the dispatcher may wish to communicate with a train crew. These signals are selectively operated by synchronous impulses sent over lines connecting the signals with the dispatcher's office. The dispatcher can stop a train at a desired point by operating the signal located at that particular point. Communication between the train crew and the dispatcher's office is obtained by means of a telephone system as described on page 242.

Interlocking System.—The underlying principle of interlocking requires that, before a signal can be cleared for the movement of a train, all switches, derails, and frog points, over which the signal governs the train movement, shall be in proper position and locked. To secure such protection for train movements it is desirable to concentrate the control of the various signals and switches at one point. The mechanism in which this concentration of control is secured is called an interlocking machine. The machine consists of small hand-thrown levers, compactly located in a frame and arranged for the operation of the circuit controllers, but restricted in their movements by both mechanical and electrical locks. The machine provides for the control

Fig. 106.—Power interlocking machine, with track model. (*Union Switch and Signal Company.*)

of as many switches by a single lever as is practical without limiting possible simultaneous traffic movements. For example, both ends of a cross-over are controlled by a single lever; also opposing signals, only one of which can be cleared at a time, may be controlled by the same lever. Safety as well as simplicity are secured by a single lever controlling conflicting signals, as the interlocking of these is obtained through lever movement and not by means of the dogs and locking mechanism which would be required were a lever used for each signal.

Intermittent Control Signals.—Elaborating upon the principle of the simple lamp signal (Fig. 105) and adding various automatic features, several companies have developed signal systems for both single- and double-track roads which have been widely adopted. A representative type built by the United States Signal Company will be described. It operates from the trolley circuit and consists of one signal box and trolley switch at either end of the block connected as in Fig. 107 and requiring two wires

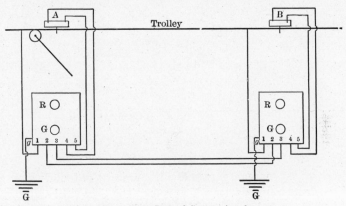

Fig. 107.—United States signal.

throughout the length of the block. A car entering the block at *A* makes a momentary connection between the trolley wire and wire No. 4, as the trolley wheel operates the iron-tongue switch mounted on the trolley wire. This momentary connection, closing the circuit to the ground through a relay and a suitable resistance, completes the permanent circuit connecting the trolley wire through No. 1, the green lamp at *A*, the signal line wire, the red lamp at *B*, through resistance in box *B* to ground. Other cars entering at *A* do not change the signal setting, but a car leaving the block at *B* energizes wire No. 5 through the agency of the overhead trolley switch and trips the relay which extinguishes the red light. A car entering at *B* performs the reverse operation, lighting the green light at *B* and the red signal at *A*. The boxes and the switches are, therefore, interchangeable.

Red and green discs are displayed in some types of this signal for day use, although the lights are commonly used as day signals as well. This type of signal has given a fair degree of satisfaction although its maintenance expense is high, especially because of the damage by lightning. In fact, it is very difficult to design a signal operating upon a grounded circuit which will not be seriously affected by lightning. The widely varying voltages on the various sections of the average interurban lines a so introduce difficulties in the design of signals to be operated from the trolley circuit. It should be noted that in this system the motorman is assured that the red signal has been displayed at the farther end of the block if the green light appears at the entering end. This fact is seldom determined by the steam-railroad engineer who relies upon the automatic block signal to give the danger indication without actually observing the signal movement himself. It should also be noted that the car controls only as it enters or leaves the block and that while within the block it has no control over the signals.

On account of its comparatively low first cost, the intermittent-control type of signal has been used quite widely in both interurban and suburban service in the past. Present practice, however, seems to tend toward using it in suburban service only.

Some of the more recent types allow permissive following movements by adding a device which counts the cars "in" and "out" of a block and does not permit the signals to return to "clear" until all cars have been counted out. The signal aspects also conform to the latest recommendations of the A. E. R. A., namely:[1]

Red: Stop, do not operate trolley switch.

Green: Proceed by trolley switch to operate signal. Proceed if green aspect changes to red light over yellow light on passing trolley switch.

Red and Yellow: Block is occupied by a car running in the same direction. Proceed by trolley switch and if yellow light changes to the opposite side of the red one, proceed under control.

To give these aspects or indications four lamps are required, one green, one red, two yellow. The yellow lamps are arranged side by side just below the red one.

A similar system of trolley-contactor type of light signals, providing three indications, is illustrated in Figs. 108 and 109. The details of the installation upon the pole, the track and

[1] *Proc.* A. E. R. A., 1913.

trolley connections and the possible indications will be obvious from the figures.   The signals give three indications:

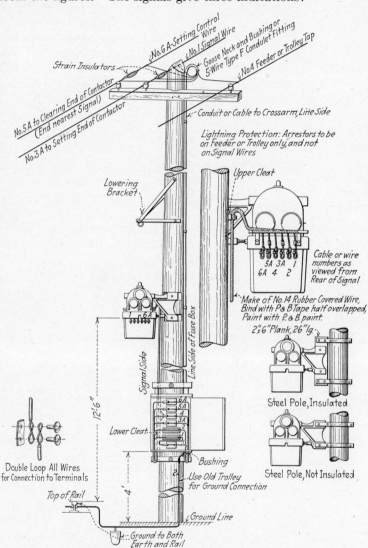

FIG. 108.—Details of signal mounting and wiring for wood and steel poles, type C. D. Signals.   (*Nachod Signal Company.*)

1. No Light, No Disc: Neutral indication. Dark, blanks normally displayed when the block is not occupied.   It mean,

that the car is free to proceed under the contactor to take the block. It is equivalent to having no orders.

2. White Light, White Disc: Permissive indication. It means proceed through the block; the opposing signal has been set to stop. It is equivalent to orders to proceed.

3. Red Light, Red Disc: Stop indication. It means stop and wait behind entering contactor until indications return to neutral. It is equivalent to orders to stop.

Fig. 109.—Overhead contactor, directional type. (*Nachod Signal Company, Inc.*)

Steam-railroad Practice.—As the track-circuit block-signal systems used with electric roads have been patterned after the more simple steam-railroad installations, a description of the latter will aid in understanding the former. The two rails (Fig. 110) for a block in length are insulated from one another and also from the adjacent rails of neighboring blocks by means of insulated rail joints *C*. The various rail lengths of a single block are bonded together in a manner similar to that described in Chap. XVII, but with much smaller wire bonds. A gravity or storage battery *D* of 1 or 2 volts e.m.f., located in a manhole below the frost line, is connected between the rails at one end of the block. At the other end of the block a sensitive relay *R* is connected across the two rails. This relay is usually mounted in the base of the signal tower and thereby protected from the weather. Where there is no train in the block the battery supplies current to the relay by way of the two rails and the signal is held in the "clear" position. As the first trucks *W* of a train enter the block, however, the wheels and the axles short circuit the relay and it opens, closing the local circuit, which throws the semaphore and colored roundels into the "danger" aspect. The

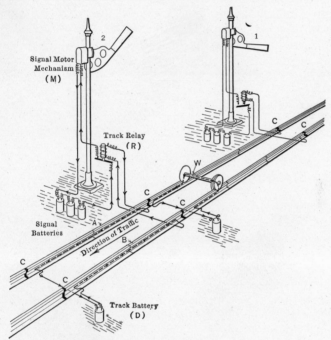

Fig. 110.—Perspective of track circuit.[1]

signal is locked in this position until the movement of the last truck of the departing train from the block removes the short circuit, closes the relay, and clears the signal.

Such is the very simple circuit and mechanism of the automatic nlock signal for steam railroads, and although its first cost has been sufficiently high to render its adoption rather slow, its maintenance is not excessive and its positive operation is to be depended upon. In fact, in one instance but one failure to operate

[1] Reproduced from General Railway Signal Company Publication.

in 250,000 was the record of operation on a large signal system during the period of a year.

Track-circuit Block Signals.—With the electric railroad, which makes use of the track rails for the return of heavy currents to the substation or the power house, the problem becomes a more difficult one, as the rails are no longer free for sectional insulation as in steam roads. One method of overcoming this difficulty which would naturally suggest itself is to use one rail for signal purposes and the second rail for the return of power current. The further use of the alternating current for the signal relay would permit selective operation of the latter without interference

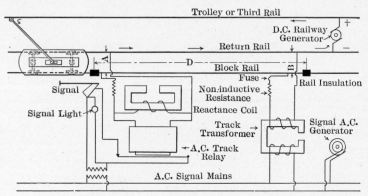

FIG. 111.—Single-rail alternating-current block signal.

from the power current. Such a system is successfully used in the New York subway, its principle of operation being illustrated by Fig. 111.

By referring to this figure it will be seen that one rail, termed the "block rail," is insulated in sections one block in length, constituting a circuit for signal current only. The other rail carries the current from the trains and also acts as a common return circuit for the signal system. Alternating current for the signal circuit and also for the signal lamps is supplied through transformers from single-phase, alternating-current mains paralleling the tracks. If the power current is flowing in the return rail from left to right, the voltage between rails at B will be slightly less than that at A, due to the fall of potential in the rail. This will cause some of the direct current to pass through the relay con-

nected between the rails at A, thence through the block rail and
the transformer secondary to the return rail at B, the latter
forming a high-resistance shunt path to the length of return rail
AB.　In order to limit the amount of this current which would
otherwise produce a unidirectional magnetic field in the relay
and the transformer, high non-inductive resistances are inserted
in series with the relay and transformer secondary and a reactance coil shunted across the relay.　While the direct power current following the block rail will pass freely through this reactance,
the signal alternating current will be prevented by the impedance

Fig. 112.—A New York subway signal installation.

of the reactance coil from taking that path and will, therefore,
pass through the relay.　As an additional precaution in the case
of the transformer, an air gap is introduced into the magnetic
circuit to reduce to a minimum any magnetic flux which might
be produced by the relatively small-leakage direct current.

With these added precautions the relay system operates
exactly as in steam-road equipments, except that the relay must
be of the alternating-current type.　A relay depending upon
torque produced by eddy currents induced in an aluminum disc
being acted upon by the magnetic field set up by the current in
the relay has been adopted for this purpose.

In the New York subway installation of this system the alternating-current distribution is at 500 volts and 60 cycles, the track transformers stepping the potential down to 10 volts, while the signal lamps are operated at 55 volts. The resistance of the track and signal circuit is such as to impress approximately 5 volts upon the relay. The power factor of the circuit is in the neighborhood of 80 per cent and the power taken by an average block but 80 watts. A typical installation is represented in Fig. 112.

Block Signals for Alternating-current Roads.—When the problem of equipping electric roads operating with alternating

FIG. 113.—Impedance bond. (*Washington, Baltimore & Annapolis R. R.*

current in the track rails arose, it may be readily seen that still further difficulties were encountered. The problem was fairly well solved, however, by the development of the two-rail signal system making use of impedance bonds (Fig. 113), and this solution marked the beginning of a new era in the development of the new railway signal systems. Practically all of the automatic block signals which are being installed on both alternating- and direct-current railways at present are of this general type. They are being installed on a number of steam roads, the high battery-maintenance expense of the older type of steam-road signals more than offsetting any disadvantages possessed by modern alternating-current signals. The fact that state laws in some states require the installation of the automatic block signals of a type satisfactory to their railroad commissions on all railroads operating within their limits has done much to hasten the development of a cheap and reliable automatic block signal operated with track-circuit control.

The principle of this type of signal system, similar to that operating on the single-phase terminal electrification of the New York, New Haven & Hartford R. R. in New York, is illustrated in

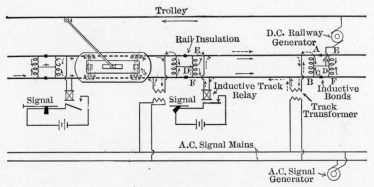

Fig. 114.—Double-rail alternating-current block signal using inductive bonds.

Fig. 114. It will be seen that each rail is insulated at the ends of the block, as in steam-railroad practice, but inductive bonds of sufficient current-carrying capacity to carry the train current are installed between the rails at *AB* and *EF*. The middle points of the adjacent bonds are connected together, so that there is a complete electrical circuit from train to power house by each rail, this circuit involving one-half of each bond at every block. This connection tends to neutralize the e.m.fs., due to the power current, which are set up in the inductive parts of each bond. These bonds are carefully designed so that their counter e.m.f., due to any unbalancing of the power current in the rails, will not be great at the frequency of 25 cycles or below, at which the train motors operate, but will be sufficiently great to produce a useful difference of potential between the rails in the signal circuit which is operated at 60 cycles. In other words, a very interesting application is made of the theory that the reactance of a coil is proportional to the frequency and the bonds are, therefore, designed to operate upon one frequency only.

The immediate source of power is the transformer, as in the single-rail system, but in this case the power current is sufficiently well balanced in the two rails to prevent unbalanced currents flowing in the transformer and the air gap in the magnetic circuit is, therefore, omitted. The transformer is designed with a relatively high leakage factor, however, in order that the current may not be excessive when the secondary of the transformer is short circuited by the train in the block. It will be noted further that, for the above reasons, the auxiliary resistances and reactance shunt across the relay may be omitted.

With these changes and a slight change in the design of the relay, the system operates as in a single-rail design. The direction of the power current is shown by full lines and that of the signal current by dotted lines in Fig. 114.

Single-track Signaling.—The continuous-track-circuit signals just described were developed for use on double-track roads. Suitable signals of this type for use on single-track roads are a

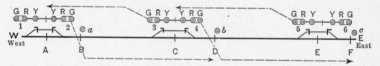

Fig. 115.—Single-track signals with preliminary track circuits.

very recent development. On a single-track road the block signal must guard against both following and opposing movements. The system must be an "absolute," or "permissive" for following movements.

The signals on a single-track road are controlled by relays similar in design to those used in double-track systems, the difference being rather in arrangement of the apparatus and connections than in the fundamental apparatus. Figure 115 shows the arrangement of the signals in a single-track block system, manufactured by the General Railway Signal Company, which is being used on a number of interurban roads at present, and illustrates a method of diagramming signals which is commonly used by signal engineers.

A typical installation of this type is shown in Fig. 116. The line WE represents the track. Three sidings with centers at A, C, and E are shown. The block length is AC (or CE). The dashed lines parallel with the track indicate the controlling limits of the various signals, *i.e.*, a car on the track under the dashed line causes the signal to which the dashed line is connected to operate. Ends of track circuits are indicated by short lines drawn at right angles across the track. The track between the right-angle marks at the sidings is not connected to the signal system.

Fig. 116.—Typical installation, single-track signal. (*General Railway Signal Company.*)

The various signals are 1, 2, 3, etc. Pairs of signals, such as 1 and 2, are, of course, mounted in a single lamp housing located either on a pole line or a special signal mast; the signals, however, are shown pointing in the direction of the traffic which they control. Since this system permits following movements, three lamps are required. The sections AB, CD, etc., are known as "preliminaries." Their function in this particular system is to guard against the possibility of two opposing trains entering a block at the same time or instant and thus neither one getting a stop indication. The length of these preliminary sections depends on the distance covered by a train in making a service stop and varies from 1,000 to 3,000 ft.

The operation of the system is briefly as follows:

Assume an eastbound train approaching A. If the block AC is empty, signal 2 will indicate clear or the green lamp will be lighted. As the train passes A the green lamp will be extinguished and the yellow lamp will be lighted, giving a permissive signal to a following train. At the same time signal 3 indicates red, thus blocking all opposing movements at C. The block indicator b, which is a sort of distant signal placed at the beginning of the preliminary section, is lighted whenever the block AC is occupied. A westbound train entering the preliminary CD causes signal 2 to indicate the red but does not affect 3 until it reaches C. Thus, if a westbound train passes D at the same instant as eastbound train passes A the eastbound train will not receive a danger indication but the westbound train will be stopped at C. In order to facilitate the switching operations a special device controlled by

FIG. 117.—Single-track signals with intermediate signals.

the track circuits and known as the switch indicator is used. This indicator is placed at each switch and shows whether or not the block is clear. If desired, three-position semaphore signals may be used in place of the lights.

Another type of signal (Fig. 117), manufactured by the Union Switch & Signal Co., which is being installed on a number of electric railways, makes use of "intermediate signals" instead of preliminary track sections to guard against opposing trains entering a block at the same instant. It also permits following movements.

This system is indicated as using semaphore signals, although light signals may be used if desired. Only one track circuit per block is used and it is fed from the center. Two track relays, one at each end of the block, are used. A car entering at A causes danger indications to be shown at signals 2, 3, and 5. If both cars entered the block at the same instant they would not get the danger indications at the home signals 2 and 5, but would be blocked at 3 and 4, which are staggered enough to permit both trains to come to a stop without colliding with each other.

The permissive-following indications are secured in the following manner: A car entering the block at *A* does not cause signal 4 to indicate until it is near the center of the block. The electrical connections are such that after signal 4 has been operated by an eastbound train signal 2 will change from the danger to the permissive indication, thus allowing the second train to enter the block under control.

Figure 118 shows the layout of signals on a typical block, with contactors on double track. The signal is located along the single track near the switch point, with a setting contactor one or two

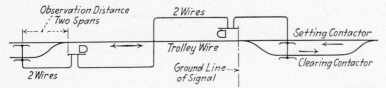

Fig. 118.—Signal layout, contactors on double track. (*Nachod Signal Company.*)

spans back of the signal. This arrangement permits the motorman, before passing the signal, to observe the change of the signal indications caused by the passage of his car under the contactor. Placing the trolley contactor on the double track instead of the single track enables him to take the block before he passes the switch point into the single track, and obviates any possible backing through the switch point. The clearing contactor is located in the other track at such a point that the trolley wheel touches it immediately after the car is in the physical clearance. This usually requires the clearing contactor to be nearer the frog than the setting contactor. The trolley contactors are directional, or have a sense of direction, so that the car entering a block under any contactor sets the signals of that block, and backing out again under the same contactor clears them.

Cab Signals.—As stationary signals are sometimes obscured by smoke, steam, fog, or blinding storms, and as train crews are not infallible but will sometimes overlook a danger signal even when the indication is very clearly given, much effort has been expended in trying to develop a satisfactory cab signal.   One type has already been described.   A number of other types are being tried at present.   In general, these signals are controlled by track circuits similar to those used with stationary signals, use being made of a third-rail section or other form of contact device to communicate the indication to the cab signal.   The development and the installation of a satisfactory type of cab signal will go a great way in solving the problem of safe train operation.

Highway Crossing Signals and Flagman.—These signals are designed especially for electric railways and are both controlled

Fig. 119.—Nachod highway crossing signal.   (*Milwaukee Electric Railway and Light Company.*)

and operated by the power from the trolley wire.   As the power supply is not limited, therefore, various moving-part aspects, such as a red disc, a "wig-wag" carrying a light and swinging like a pendulum, or the ringing of a bell, are available.   The

signals are heavily insulated against lightning and other acciden-
tal high voltages which occur in a trolley line. The various
elements are separately insulated from the ground, so that a
breakdown in insulation of one element will not affect the other
warning elements. Where a number of warnings are given they
are separate and independent. The signals are governed by space

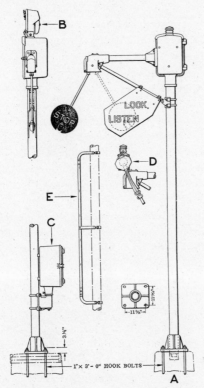

FIG. 120.—Three aspect flagman. (*Union Switch and Signal Company.*)

interval and not by the time interval. The warning is given at
the starting contactor when the car reaches the danger zone, and
is discontinued at the stopping contactor at the highway the
instant the car is out of this zone. In some systems the bell
will ring for so many seconds, it being presumed that the car will
have passed the crossing by that time. This time is usually
made longer than necessary.

Under normal conditions this flagman indicates the approach of a train by swinging the red banner upon which appears the word "STOP," and displaying a red light attached to the banner. When no train is approaching, the banner is held to one side between two screens, upon which is painted "LOOK and LISTEN," and the lamp suspended from the banner is not lighted.

Automatic Train Stops.—Some of the elevated railways have used automatic train stops for a number of years. While desirable for all classes of service, they are particularly useful where trains must be operated at high speeds and small headways. One type of automatic stop consists of a projecting arm outside of the right-hand rail which is controlled by the track circuit and is raised when the signal indicates danger. This engages a rocker arm on the locomotive or first car which operates the air brakes if the train moves past the block entrance. Some of the roads using automatic stops have found that the installation of the stops greatly increased the alertness of the train crew and made for better discipline, because the stopping of a train by means of the automatic stop is in the nature of a demerit charge against the train crew.

Headway Recorders.—Unwarranted layovers that result in irregular schedules, unnecessary high speeds, damage to equipment, waste of power, and dissatisfaction of the patrons may be avoided by the use of automatic headway recorders. These automatic headway recorders deliver each day in a graphic form a complete history of all car movements at points of installation during the 24-hr. period preceding. A car passing under the contactor prints a mark on a clock-driven chart, the location of which mark shows the time of its passage. The chart shows all cars both ways for a whole day.

CHAPTER XX

TRACK LAYOUT AND CONSTRUCTION

The electrical engineer of a proposed electric interurban railway is often called upon to determine the right-of-way and superintend the track survey and construction, although in the large city systems or extensive interurban developments a technically trained civil engineer is usually given this responsibility. In either case the electrical engineer should be familiar with such general features of the problem as may be herein outlined.

Right-of-way.—After several proposed routes have been suggested for the new railway, possibly with the aid of rough preliminary surveys for each, and detailed notes taken of the advantages and disadvantages of each, involving the topography of the country, the number of intermediate towns and the amount of tributary population served, possible schedules, etc., it is necessary to decide upon one route. This is usually determined by the officials of the company in conference with the engineer. With this decision in mind, the problem of obtaining the right-of-way presents itself and it is often policy not to make the above decision public until after the greater portion of the right-of-way has been secured. In fact, it has sometimes been found advisable to propose publicly two possible routes and even go to the extent of purchasing options on land along each in order that an element of competition may enter, preventing land and options from assuming exorbitant values along the desired route.

Great diplomacy must be exercised by the advance real estate agent in order to secure the desired route at a reasonable figure and without too many concessions, which often complicate the schedules and embarrass the company when operation begins. It must always be remembered that much of the future traffic will come from those with whom these preliminary negotiations are made.

If satisfactory locations cannot be secured, either because of opposition to the proposed road or too high prices being placed

267

upon the land, right of eminent domain may be secured through the court and certain sections of the route condemned and thereby purchased at a value appraised by the court or a commission appointed by the court. As this proceeding makes public the proposed route and prejudices some against the company, it should be avoided if possible, but if found necessary, it should be postponed until the rema'nder of the land has been secured.

It will be noted that the above discussion presupposes a private right-of-way for the road. Such a route is generally much to be preferred, except with'n the limits of intermediate towns, and even in the latter case a route but a few blocks from the center of town on a back street with little traffic, where speeds may be fairly high and frequent curves avoided, should be given serious consideration. In some instances interurban railroads run for miles along country roads, but it is usually done at the expense of low schedule speeds and high maintenance charges, due to restrictions often imposed by town boards and street commissioners, not to mention frequent and serious accidents. A slightly larger first cost for a private right-of-way is justified in most cases not only from the standpoints of schedule, safety and independence from ordinances stipulated by outsiders, but from the purely financial consideration as well.

A right-of-way at least 100 ft. in width should be secured to allow for possible double track with necessary cuts and embankments provided with adequate drainage ditches. Such a strip of land averages 12 acres to the mile.

With the route approximately determined and the right-of-way secured, a final survey should be made to locate the exact line for the track and to determine the profile. With the exact profile plotted, the grade line may be drawn consisting of an average line through the profile representing a series of grades, with none exceeding 2 per cent if possible, and with as close a balance between "cuts" and "fills" as may be secured in order that the haul for excavation and embankment may be a minimum. While grades as high as 7 or 8 per cent sometimes exist on interurban roads, it will often be found that when the first cost of the extra-heavy car equipment and possibly the station equipment necessary to operate on these grades, together with the annual cost of extra power required, are balanced against the fixed charges on the extra cost of reducing the grade by means of a deeper cut or a slight change of route, the latter policy would have been the better of the two.

Before accurate estimates can be made or contracts let for preparing the subgrade, it will be necessary to learn something more of the character of the subsoil. It will be assumed that the general nature of the country and its geological formation were carefully noted during the preliminary survey, since the decision of the proper route depends largely upon such a study, especially when a river is to be paralleled and possibly bridged occasionally. It is now necessary, however, to have test borings made as deep as the deepest proposed cut at intervals along the

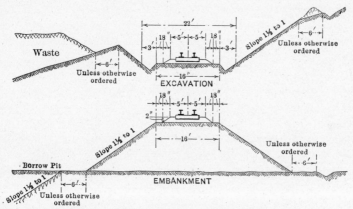

FIG. 121.—Typical interurban roadbed construction.

line sufficiently frequent to obtain a good idea of the type of excavation to be expected and the necessity of driving piles or installing mattress concrete or timber in case of possible quicksand. A contract can usually be placed for such borings with their results either represented to scale on a drawing for each station or, better, by a glass tube filled to scale with the various strata of subsoil found.

With this information at hand, a series of cross-sections at right angles with the base line at stations 100 or 200 ft. apart, or possibly less where the profile is very irregular, may be made and the volume of excavation and embankment calculated. A list of cut and fill expressed in cubic yards of each type of subsoil from solid ledge to soft clay may then be made for each mile of road and estimates readily calculated and contracts signed. Typical sections of cuts and embankments will be found in Fig. 121, while estimates of their respective costs in the South will be found at the end of the chapter. These latter values vary greatly with local conditions and are usually based upon a certain maximum length of haul between a cut and the corresponding fill into which the excavated material may be deposited.

A certain area of so-called "free haul" is established which may vary somewhat for the various stations along the proposed line. This "free haul," which is a convenient unit upon which to figure contract estimates and bids, is based upon the distance within which excavation may be balanced against fill, due allowance being made for shrinkage of the latter. Contracts and bids usually name a price per cubic yard for grading within the "free haul" area and an additional price per unit for all "overhaul." The "overhaul" is determined by subtracting the "free haul" from the distance between the centers of gravity of the remaining excavation and final embankment.

Excavation and grading may be undertaken in connection with small jobs with the use of hand shovels, wheelbarrows, scrapers, and wagons. Although the unit cost may be higher than for larger contracts, the smaller volume handled may warrant the selection of this method. For such work as the construction of a new interurban line, however, power shovels and industrial narrow-gage railway trains hauled by dummy locomotives would usually be warranted. A figure presented by the Lake Shore & Michigan Southern R. R., quoted by Richey,[1] covering the cost of grading third and fourth track for the above road with a haul not exceeding 5 miles, is given in the following table. This includes loading, unloading, and leveling ready to lay ties, and covers both labor and supplies. It is, however, exclusive of interest, depreciation, explosives, and overhead charges.

TABLE XXI.—COST OF GRADING

Gravel pits with 15 ft. face	$0.11 cu. yd.
Earth cuts 3 to 10 ft. deep	0.15 cu. yd.
Shale cuts, all blasted	0.21 cu. yd.
Rock cuts, requiring blasting and breaking up	0.25 cu. yd.

[1] See RICHEY, "Electric Railway Handbook."

The labor and supplies in the above table are based on the following units:

Foreman............................... $75.00 per month.
Laborers.............................. 0.15 per hour.
Steam shovel crew (8 men, 10 hours)........ 25.00 per day.
Train service, labor and supplies........... 28.00 per day.

Trestles.—In localities where low elevations must be spanned, and especially where the subsoil is of questionable bearing capacity, the choice between wooden trestles, structural steel, and masonry is often made with difficulty. The *Engineering News* sets forth the following arguments in favor of wooden trestles for preliminary construction at least. These are particularly forceful, of course, in sections where timber is cheap.

A well-built timber trestle, while it lasts, is a very solid and safe structure, and it lasts normally in good condition for from 5 to 10 years while much hastily built masonry gives out in 1 or 2 years.

There is more time to determine accurately the size of opening needed and thus avoid needless washouts; besides, well-built timber structures are less likely to wash out suddenly.

The time of construction is shortened materially, often an important consideration.

The masonry, when at last built, is almost certain to be better built and of better stone. Haul, then, is of less importance and there will be more time to secure good materials. The roads are few on which any large proportion of the original masonry is in good condition after 10 years. This is especially true of the smaller structures, such as cattle guards and open culverts, which are often so poor as to shake to pieces in a few months. The lesson that the smaller the structure the larger and better dressed must be the stones composing it, if it is to be durable, is one which engineers are slow to learn.

It is easier to introduce long and high fills afterward to be filled by train, or replaced by masonry or iron, and thus to secure a better alignment and avoid rock cutting or other objectionable work.

A very large part of the total cost of the line in its permanent form is postponed for 6 to 8 years past the trying years of early operation, thus not only saving the interest on the cost of the permanent work but going far to protect the company from the danger of early insolvency, which has proved so deadly to many overconfident companies.

The only necessary disadvantages are the liability to decay and fire. To guard against the former is a mere question of inspection. The danger from fire is a real one and every year has its record of accidents resulting therefrom, but if the danger is real it is small.   There are few such accidents and those mostly from gross carelessness.   In proportion to their number, accidents from iron structures have been vastly more numerous and more fatal, and the same is true in substance of small masonry structures where the great liability to washouts is a serious matter.

Ballast.—It is safe to say that the experience of interurban roads which have been operating for some time demonstrates the fact that money expended in first-class subgrade construction and rock ballast proves to be the most economical in reducing maintenance charges and providing a smooth-riding roadbed which does not quickly wear out both itself and the rolling stock.

The ballast, which is that portion of the roadbed upon which the ties are placed, should be sufficiently porous to permit the water to run off freely.   The best ballast is recognized to be crushed rock capable of passing through a $2\frac{1}{2}$-in. ring.   Coarse gravel, however, makes a very good substitute and is very often used because of its lower cost.   Fortunate, indeed, is the road that secures with its right-of-way one or more borrow pits containing good ballast gravel.   This ballast is laid for a depth of 6 to 18 in. under the ties, and should cover the ties to the base of the rail.

Gravel ballast will range from 15 to 40 cts. per yard, while rock ballast will vary from maximum values of gravel to 75 or 80 cts. per yard laid in place ready for ties.

Ties.—Now that the scarcity of good lumber is beginning to be felt, with a corresponding increase in first cost, the selection of suitable ties and their treatment to insure long life is becoming a serious problem.   Pine, cedar, white oak, red oak, fir, and chestnut are the woods in most common use.   The choice between these depends largely upon the variety which is native in the locality in which the road is being built.   Cedar is probably as long lived as any, while the ability of white oak to hold spikes is probably greater than any other wood.   While this variety of tie is generally too expensive to use throughout, it is often specified for curves where the strain on spikes is, of course, greatest.

Herrick gives in the following table an approximate length of life for the different varieties of ties as determined by Mr. Hough.[1]

[1] HERRICK, A. B., "Practical Electrical Railway Handbook."

TABLE XXII.—LIFE OF TIES

White oak.............................. 7.4 years
Red oak............................... 5.0 years
Chestnut.............................. 7.1 years
Southern pine......................... 6.5 years
White pine............................ 6.5 years
Red cedar............................. 11.8 years

It is generally considered advisable to specify preservative treatment for ties in order to increase their life, although it is difficult to determine from experience thus far just how much the life is extended thereby. Ties which have been embedded in concrete in city construction have shown particularly long life, averaging from 10 to 20 years with many rail replacements. The replacement of rails and the removal and replacement of spikes during realignment often shorten the life of a tie when it has not decayed. Screw spikes have been proposed to obviate this difficulty, but they are little used at present because of their higher first cost and the greater time required for installation and removal.

It has been found recently that screw spikes used with chloride of zinc treated ties have very short life, due to the galvanic action between the zinc salts and the steel of the spikes. This, together with the difficulty noted below which ties thus treated sometimes introduce in the operation of signals, have brought about the rather general use of hardwood ties without treatment or softwood ties confined to creosote treatment.

Reinforced-concrete and steel ties have been experimented with, especially abroad. Whereas concrete and steel substructures are replacing ties to a large degree in city streets, the wooden tie for interurban or steam-railroad use has not been replaced to any extent in this country.

The dimensions of ties for interurban use are similar to those for steam roads, averaging 6 in. by 8 in. by 8 ft., although 5-in. ties may be found occasionally. In third-rail construction a longer tie is installed every 10 ft. to act as a support for the third-rail insulator. The spacing of ties will be found to vary from 15 to 30 in., but an average dimension may be taken as 2 ft. Ties which lie under the rail joints are placed nearer together, but their exact spacing is dependent upon whether a suspended or a supported rail joint is used, as will be described later.

One consideration in connection with the selection of ties which has received very little attention is the effect of preservative treatment upon their resistance. This is of particular value only where the automatic block signals are installed. From the discussion of the previous chapter it will be seen that if the resistance of the ties be greatly reduced they will act as a shunt to the relay and possibly interfere with its proper operation. Tests made at Purdue University[1] upon the resistance of ties, recorded in the report of the Wood Preservation Committee of the American Railway and Maintenance of Way Association, prove that ties follow the laws of insulators in general, but that when

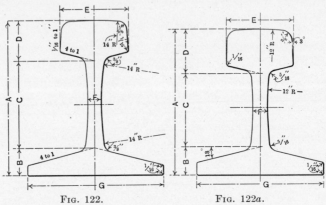

FIG. 122.   FIG. 122a.

FIGS. 122 and 122a.—Standard "T" rails for shallow paving.

treated with the chloride of zinc preservative process their apparent resistance is lowered. Calculated results based upon the data of these tests, assuming wet treated ties in wet ballast, show values of resistance sufficiently high to prevent serious interference with signals. Cases in practical operation have been reported, however, in which such interference has been present.

Rails.—In the selection of rails also, steam-railroad practice has been followed to a great extent, although the weight of rail used is, on the average, less with the interurban roads. This is possible because of the lighter weight of trains and the absence of reciprocating motion. The interurban roads make use of the T-rail almost exclusively, averaging in weight from 70 to 80 lb.

[1] BUTTERFIELD, J. T., Graduate Thesis, Purdue University, 1910.

per yard. In city streets a wide variety of rail sections will be found, from the T-rail to the various shapes and sizes of grooved girder rails. The T-rail has been rather generally

TABLE XXIII.—DIMENSIONS OF STANDARD T-RAILS IN INCHES

Type of rail	Figure 122			Figure 122a		
Wt. per yard, lb........	80	90	100	80	90	100
Height A.......:......	$5\frac{1}{8}$	$5\frac{5}{8}$	6	$4^{15}\!/_{16}$	$5^{17}\!/_{64}$	$5^{41}\!/_{64}$
B.............	$3\frac{1}{32}$	1	$1\frac{1}{16}$	1	$1\frac{1}{32}$	$1\frac{5}{64}$
C.............	$2^{23}\!/_{32}$	$3\frac{5}{32}$	$3\frac{3}{8}$	$2^{15}\!/_{32}$	$2\frac{5}{8}$	$2^{55}\!/_{64}$
D.............	$1\frac{7}{16}$	$1^{15}\!/_{32}$	$1\frac{9}{16}$	$1^{15}\!/_{32}$	$1^{39}\!/_{64}$	$1^{45}\!/_{64}$
Width of head E........	$2\frac{1}{2}$	$2\frac{9}{16}$	$2\frac{3}{4}$	$2\frac{7}{16}$	$2\frac{9}{16}$	$2^{21}\!/_{32}$
Thickness of web F.....	$3\frac{3}{64}$	$\frac{9}{16}$	$\frac{9}{16}$	$3\frac{5}{64}$	$\frac{9}{16}$	$\frac{9}{16}$
Width of base G........	$4\frac{5}{8}$	$5\frac{1}{8}$	$5\frac{1}{2}$	$4\frac{7}{16}$	$4^{49}\!/_{64}$	$5^{9}\!/_{64}$

objected to by city authorities because of the danger to vehicular traffic offered by the projecting head of the rail and the difficulty in paving close to the rail with standard paving blocks. Two

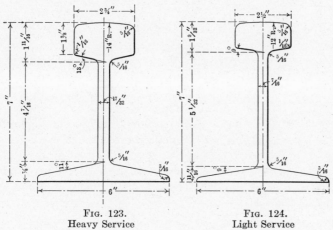

FIG. 123.
Heavy Service

FIG. 124.
Light Service

FIGS. 123 and 124.—Standard "T" rails for paved streets.

sizes of girder rails, 7 and 9 in. in height respectively, have come into general use, the latter being preferred from the standpoint of ease in paving.

The A. E. R. A. in 1910 adopted a standard T-rail for city streets for use except where the traffic is confined to the railway strip or is so congested that the strip is continually used by vehicles. The dimensions of this standard for various weights of rails are indicated in Table XXIII, which refers to Figs. 122 and 122a.

For the heaviest service, in connection with deep-block pavement, the 7-in. T-rail, known as "Section A" (Fig. 123), weighing 100 lb. per yard, was adopted. Light service is provided with an 80-lb. rail, shown in Fig. 124, known as "Section B."

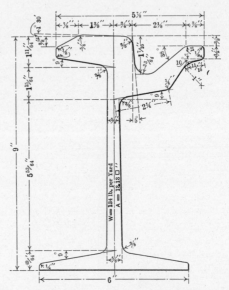

Fig. 125.—Standard girder rail for heavy service.

In heavy city service, in connection with deep-block pavement when vehicular traffic is congested, the girder rail (Fig. 125) is used. A section similar to Fig. 125 in all respects except that of height, which is 7 in., was also adopted by the Association in 1913.

In view of the many difficulties that necessarily have had to be overcome in the manufacture of rails to meet the more exacting demands of heavier trains and higher speeds, and because of the fact that the selection of proper rails is not a problem of road construction alone but of maintenance of way as well, it seems desirable to list in detail the more important specifications which have been approved by the A. E. R. A. and the A. S. T. M.

Specifications for Open-hearth Steel Girder and High T-rails

The steel shall be made by the open hearth process.

Bled ingots, and ingots or blooms which show the effects of injurious treatment, shall not be used.

A sufficient discard from the top of each ingot shall be made at any stage of the manufacture to obtain sound rails. When finished rails show piping, they may be cut to shorter lengths until all evidence of this is removed.

The steel shall conform to either of the following requirements as to chemical composition, as specified in the order.

TABLE XXIV.—CHEMICAL PROPERTIES AND TESTS OF RAILS

	Class A	Class B
Carbon, per cent................	0.60–0.75	0.70–0.85
Manganese, per cent..............	0.60–0.90	0.60–0.90
Silicon, per cent.................	not over 0.20	not over 0.20
Phosphorus, per cent.............	not over 0.04	not over 0.04

To determine whether the material conforms to the requirements specified in paragraph 4, an analysis shall be made by the manufacturer from a test ingot taken during the pouring of each melt. Drillings for analysis shall be taken not less than ⅛ in. beneath the surface of the test ingot. A copy of this analysis shall be given to the purchaser or his representative.

A check analysis may be made from time to time by the purchaser from a test ingot or drillings therefrom furnished by the manufacturer.

The test specimen shall be tested on a drop test machine of the type recommended by the American Railway Engineering Association. The specimen shall be placed head upward on the supports of the machine, and shall not break when tested with one blow in accordance with the following conditions:

TABLE XXV.—PHYSICAL PROPERTIES AND TESTS OF RAILS

Weight and height of rail	Temperature of specimen, degrees Fahr.	Distance between supports, feet	Weight of tup, pounds	Height of drop	
				Class A	Class B
Rails weighing over 100 lb. per yd. and 7 in. in depth..	60–120	3	2,000	15	12
Rails weighing 100 lb. or less per yd. or 7 in. or less in depth....................	60–120	3	2,000	13	10

The atmospheric temperature at the time of testing shall be recorded in the test report.

The testing shall proceed concurrently with the operation of the works.

Three rails, each from the top of one of three ingots from each melt, shall be selected by the inspector, and a test specimen shall be taken from each of two of these.

Drop test specimens shall not be less than 4 or more than 6 ft. in length.

Two drop tests shall be made from each melt.

If the result of the drop test on only one of the two specimens representing the rails in a melt does not conform to the requirements specified in Section 7, a retest on a specimen from the third rail selected shall be made and this shall govern the acceptance or rejection of the rails from that melt.

The cold templet of the manufacturer shall conform to the specified section as shown in detail on the drawing of the purchaser, and shall at all times be maintained perfect.

The section of the rail shall conform as accurately as possible to the templet, and within the following tolerances:

The height shall not vary more than $\frac{1}{64}$ in. under nor more than $\frac{1}{32}$ over that specified.

The overall width of head and tram shall not vary more than $\frac{1}{8}$ in. from that specified. Any variation which would affect the gauge line more than $\frac{1}{32}$ in. will not be allowed.

The width of base shall not vary more than $\frac{1}{8}$ in. under that specified for widths less than $6\frac{1}{2}$ in.; $\frac{3}{16}$ in. under for a width of $6\frac{1}{2}$ in.; and $\frac{1}{4}$ in. under for a width of 7 in.

Any variation which would affect the fit of the splice bars will not be allowed.

The base of the rail shall be at right angles to the web; and the convexity shall not exceed $\frac{1}{32}$ in.

When necessary on account of the type of track construction, and notice to that effect has been given to the manufacturer, special care shall be taken to maintain the proper position of the gage line with respect to the outer edge of the base.

Unless otherwise specified, the lengths of rails at a temperature of 60°F. shall be 60 and 62 ft. for those sections in which the weight per yard will permit.

The lengths shall not vary more than $\frac{1}{4}$ in. from those specified.

Shorter lengths, varying by even feet down to 40 ft. will be accepted to the extent of 10 per cent by weight of the entire order.

The weight of the rails per yard as specified in the order shall be maintained as nearly as possible after conforming to the requirements specified in Section 4.

The total weight of an order shall not vary more than 0.5 per cent from that specified.

Payment shall be based on actual weights.

Rails on the hotbeds shall be protected from water or snow, and shall be carefully manipulated to minimize cold straightening.

The distance between the rail supports in the cold straightening process shall not be less than 42 in. except as may be necessary near the ends of the rails. The gag shall have rounded corners to avoid injury to the rails.

Circular holes for joint bolts, bonds, and tie rods shall be drilled to conform to the drawings and dimensions furnished by the purchaser.

In Class A rails the tie rod holes may be punched.

The ends shall be milled square laterally and vertically, but the base may be undercut $\frac{1}{32}$ in.

Rails shall be smooth on the head, straight in line and surface without any twists, waves, or kinks, particular attention being given to having the ends without kinks or drop.

All burrs or flow caused by drilling or sawing shall be carefully removed.

Rails shall be free from gag marks and other injurious defects of cold straightening.

The composition of the third or conducting rail may be such as to result in a much softer and lower resistance rail. Armstrong gives the following analysis for such rails:

TABLE XXVI.[1]—ANALYSIS FOR THIRD RAILS

Carbon not to exceed	0.12 per cent.
Manganese not to exceed	0.40 per cent.
Sulphur not to exceed	0.05 per cent.
Phosphorus not to exceed	0.10 per cent.

[1] ARMSTRONG, A. H., "Electric Traction."

The use of manganese steel for the centers of special work and even for complete frogs, switches, and curves has been recently given a great deal of attention because of its long life. While it seems to be the consensus of opinion among railway operators that the latter uses of manganese steel are advisable only in extreme cases of heavy wear, the adoption of replaceable frog and switch points of this material is very heartily sanctioned.

Rails of Steel Alloys.—It may have been inferred already from the chemical specifications set forth in Table XXIV that the amounts of various chemicals present in steel rails greatly change the physical properties and life of the latter.   Carbon, of course, increases hardness at the expense of ductility, while phosphorus makes the rail brittle and of coarse crystalline structure.   As the safe temperature possible for finishing rails is also lowered by the presence of phosphorus, the latter must be kept to a minimum.

Some other elements have, however, been added to steel rails to good advantage.   The difficulty of the problem lies in the sacrifice in ductility and low first cost which must be made in order to obtain hardness.   The addition of about 0.1 per cent of titanium or the use of ferrotitanium tends to make the steel more homogeneous and thereby allows the percentage of carbon to be increased with no loss of ductility or shock-resisting qualities. Whether the increased expense of this alloy is warranted remains to be determined by longer experience.   This treatment can be applied to either Bessemer or open-hearth processes.

In particular locations in the track where the rails receive very hard wear, such as at curves, frogs, or crossings, ferromanganese steel has been used to advantage.   The addition of from 12 to 15 per cent of manganese to the open-hearth steel adds greatly to its hardness without seriously limiting its ductility.   Since this steel must be quenched in water when red hot, which, in turn, results in much care and time being spent in the straightening process, and since this steel cannot be machined or drilled after quenching, its first and installation costs are greatly increased.

Until the so-called Cuban ore, containing about the correct percentages of nickel and chromium, was used in the manufacture of steel rails, much trouble with broken rails was experienced where the nickel-chrome steel was employed.   This new ore, requiring only a slight addition of nickel in the furnace, has been converted into rails during the last few years by both the Bessemer and the open-hearth processes.   These rails seem to have the desirable hardness without corresponding increase of cost.   They have not been in use long enough, however, to determine what the increased life and wearing qualities may be.

Rail Joints.—Aside from the mechanically rigid rail joints produced by cast welding, thermit welding, and electric welding discussed in some detail in Chap. XVII, several other types of rail joints in rather more common use should be mentioned.   The simplest and cheapest joint is, of course, the four- or six-bolt fish plate clamped on either side of the rail ends. This construction allows considerable vertical motion to the ends of the rails as the train passes over them, causing the heads to be soon flattened. The rail must, therefore, be replaced or shortened because of its worn condition at the end before it is seriously worn elsewhere.

The other types of joints most commonly used are the Atlas, Continuous, and Weber joints, all of which make use of combined splice bars and tie plates differing but slightly in design, *i.e.*, they all furnish an iron plate between the foot of the rail and the tie, which plate is generally notched to receive the spikes in order to prevent creeping. The Weber joint makes use of a single plate cast in one piece with one of the vertical plates, while the other joints involve two half plates split longitudinally under the center of the rail.

The use of tie plates is a matter open for discussion. They probably increase the life of the ties, especially when rather soft wood is used, by preventing chafing between rail and tie, but many engineers are not convinced that this gain warrants the extra expense.

Rail joints may be of the "suspension" or "supported" type, the former having the rail ends between ties, while the latter provides a tie directly under the ends of the rails. The former seems to be in more general use. In case the Atlas rail joint be selected the suspension type must be used, as this joint requires transverse bolts through the casting under the rail flanges at the end of the rail.

Both 30- and 60-ft. rail lengths are in use, the former being preferred in interurban construction because of less expansion troubles therewith and the greater ease of handling the shorter length on curves. Where the above features are not objectionable, however, the 60-ft. rail has the advantage of fewer joints and bonds, thereby reducing slightly the first cost and maintenance charges. The shorter rail lengths are meeting with increased favor.

Rail Corrugation.—For several years rails subjected to heavy traffic have been found to wear in the form of corrugations, which may become of such magnitude that they must be ground to a depth of 0.6 in. in severe cases in order to remove the irregularities. Although several plausible theories have been advanced, the cause of this trouble has not been satisfactorily explained, for the widely varying conditions under which the corrugations are found are hardly fulfilled by any one theory.

For example, corrugations are found more often in the following cases:

High girder rails in paved streets.

Outside rail of long radius curves.

Rails rigidly supported on concrete foundations.

One portion of a single rail may be affected while other portions of the same rail are free from corrugation.

Rails corrugated in one section of track are found to wear smooth when located elsewhere.

Time required may vary from 48 hr. to several years.

Reproduced immediately after grinding in some cases and eliminated in others.

Corrugations are absent under the following conditions:

Practically all steam railroad tracks.

Nearly all T-rails, especially on interurban road, except near stations or where cars are started or stopped under abnormal conditions.

Some of the theories which have been advanced to explain the cause of corrugation are:

Chattering of brake rigging during stop.

Nosing of wheels transversely across rails.

Chattering of rolls when rails were rolled.

Alternate hard and soft spots in composition of rails.

Cold-rolling action of wheels on rails.

The last theory seems to be the most plausible one offered thus far, and nearly all conditions of corrugation can be explained thereby. This has been outlined in considerable detail by Pellissier[1] and Gidanski.[2]

The contact area between wheel and rail is so small that the pressure may exceed 40,000 lb. per square inch in practice. This is very near, if not in excess of, the elastic limit of the rail. It would be safe to say, therefore, that the elastic limit is often exceeded with the wheel in motion. Where this takes place it would have a tendency to cause the metal to flow slightly until the density was increased sufficiently to withstand the force of the

[1] PELLISSIER, G. E., "A New Theory of Rail Corrugation," *Elec. R. Jour.*, Sept. 30, 1911.

[2] GIDANSKI, C. M., "Rail Corrugation," *Elec. Ry. Jour.*, Dec. 27, 1913.

wheel. The wheel would then tend to ride over the place of high density and start the metal to flow just beyond this point. The coning of the tread can be shown to aggravate this effect and produce the shape of groove which is actually found in practice.

As grinding the head of the rail is the only satisfactory remedy for this trouble, and since the effect will often recur quickly after this rather expensive treatment has been applied, it proves to be a problem of rather difficult solution. It can be safely said, however, to offer a very good argument against the use of too rigid a substructure for the support of the rails.

It is expected that the investigations now being carried on by the Rail Corrugation Committee of the A. E. R. A., of which Prof. D. D. Ewing of Purdue University is chairman, will offer further explanation of this peculiar phenomenon.

Roadbed Construction.— Whereas the interurban roadbed consists merely of a natural subsoil or fill, well drained with side

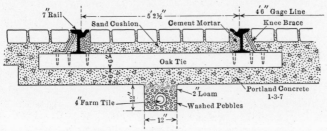

Fig. 126.—Standard track construction, Cincinnati, Ohio.

ditches and covered with gravel or crushed rock ballast to a depth of from 6 to 18 in. under the ties, the problem of roadbed construction in city streets is a more difficult one. A trench is first excavated slightly greater in width than the length of the ties and of a depth depending upon the type of foundation to be used. Although the old method of excavating a transverse trench for each tie is now practically obsolete, many companies are keeping lengths of ties to a minimum and reducing the foundations and ballast as much as possible in order to decrease excavation costs. The use of the longitudinal concrete beam construction under the rails is little in favor at present.

Although most engineers will agree that the roadbed should be well drained, comparatively few roads are going to the expense of installing longitudinal tile drains under the ballast of single

track or between the tracks of a double-track road.   Cincinnati,
Kansas City, Cleveland, Seattle, and some of the other large
cities claim good results from such tile construction.   Where
installed, it has been found desirable to use bell-and-spigot sewer
tile rather than the soft agricultural drain tile.   The latter is
found to crush and fill up too easily under heavy traffic conditions.

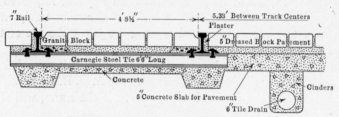

Fig. 127.—Standard track construction, Cleveland, Ohio.

Sections taken through standard roadbeds using drains are seen
in Figs. 126, 127, and 128.

Opinions of expert railway engineers differ as to whether the
roadbed should be perfectly rigid or somewhat flexible.   With the
former construction the rolling stock is believed to suffer to a
greater extent and rail corrugation seems to be more marked.   It

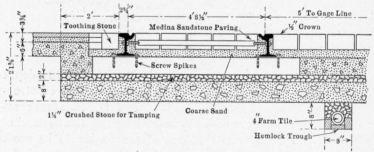

Fig. 128.—Standard track construction, Buffalo, N. Y.

is also difficult to construct where traffic cannot be readily diverted
from the track.   With the flexible construction, ties have
shorter life and rails are more readily thrown out of alignment.
The simplest form of flexible construction, which is not unlike
that common in interurban practice, with the exception of
pavement, is indicated in Fig. 129, a construction which has
been adopted as standard in Minneapolis.

In the more elaborate sections shown in Figs. 126, 127, and 128 a concrete sub-base is first laid in the excavation, followed by a cushion of sand for the ties and pavement. In the Cleveland construction it will be noted that steel ties have been grounded into the concrete sub-base without a cushion, while in Milwaukee standard practice with macadam pavement calls for a layer of concrete over layers of crushed stone and coarse-rock ballast.

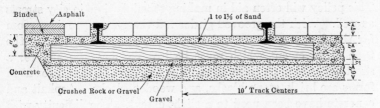

Fig. 129.—Standard track construction, Minneapolis, Minn.

The use of screw spikes should be noted in the Cincinnati track as well as knee braces which replace the tie rods with the girder rails.

The use of tie rods to prevent the overturning of high girder rails is difficult with heavy block paving. In some installations these rods of round section are placed low on the rail, and therefore under the paving blocks, while in other cities a thin, flat rod

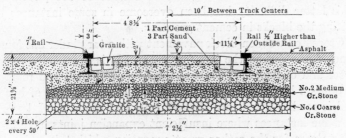

Fig. 130.—Standard track construction, Milwaukee, Wis.

is used which will fit in the joints between paving blocks, as in Fig. 128. In at least one city interference with the blocks has been avoided and at the same time the desirable high connection on the rail has been maintained by an offset rod of round section passing under the paving blocks.

Pavement.—The railway company is usually required to install and maintain the pavement between tracks and for a distance of

2 ft. or more outside.   If paving blocks are used with anything but a 9-in. girder rail a special block must be secured to fit the rail and provide a groove inside the rail sufficient to allow the wheel flange to pass without forming a dangerous rut for vehicular traffic.   Such grooves are rapidly worn away by the latter traffic and the railway company endeavors, therefore, so to design the track and paving that the vehicles will not be attracted thereto. This policy will often aid in making schedule time in city streets as well.   With the grooved girder rail the groove provides room for the flange.   In many cities the city authorities specify the type of pavement which must be installed between and for a short distance upon either side of the tracks.   The most common forms are brick, stone blocks, and wooden blocks.   Asphalt and concrete have been used to a slight extent.   The difficulty with these types lies in the fact that frequent removal for repairs is not only accompanied with much labor and expense, but there is no salvage of material for replacement as there is with practically all types of block pavement.

Blocks, however, have the disadvantage that it is practically impossible to make such pavement watertight.   If not watertight, the life of ties and wooden blocks is greatly impaired and the freezing of water under and between blocks is very likely to cause bulging and cracking of the surface of the pavement. This latter difficulty has been overcome in some instances by setting the blocks in cement grouting.

Creosoted wooden-block pavement with a tar binder has found much favor during the last few years.   It is practically waterproof and of long life, while not difficult to install and replace. It offers a less slippery and harsh surface for the feet of horses and is readily fitted into shallow rails and round special work. In some instances where insufficient expansion joints have been left to care for the rather great expansion which takes place in hot weather, difficulties with upheaval of the paved surface have been met, but properly installed wooden blocks have produced a cheap, efficient, and long-lived pavement in many large cities, even when subjected to heavy vehicular traffic.

Special Work.—Special work, which is the term given to track switches, frogs, crossings, and, indeed, practically all track construction not made up of standard rails, is usually subjected to relatively heavy traffic and a correspondingly great amount of

Estimated Cost of Roadbed Construction

	Labor	Material	Total
Clearing and Grubbing.			
68 acres at $45..........................	$3,060	....	$3,060
Grading.			
Solid rock 8000 yd. at $0.75..............	6,000	....	....
Loose rock 35,000 yd. at $0.37	12,950	....	....
Earth, 716,000 yd. at $0.145	103,820	....	122,770
Culverts.			
150 Culverts varying from 18″ to 60″ diam..	....	9,420	....
Total 4573′.			
Hauling and placing.....................	995	....	....
End walls 1300 yd. at $8.................	10,400	....	20,815
Timber Bridges.			
41 Pile bridges, 4752 lin. ft. at $8.80.......	14,000	27,818	....
1 Frame bent bridge, 800 lin. ft. at $10.25..	2,730	5,470	50,018
Steel Bridges.			
9 Steel spans ranging from 30′ to 130′, 700,520 lb. erect. at 4⅛ cts.	3,502	25,395	....
Concrete piers, 2300 yd. at $7.20..........	8,280	8,280	....
Deck, 2300 yd. at $2.50.................	675	1,300	47,432
Track.			
Rail 80 lb. 33′, 8431.7 tons at $33.515.....	....	282,588	....
Angle bars, 21,690 prs. at 0.86	....	18,653	....
Track bolts, 86,762 at 0.04	....	3,471	....
Track spikes, 2010 kegs at $5.60.....................	....	11,256	....
Bonds, 21,160 at 0.60.................	3,196	9,500	....
Cross bounds, 67 total......................	....	....	600
Track ties, 169,860 at 0.65.............	....	110,409	....
Switches compl., 18 at $150.............	....	2,700	....
Labor.............................	26,548	....	468,921
Ballast.			
Local gravel or lime rock.................	130,000	....	130,000
Fencing (Wire).			
26,900 rd......................	5,380	11,112	16,492
Miscellaneous.			
Railroad crossings at $300...............	200	1,000	....
Highway and private crossings at $47....	1,150	4,490	....
Signs.................................	100	300	7,240
Grand total...............	....	....	$866,748

wear. This special work is sometimes made up of sections of rails set in steel castings, or it may be entirely a steel casting. Recent practice tends toward the use of manganese steel for such castings where the expense seems warranted, while in other cases manganese steel "points" are inserted in the casting at the proper location to receive the greatest amount of wear. Much difference of opinion is expressed as to whether these inserts should be made removable or permanently installed. If the former practice is adopted, it is very difficult to replace satisfactorily the worn-out insert, as the remainder of the casting is usually badly worn also. Even with manganese steel points, however, some saving is probably possible if the construction of the special work is so designed as to permit of their replacement.

Considerable advance has been made during the last few years in the standardization of special work, particularly by the A. E. R. A. This is of advantage not only to manufacturers, who may decrease materially their patterns and tools, but to operating companies because of increased ability to obtain prompt shipments and to order and replace parts intelligently with little chance of error. To this end the switch laid out upon a 100-ft. radius curve has become the most popular standard, while frogs and mates may be readily specified by number from a comparatively small standard list, the number indicating a distinct casting with certain field dimensions. These standards are clearly set forth in the manual of the association named.

Estimates.—Whereas the cost of materials varies greatly in different portions of the country, estimates or actual costs of construction must be taken with a great deal of caution. They seem to be of sufficient value as a study of approximate relative values, however, to warrant listing herein. Such an estimate covering the construction for an interurban line 63 miles in length in the South will, therefore, be found on page 287.

The estimate represents an expenditure of $13,700 per mile for roadbed and track, exclusive of engineer's fee and contractor's profit. It is interesting to note that of the above total 37.8 per cent is labor and 62.2 per cent material.

CHAPTER XXI

CARS

Car Selection.—Notwithstanding the fact that electric traction has been developed within a comparatively few years, cars which are now operated upon the various city and interurban lines of the country range from the 20-ft. single-truck made-over horse cars to the 70-ft. magnificent limited double-truck parlor cars weighing from 50 to 70 tons and provided with all the conveniences of the Pullman coach. With this array of possible rolling stock to choose from, the problem of car selection for a proposed road or for additions to present equipment on city or interurban systems is a difficult matter. Too little attention has been given to this problem in the past, the questions of sufficient seating capacity and finish often being the principal considerations in the selection of cars. These factors are, of course, of prime importance, for the public patronage is not only dependent upon the ability to obtain a seat in a car, especially upon a long journey, but also to a surprising extent upon the appointments of the cars with respect to personal convenience. Track and street conditions often impose limits on the dimensions of cars which may be used on a given road. The class of service in which the car is to be used, whether city, suburban, or interurban, defines to a certain extent the type of car. In city service local conditions, such as climate, topography, size of city, kind and location of industrial works, volume of vehicular traffic, distribution of population, and social characteristics of the people, enter more or less directly into the problem of car selection and influence the choice of type. The main questions in the problem, however, are:

1. Method of fare collection.
2. Location and arrangement of entrances and exits.
3. Seating and standing capacity.
4. Dimensions and weight of car.

These questions are largely determined by:

1. Average length of ride per passenger.
2. Average number of passengers per car-mile.
3. Average number of stops per mile.
4. Maximum safety in operation.
5. Cost of operation and maintenance.

In the selection of cars for interurban service some of the more important points to be considered are:

1. Nature of traffic, whether passenger, freight, or express.
2. Length of road.
3. Social conditions.
4. Schedule speed.
5. Condition of roadbed and structures.
6. Convenience of patrons.
7. Nature of competition if competition exists.
8. Whether or not the road enters the cities along its route over private right-of-way or over city streets.

Fig. 131.—Electric locomotives used in 1885.

At the present time careful engineers are studying the problems of car selection and design as they have never been studied before and much emphasis is being placed on the economic ratios "weight of car per seat," "weight of car per square foot of floor area," and "weight of car per foot of car length."

Car Bodies.—It was in Baltimore August 10, 1885, that the first electric railway service in the United States was inaugurated. The illustration shows one of Leo Daft's electric locomotives or tractors, which pulled regular street cars. The third rail between the tracks carried the power except at crossings where an overhead contact was made. With the gradual increase in speed of cars there came an increasing number of wrecks, which soon proved the average car construction to be unsuitable for withstanding severe strains and thereby protecting passengers to some extent from injury in case of collision. Then came a period of marked increase in the weight of cars, with correspondingly increased capacity not only of car equipment but of feeders, substation, and power-station capacity as well. Quite

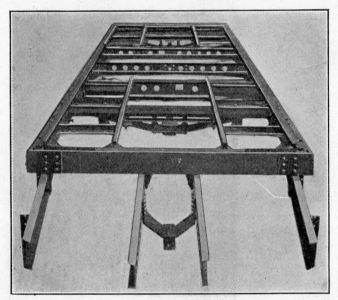

Fig. 132.—Steel frame car construction.

recently, however, another reaction has taken place, for it has been found that the desired strength to resist the abnormal forces in service may be obtained by proper design with even less weight. This apparently paradoxical condition is partly due to the fact that the use of steel in place of wood will give greater strength with less weight and also that a car may be constructed as a double truss, the side frames acting as one truss to transfer the load to the bolsters and the bolsters, in turn, acting as transverse trusses between car sills and truck support. For steel-frame construction, see Fig. 132.

The better types of recently designed car bodies are either all steel or partly steel. The great advances made within the past few years in the art of sheet-metal working have made it possible to construct pressed-steel shapes cheaply in almost any form desired. These shapes are much used in modern car-body construction. All-steel cars are fireproof and in case of wreck they do not telescope readily, nor do they break up into dangerous splinters. The car floors used in these cars are of the so-called "monolithic type," and are made by spreading either a plain or a reinforced cement on a base of galvanized iron and special shapes.

The monitor-type roof (Fig. 141), is rapidly being replaced by the arch type (Fig. 142), which is stronger, lighter, and easier to construct and gives greater headroom for a given height of car.

Metal and composition ceilings are being used instead of the wood veneers used a few years ago. These new ceilings are fireproof and do not warp or shrink.

The desirable reductions possible in cost of power, car repairs, track repairs, fixed charges on power plant and distribution system with decrease in weight of cars are very clearly pointed out in a paper by M. V. Ayers, then electrical engineer of the Boston & Worcester Street Ry., before the American Association in 1909. In this paper formulas are developed for the foregoing cost reductions and suggestions are given for possible decrease in weight of cars without curtailment of strength. Aside from the above truss design and steel underframing, the use of aluminum and cast bronzes in place of iron, softwoods in many places instead of hardwoods, and the reduction in the weights of motors with forced ventilation are mentioned.

Other marked advances are the standardization by the above-named association of the heights of couplers, platforms, bumpers, and many other construction details of both city and interurban cars,[1] and the use of corrugated-iron buffers or "anticlimbers" to prevent telescoping of platforms in case of collision. Such telescoping was the cause of much damage in several very serious interurban wrecks in the Middle West.

Trucks.—The truck primarily consists of two pairs of wheels and axles upon whose journals a steel framework is supported by

[1] A. E. R. A., "Engineering Manual," 1914.

means of combined helical and elliptical springs. This framework serves not only to take the weight of the car body, but also to form a support for the brake rigging and a portion of the weight of the motors. Since the axles are held in a position parallel to each other by the fixed journal boxes, the distance between axles cannot exceed a certain value, generally 7 ft. 6 in., because of difficulties in following curves of short radius in the track. With this limitation and with the further fact dem-

Fig. 133.—Arrangement of Brill 27–MCB Truck for removing bolster springs.

onstrated by practice that single-truck cars tend to rock badly in the direction of motion, the length of single-truck car bodies must necessarily be limited to from 22 to 25 ft. overall. For the longer cars two trucks with king pins located as near the ends of the car as possible without interfering with vestibule supports must be used.

With either type of truck the motors are suspended with two babbitted boxes, cast in one side of the motor frame, bearing on the car axle, and the opposite side of the motor is hung by means of a flexible link from the truck frame. The so-called "nose" suspension provides but one support between motor and frame, while the "yoke" suspension, as the name implies, furnishes two such connections. With these suspensions the motor is permitted to swing slightly about the car axle as a center as the car passes over irregularities in the track, thus keeping the pinion on the motor shaft at all times in mesh with the gear on the car axle.

Trucks are provided with car wheels ranging from 22 to 37 in. in diameter, the larger sizes being generally used in heavy interurban traction. Wheels are constructed of cast iron with chilled treads, cast steel, or a combination of cast-iron centers with steel rims. The latter type has now been largely replaced on interurban roads by the cast-steel wheel, as some difficulties were encountered, due to the steel rims working loose in service.

FIG. 134.—Brill standard safety car truck.

Wheels may be returned four or five times before scrapping is necessary, a reduction of from ¾ to 1½ in. in diameter being possible before wheels must be discarded. Steel wheels will range from four to five times the mileage of cast-iron wheels and the latter are considered unsafe above 30 m.p.h. Wheels varying as much as 2 in. in diameter have been successfully used on different axles of the same car, although those on the same axle must be of the same diameter. The wheels are forced on the axles under hydraulic pressures of from 25 to 50 tons, depending upon the type of wheel and size of axles.

Car axles are turned from cold-rolled steel and vary in diameter from 4 in. with the smallest motors up to 7 in. with 200- and 250-hp. motors in heavy service.

Formerly, it was general practice to lubricate truck journals by means of cotton waste, soaked in grease, packed in the journal box. While this method is still used to a limited extent, the best practice at present is following the lines laid down years ago by the steam railways, namely, the use of oil-soaked woolen waste, packed in a large journal box and surrounding the part of the journal not covered by the "brass."

Trucks are provided with side bearing plates upon which similar plates on the under side of the car must rest when the latter is unequally loaded or upon curves to prevent too great tilting of the car.

As a result of the success achieved by the Birney safety car, there has been a tendency on the part of many railways to look with more favor upon the use of single-truck equipment. It is designed to eliminate the galloping and most uncomfortable riding-action characteristics of the existing types of single trucks. This is accomplished by supporting most of the car body and passenger weight on the extreme end of the truck.

The "maximum-traction" truck is being used to a wide extent under modern light-weight, low-platform cars. It is particularly well adapted to the form of construction used in the "stepless" center-entrance cars (Fig. 143).

Motor Equipment.—The question of whether a two- or four-motor equipment should be installed must receive careful thought. Previous chapters have described the method of determining the total power required for the car, but whether this should be supplied by two or four motors is quite another problem. With single-truck and maximum-traction truck cars two motors only are possible. In standard double truck cars, four-motor equipment is probably most commonly found, although many roads are operating with but one motor per truck. Tests which have been made with the same car equipped in both ways disclose the fact that, under certain conditions, such as heavy grades, large number of stops per mile, and severe climatic conditions, the four-motor equipment will require less power for the same schedule. This is largely due to the distribution of torque over the larger number of driving wheels. This torque distribution, as well as the reserve capacity over that called for by the theoretical calculations, especially under the abnormal conditions of snow fighting and making up lost time, is usually considered of tangible monetary value by traction managers.

For these reasons the four-motor equipment has generally found favor where heavy cars are used. While the control equipment and car wiring are slightly more complicated with the four-motor equipment, the ability to use two motors, ordinarily with one on each truck, in case of failure of one or more of the other set is worthy of consideration. In short, the continuity of service and the maintenance of schedule speed must be thought of as well as first cost of equipment and operating expense.

Figure 135 shows the Baldwin truck, which is especially suitable for heavy, high-speed, electric-railway service, or for use under motor cars on electrified sections of steam lines.

Fig. 135.—Baldwin truck for interurban cars.

This truck is of the equalized pedestal type with angle-iron end frames. The side frames are of forged iron, and they are secured to the end frames by corner gussets, and to the channel transoms by heavy cast-steel gussets which support the brake rigging. This provides a rigid construction and prevents "diamond pointing." The pedestals are of wrought iron, and are fitted with steel-plate wearing gibs. The equalizers are made with easy curves, and support the frames through twin helical springs, while the bolster springs are triple elliptic. The bolster is a steel casting, suspended on swing links.

Lighting.—The very unsatisfactory nature of car lighting at the present time, especially upon interurban roads, has been commented upon in a previous chapter. The reason for this, in the face of public criticism on roads where everything else is done for the convenience and comfort of the passengers, is difficult to understand. The present method of lighting is that of using several series of five incandescent lamps, each protected by fuses and connected directly between the trolley and ground so that the lights will not be extinguished when the circuit breaker opens. Several clusters are distributed throughout the hood of the car and often a light is placed over each seat. The incandescent headlight, if one be used, may be lighted in place of the vestibule light on the front end of the car by means of a snap switch. All the lights are, of course, dependent upon trolley voltage, which has been previously shown to vary over a wide range, with more than proportional variations in light intensity. A lighting system independent of trolley voltage must sooner or later replace this unsatisfactory method of car lighting.

In the high-voltage, direct-current systems the lighting circuit usually receives its energy from a dynamotor or motor-generator set, which transforms the high trolley voltage down to 600 volts for the air-compressor, lighting, and control circuits. Where alternating-current systems are used, the lights are usually fed from a small special transformer.

The use of tungsten lamps is a distinct advance over the old carbon-filament lamps, as they are much more efficient and are not affected to so great an extent by voltage variations.

The fact that low-voltage tungsten lamps are particularly well adapted to railway work has made possible a new type of lighting system that is being tried out with very gratifying results so far by a well-known interurban road[1] which has to meet severe competition from steam roads. In this system the lamps are lighted from a storage battery. The 30-volt system, which has practically become the standard in steam-coach lighting systems, is used. The batteries are charged by means of a motor-generator set, the charging being done in the daytime. The motor-generator set is of such design that its terminal voltage is not greatly affected by variations in the line voltage and, therefore, complicated voltage regulators are not required.

Arc headlights are often used on interurban cars with some provision for operation upon city streets, such as a gauze shade, reduced voltage, polarity reversal in the case of the magnetite arc, or the substitution of an incandescent lamp. These head-

[1] Michigan United Traction Company. See *Elec. Ry. Jour.*, July 18, 1914.

lights require from 4 to 4½ amp. at 550 volts, of which more than 80 per cent is wasted in external resistance. At present, high-power tungsten lamps equipped with good reflectors are being used to a considerable extent in headlight service.

Car Heating and Ventilation.—At present four types of car-heating systems are available, namely: electric, hot water, hot air, and coal stoves. First cost, cost of operation and maintenance, convenience in handling, safety, type of car, severity of climate, and nature of run are some of the factors which affect the choice of a heating system. All-steel cars usually require from 20 to 30 per cent more heat than do wooden cars operating under similar conditions. The use of double window sashes in severe weather reduces the amount of heat necessary to keep a car in comfortable condition. Interurban and other long-haul cars must be heated differently than the city car, where the length of ride is usually short and passengers do not remove their outer wraps.

Many city cars and some of the smaller interurban cars are heated by means of electric heaters provided with switches located in the vestibule which will permit several degrees of heat. Heater regulation (1) by the car crew, (2) by the dispatcher, (3) by automatic means has been tried out. While in first cost it is most expensive, the automatic method of control, in which a thermostat regulator controls the manipulation of the heater control switch, seems to give the best satisfaction. Electric heaters should be so placed that the clothing of passengers cannot come into contact with any part of the heater or cannot screen the heater so that currents of air cannot pass freely. The electric system of car heating is clean, convenient, and easily maintained, but is costly to operate. The problem of car heating, especially upon long, exposed runs at high speed in the coldest weather, is a serious one, a car requiring from 10 to 30 amp. at 550 volts for such service. One large city railway system in particular, although able to supply the demands of summer traffic with existing power-station equipment, was forced to install additional apparatus and enlarge its station in order to meet the car-heating demand in winter.

Ventilation, with the electric system, is secured in several ways. One method employs a small motor-driven blower which draws outside air through a duct from some place near the roof and forces it through other ducts which have outlets near the heaters. The foul air ascends and passes out at the ceiling through special ventilators. In another method the ventilators are so shaped that they act as "ejectors" when the car is in motion and draw the foul air out of the car, fresh air being supplied through holes in the sides of the car near the heaters. In many city cars the doors are the only means of ventilation in the wintertime. However, public opinion is becoming rather exacting on the point of ventilation, and the better types of cars are being equipped with ventilating systems. A ventilating system, to be effective, must be able to supply from 600 to 800 cu. ft. of air per passenger per hour.

In many of the newer types of cars a special type of hot-air heater is being used. A motor-driven blower draws fresh air from the outside of the car and forces it over the heating surface of an enclosed stove or hot-air heater. The air is then either discharged directly into the car or distributed by means of ducts to various parts of the car. The foul air escapes through ceiling ventilators. These heaters usually burn hard coal. They require very little attention and are very economical.

The coal stove is practically obsolete as a means of car heating.

Interurban companies, and especially those operating single-end cars, have adopted the hot-water heating system almost exclusively, the heater being located in one end of the car, preferably in the baggage compartment or motorman's cab. This system has the double advantage of low cost of operation and more even distribution of heat in the car, this being accomplished by means of pipes encircling the car near the floor, as in the cars of steam railroads. Ventilation is secured by methods similar to those described under electric heating.

Current Collection.—Little change has been made in the overhead trolley since the earliest days of electric traction, its operation being entirely satisfactory except for the very highest speeds or for the collection of very heavy currents. Large trolley wheels are used for high-speed service and each road has a particular composition for the wheel casting which it believes to be best for local conditions. Wheels should run from 5,000 to 10,000 miles before replacement is necessary.

The pantograph bow collector is coming into general use in high-voltage, high-speed service. Such a device is illustrated upon a car in Fig. 136. It is raised to the wire by air pressure, the controlling valve being in the motorman's cab. With this type of collector the alignment of the trolley wire is not important, as the collector is often 2 ft. or more in length and any transverse

Fig. 136.—Pantograph and wheel trolleys.

movement prevents local wearing of the collector. A near view for the pantograph collector built by the General Electric Company for the electric locomotives of the Chicago, Milwaukee & St. Paul Ry. is shown in Fig. 137.

Fig. 137.—Sliding pantograph trolley. (*Chicago, Milwaukee & St. Paul R.R.*)

The third-rail shoe for collecting heavy currents from the third rail mounted beside the running rails has been referred to previously. A view of one of the many types may be found in Fig. 138. Some difficulty has been encountered in the past with this construction in winter, for if sleet be allowed to form on the rail the shoe tends to ride on the sleet and a poor contact with much arcing results. Various methods have been devised to overcome this difficulty with more or less success. Those most used are a steel brush or scraper placed ahead of the shoe and the sprinkling of the third rail with brine.

FIG. 138.—Third rail shoe and mounting.

Car Wiring.—A great deal of laxity has existed in the past in regard to car wiring and many accidents and fires have resulted in consequence. As the Underwriter's Code does not rigidly apply, since cars are not insured, the tendency has been to use little care in running the wires under the car. Rubber-covered wire is, of course, used, but it is customary to group all the wires together in one or two cables in a length of canvas hose hung from the car sills and extending from motors to controllers. The cable extending from the trolley base is supported on the top of the car roof by means of brass clips and is carried either into the car vestibule to the circuit breaker with only the insulation of the wire or, in the case of master control, it is carried down one of the corner posts of the car in molding.

The Fire Underwriters[1] have drawn up a code of rules for car wiring and many improvements have resulted therefrom. Asbestos-lined conduit is now often laid under the seats of the car for the installation of cables, while in the better types of construction, iron conduit is installed as in building wiring. Present practice also involves the use of asbesto-lumber or galvanized-iron protection between wiring and wooden-car frames, especially over the rheostats. Car-wiring diagrams will be considered under Types of Control, Chap. XXIV.

Special Types of Cars.—The preceding discussion applies to all types of cars. The special features of cars designed for a particular service will be outlined below.

Pay-as-you-enter Cars.—The introduction of this type of car a few years ago practically revolutionized the construction of cars intended for city, suburban, and light interurban service.   Briefly stated, the advantages of the pay-as-you-enter system are as follows:

1. The number of platform accidents is greatly reduced.

2. The conductor can collect all fares.

3. Passengers within the car are not disturbed by the conductor walking back and forth, and outgoing passengers are not blocked by incoming passengers.

4. The conductor has better supervision over the car.

An apparent disadvantage is the increased length of stop, but this has not proved to be serious, as the platforms in this type of car are very large, and when this platform is filled the car is started. The fares are paid before the passengers enter the car but during the period the car is in motion. This procedure, together with the time saved by the conductor being in a position to start the car promptly, has permitted the same schedule to be maintained in several cities with less cars when this type of car has been adopted.   Views of cars equipped with prepayment devices will be found in Figs. 139 and 140. These cars are frequently designed for single-end operation.

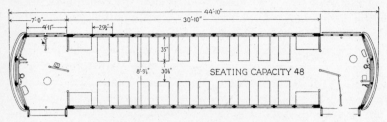

FIG. 139.—Plan of one-man, two-man car.

FIG. 140.—Platform of one-man, two-man car.

These cars are adaptable to one-man operation during the non-peak periods, and for operation with two men or in trains during the rush hours. In addition to the dead man's control and safety-device equipment, characteristic of the safety car for one-man operation, wherein it is impossible to open the front-entrance or exit doors until the brakes are applied or to start the car until they are closed, provision is also made for absolute safety when operated as a two-man car or in two-car trains.   In the former, the conductor cannot open the rear doors until the brakes have been applied and the motorman cannot get the light signal to start until these doors have been closed.   Likewise, in a two-car train the brakes must first be applied before any of the doors can be opened, and all the doors must be closed before the motorman has the signal to proceed.

Another innovation included in the equipment of these new cars is the use of air and electric couplers, which permit the coupling of two cars of this type, connecting the two air lines and the various electric circuits, with one impact of the two drawheads. If the cars should become uncoupled, the emergency brakes would be automatically applied.

Another safety feature is obtained through an emergency cord, which extends through the cars of the train, enabling either conductor to bring the car to a stop regardless of the position of the motorman's brake-valve handle.

The prepayment plan of fare collection may, of course, be used with any type of car.   In order, however, to make the best possible use of the advantages offered by the prepayment system, the following devices and modifications in car construction were introduced:

1. Means for separating the incoming and outgoing passengers.

2. Large platforms or vestibules with unobstructed openings into the car body.

3. Means of controlling the doors.

City Cars.—In the smaller cities where traffic is not particularly heavy, the 20-ft., single-truck car with the longitudinal seats is still used.   The corresponding summer equipment would be a 20-ft., 10-bench, single-truck car with running board.   Officials differ as to the advisability of maintaining a double motor equipment, and many of the smaller roads shift the equipment twice a year from one type of car to the other.   With single trucks this involves considerable labor, but if double trucks be used the trucks complete with motors can be changed with little trouble. Where summer traffic is heavy, especially to summer resorts, the

35-ft., 15-bench, double-truck open cars or small trailer cars are used.

In the large cities the convertible or semiconvertible double-truck cars (Fig. 141) with either transverse seats throughout or a

FIG. 141.—Monitor-roof-type city car.

combination of transverse and longitudinal seats, are still being used, although many of them have been equipped with the various prepayment devices. Figure 142 shows a typical modern car of the same general design. These cars are used throughout the

FIG. 142.—Arch-roof-type city car. (*The J. G. Brill Company.*)

year. This avoids duplication of equipment and the dangers incident to the operation of the running-board type of car in congested districts. Cars with transverse seats are much more comfortable, especially for long rides, but they do not permit rapid ingress and egress, nor do they provide the standing room for a given size of car that the longitudinal seats furnish.   The combination of both types of seats for long cars, with the section of transverse seats in the center of the car, permits the long-haul passengers to ride in comfort and yet furnishes more readily accessible seats and standing room for the local traffic.

It will be noted that the newer type of car has tightly closed, folding doors, folding steps, enclosed hand grips, marked openings, shielded drawbar, and, in general, offers no opportunity for careless passengers to hang on outside of the car.   The doors are operated either by compressed air or manually by means of a system of levers, and are always closed before the car starts.   The bulkheads or partitions which separate the platform from the main part of the car body are often eliminated in modern cars. By so doing greater capacity is secured and there is less obstruc-

Fig. 143.—Stepless center-entrance car.   (*Kuhlman Car Company.*)

tion to the entrances and exits.   Pipe railings, as indicated in Fig. 140, divide the incoming from the outgoing passengers. Most of these special features are found on all new cars of all types intended for city service.

The "stepless," center-entrance car (Fig. 143) introduced in New York City a few years ago, is becoming an extremely popular type of car for service in large cities.   These cars are found in various modifications.   The body is mounted on low-wheeled, maximum-traction trucks and the entrance is only a low step above the street level.   A couple of low steps or one step and an incline or "ramp," completes the passageway from the entrance platform or "well" to the car deck proper.   These cars can be loaded and unloaded very quickly and because of the absence of end platforms have great seating capacity.   The car shown seats 51 passengers.

The "near-side" car (Fig. 144) is being used to an increasing extent, particularly for one-man operation. In the larger cars, both conductor and motorman are in the front end. The front doors are used in service, the rear door being an emergency exit. All doors are controlled by the motorman and are either of the

Fig. 144.—Near-side car. (*The J. G. Brill Company.*)

manual- or power-operated type. The car is particularly well adapted for one-man operation on lines which handle light traffic. Only one stop per block is required even when the cross-street traffic is heavy, because the car stops on the "near side" of a street intersection and loads from the sidewalk line. Plat-

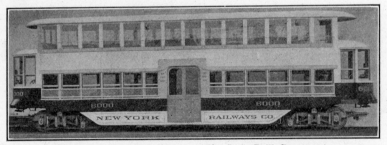

Fig. 145.—Double-deck car. (*The J. G. Brill Company.*)

form accidents are reduced to the minimum and the number of collisions with vehicles on intersecting streets are greatly reduced when this type of car is used.

Several companies operating in large cities have again introduced types of double-deck cars (Fig. 145). A construction similar to that of the low center-entrance car has eliminated part of the objections that were formerly urged against this type of car. As these cars will seat a very large number of passengers, they are particularly well adapted to the carrying of large masses

Fig. 146.—Center-aisle open car for Honolulu. (*J. G. Brill Company.*)

of passengers, such as must be handled at certain periods of the day in the vicinity of large industrial works.

The type of the car shown in Fig. 146 is typical of the country in which it will operate, permitting the passengers to enjoy the

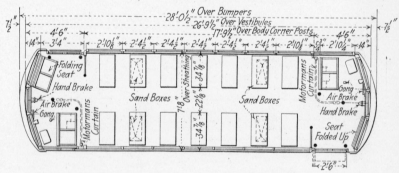

Fig. 147.—Floor plan of standard safety car.

pleasant climate and at the same time affording protection from the sun and the rain.

Birney Safety Cars.—During the last few years the Birney Safety Car has become exceedingly popular. These cars are operated by one man and, therefore, the cost is reduced.

Due to the fact that they are lighter in weight they use less power and can be run at higher speeds.

Suburban Cars.—This service in large cities is maintained with the semiconvertible and the stepless double-truck type of cars.

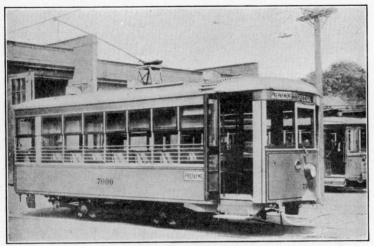

Fig. 148.—Standard safety car.

The car bodies are usually larger and the motor geared for higher speeds than are used for city service.

Fig. 149.—Open-running-board car.

Open, running-board cars are used much more in the East than in the Middle West for suburban service. Such a car, 42 ft. 6 in. in length and weighing 13 tons without electrical equipment, is shown in Fig. 149.

Interurban Cars.—Cars which have been developed for interurban service, which has recently grown so rapidly, particularly in the Middle West, are patterned after the steam-railroad coaches. They often reach lengths of 68 ft. and weights of 50 tons. These cars have transverse seats and are divided into four compartments, for motorman's cab, baggage, smoking, and main passenger service, respectively. This design often precludes double-end operation. A plan view of such a car may be seen

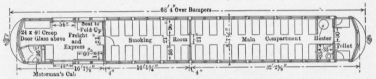

Fig. 150.—Plan of interurban car.

in Fig. 150, while a similar car designed as a sleeper and operated upon the Illinois Traction Company's lines between St. Louis and Peoria, Ill., is illustrated in the plan view of Fig. 151.

The better classes of interurban cars now being built are of all-steel construction. A typical all-steel car embodying all of the latest refinements in car design is illustrated in Fig. 152.

A light, low-wheeled, center-entrance car somewhat similar to Fig. 143 has been tried out in interurban service by one inter-

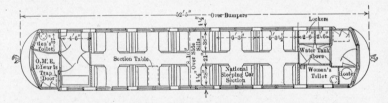

Fig. 151.—Plan of sleeping car.

urban railway company[1] operating a short road which enters a large city over the tracks of the city railway system. No difficulty has been encountered in handling the traffic and maintaining schedules formerly handled and maintained by cars weighing two or three times as much. The great passenger-carrying capacity, low energy consumption, and facility for operation on congested streets, which these cars possess, have opened a new field for them in this class of interurban service.

[1] "Pittsburgh Railways," *Elec. Ry. Jour.*, p. 250, Aug. 8, 1924.

Elevated and Subway Cars.—In the elevated and subway service in the largest cities a slightly different type of car is required, although it is patterned closely after the interurban car.

Fig. 152.—All-steel interurban car.   (*St. Louis Car Company.*)

Exits are so located as to be flush with the platform floors, no steps being necessary.   In Boston and New York both side and end doors are provided and with the traveling public trained

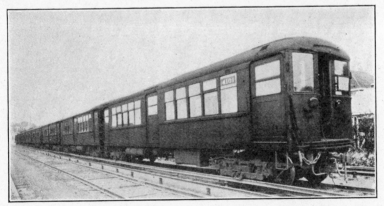

Fig. 153.—Chicago elevated eight-car train.

to enter by the end door and leave the car by the side door, some time is gained at the station.   Both transverse and longitudinal seats are provided.   These cars are designed to operate in trains, each train consisting of both motor cars and trailers, all motor cars being operated by means of the multiple-unit control from the motorman's cab of the forward car. In the Boston subway, steel cars are now being adopted, one of this type being illustrated in Fig. 154.

While the life of passenger cars will vary from 10 to 20 years, depending upon the type, severity of service, and the attention which they receive in the shops, obsolescence has been the reason for discarding most of the cars used thus far, *i.e.*, traffic demand has required that larger and better cars replace those in operation before the latter were actually worn out.

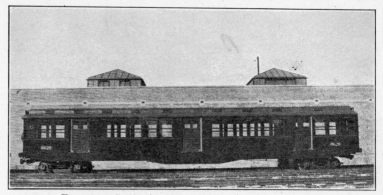

Fig. 154.—Steel motor car, used in Cambridge subway.

Freight Cars.—The car-body construction of motor cars used in handling freight and express is similar to that of the standard express car used in steam-railway service. Sometimes these car bodies are equipped with extra-heavy underframing, trucks, and motors, and used as locomotives for hauling short trains of standard steam-road freight cars.

Storage-battery Cars.—The great improvements made during the last few years in storage batteries, bearings, and light mechanical parts, brought about largely by the wonderful development of the modern automobile, have contributed much to the success of this type of car for certain classes of service. In 1913 there were 280 of the cars in use on 45 different roads in the United States.[1] The number has increased considerably since then.

[1] *Elec. Ry. Jour.*, Oct. 4, 1913.

Storage-battery cars are particularly well adapted to meet the service requirements for:

1. Cross-town lines with light traffic.
2. Lines where either narrow streets or legal requirements prohibit overhead construction.
3. Very small roads.
4. Accommodation trains on short steam roads, and light-traffic, branch-line service in connection with large steam-railway systems.

In order to minimize the energy consumption, great care is taken in the design of these cars. Usually, all of the bearings are of either the ball or roller type, the car ends are shaped to minimize air resistance, and all unnecessary weight is eliminated.

A car purchased by the Cambria & Indiana R. R., a short coal road in Pennsylvania, has a seating capacity of 52, is 50 ft. long, and weighs 29.5 tons. It has baggage, smoking, and toilet compartments, in addition to the regular passenger compartment, and is equipped with four 25-hp. motors and 240 Edison A-12 cells for power and 10 Edison A-12 cells for lighting. The battery equipment weighs 7 tons. The car has a maximum range of 130 miles on level track and a maximum speed of 35 m.p.h.

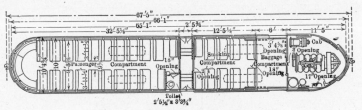

Fig. 155.—Plan of gas-electric car.

Gas-electric Car.—In several instances, particularly upon branch roads acting as feeders to trunk lines, where traffic is light and the installation of an electrical distribution system therefore unwarranted, and yet where the advantages of electric traction are worthy of serious consideration, the gas-electric car has found a place. This car not only provides for from 40 to 50 passengers, together with a baggage compartment, but also a complete power plant, a flexible distribution system, and a motor car combined. In the front end, above the floor, is located an eight-cylinder, 100/125-hp., four-cycle gas engine, direct connected to an 80-kw., 600-volt, commutating-pole, direct-current generator with exciter. A series-parallel controller regulates the supply of current from this generator to two 100-hp. motors mounted on the front trucks. Additional flexibility of control is provided by the regulation of the voltage supplied to the motors by the variation of the generator field strength. The controller is also provided with means for regulating the engine ignition and the throttle. The car may be started, stopped, and reversed with

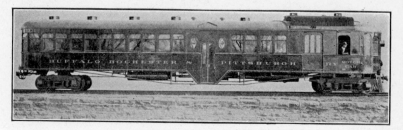

Fig. 156.—Elevation of gas-electric car.

the engine running continuously in one direction. A trolley is often provided by means of which the car may be operated on standard direct-current trolley systems without change in the control equipment.

Reports from roads where these cars have been installed show a marked reduction in operating expenses and maintenance charges over those of steam-operated trains, although their comparatively recent introduction has not permitted an accurate comparison over an extended period. A plan and elevation of one of these cars may be found in Figs. 155 and 156, respectively.

CHAPTER XXII

MOTOR BUSSES

The subject of electric-railway engineering has recently become very much interrelated with that of motor-bus transportation. Either as a competitor or as an auxiliary feeder to an urban or interurban railway, the motor bus should be considered at least from its economic standpoint, if not in its details of design and operation. Reference to the tables of Chap. II will indicate the status of the motor-bus problem from the standpoint of traffic requirements.

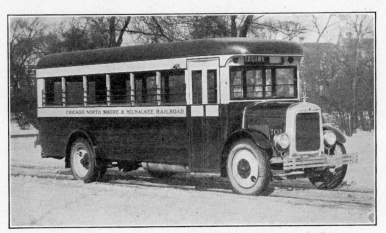

Fig. 157.—Bus. (*Chicago, North Shore & Milwaukee R. R.*)

Growth. Extent and Comparison with Electric Railways.— According to a survey by the Bureau of Census, motor busses carried approximately eleven million passengers in the United States during 1922. The electric railways carried approximately twelve billion passengers during the same period. This clearly shows that during 1922 the bus was nearly 0.09 per cent as important to the general public as the electric railway. The actual figures as given by the Bureau of Census are: busses,

11,852,276 passengers; electric railways, 12,665,300,050 passengers. Even if in the last year (1923) the electric railways carried the same number of passengers as in the year 1922, and the busses carried double their number, the bus will comparatively have very little general importance as contrasted with the electric railways. Though the bus transportation is growing with remarkable rapidity, yet it is as yet of minor consideration.

No substitute has yet been developed for the railway in hauling a large number of people. As a supplementary service, and for purposes of traffic development, the motor bus has a field of distinct usefulness. The motor bus can prove an excellent auxiliary to the present transportation system, provided it is operated under fair regulation and fair control.

In connection with the principle of coordination of service between the bus and the trolley, the report of the special committee of the U. S. Chamber of Commerce should be interesting. This report declares that the bus and the electric railway cannot permanently exist in a community and pay their way in competition with each other. There should be in each community a single reliable transportation agency rather than individual transportation units. The electric railway is the best medium for mass transportation of passengers, and should be the foundation of the suggested coordinated transit system.

Regarding regulation, the Committee states that anyone engaged in the business of common carrier by motor vehicle should be subject to regulation by Commission as to its rate and service, just as any other common carrier. Regulation by state bodies having jurisdiction over intrastate traffic has generally been accepted in this country and should be applied to motor-vehicle common carriers as well as to the other public utilities. Primarily, the purpose of all these laws is to protect the public by securing:

1. Regular and adequate service.
2. Reasonable rates.
3. Responsibility of carrier for damages which he may cause during transportation.

The Committee also points out that the present railway taxes are unsystematic, to say the least, yet amount, with imposts, to nearly $100,000,000 a year, while the maintenance of track amounts annually to even more than this sum. The tax should

Table XXVII.—Passengers by Months on North Side Bus Lines
(Chicago Motor Bus Co. in 1922)

	Passengers carried	Excess over March	Per cent of year's total
January	413,632		
February	399,186		
March	511,493		
April	613,684	102,191	1.3%
May	754,660	243,177	3.1
June	849,220	337,727	4.3
July	941,879	430,386	5.5
August	889,713	378,220	4.8
September	759,615	248,122	3.2
October	642,796	131,303	1.7
November	508,086		
December	492,027		
	7,775,991	1,871,126	23.9%

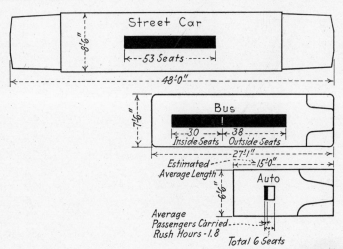

Fig. 158.—Relative area occupied and seating capacity of passenger vehicles.

be based on both gross and net returns, rather than an *ad valorem* tax, for greater tax simplification and for placing the entire expense of maintaining improved highways upon the users of these highways. This will make each form of transportation bear its fair share of the public expenditure.

In the motor bus the gasoline motor should not be put to wrong use. The gasoline and electric motors should be compared on several bases. The following leading differences may be noticed:

1. The gasoline motor is weak on acceleration.
2. Reliability is an inherent virtue of an electric motor.
3. The electric motor excels in low maintenance cost.
4. Gasoline cars necessitate large shops.
5. Gasoline cost will be a determining factor.

As the buses are very extensively used in Great Britain, where they have proved very successful, the following statistics and economic features are given for general information. The figures are taken from the Sheffield Corporation of Tramways and Motors.

AVERAGE EXPENDITURE PER BUS MILE

	1915 cents	1918 cents	1919 cents
Traffic expenses.................	6.02	9.86	14.17
General expenses................	0.74	0.76	1.06
Repair account.................	3.83	8.82	9.05
Road maintenance account........	0.11	0.29	0.40
Power expenses (gasoline).........	3.37	8.31	11.10
Total working expenses..........	14.07	28.04	35.78

COMPARATIVE FIGURES OF TRAMWAYS AND BUSSES, 1918–1919
Sheffield Accounts

	Per car mile cents	Per bus mile cents	Bus expenses are
Working expenses............	24.77	35.79	44.5% more than tram
Service of debt (capital)......	3.37	1.85	45.3% less than tram
Total expenses.............	28.14	37.64	33.7% more than tram

COMPARATIVE FIGURES OF TRAMWAYS AND BUSSES, 1918–1919. (*Continued*)
Sheffield accounts

	Cents tram per pass.	Cents busses per pass.	Bus expenses are
Working expenses..........	1.43	4.27	198% more than tram
Service of debt (capital)......	0.19	0.22	123% more than tram
Total expenses............	1.62	4.49	175% more than tram

	Tram per seat car mile cent	Bus per seat bus mile cent	Bus expenses are
Working expenses..........	0.46	1.06	131.3% more than tram
Service of debt (capital)......	0.06	0.05	[1]129% less than tram
Total expenses..........	0.52	1.11	114.1% more than tram

[1] This is an important figure and one which is overlooked by motor-bus advocates. The impression usually left is that the difference in capital expenditures is much greater.

	Per car mile cents	Per bus mile cents	Bus receipts are
Traffic receipts..............	33.13	40.91	23.5% more than tram
Traffic receipts per seat provided....................	0.61	0.122	98.0% more than tram
Average fare charged per mile	1.30	3.0	130% more than tram

The following conclusions may be drawn from the above table:

1. That the revenue expenses of running the motor bus amount to 44.5 per cent more than for the tram car. After giving the motor omnibus the benefit of comparatively lower first cost (capital), it still costs 33.7 per cent more than the tram car to operate per mile.

2. The revenue expenses per passenger carried on the motor omnibus are 198 per cent more than on the tram car. The total expenses per passenger carried are 176 per cent more on the bus than on the tram car.

3. That for the seats provided, the omnibus revenue expenses are 131.3 per cent higher than the tram-car revenue expenses. The total expenses per seat provided are 114.1 per cent higher on the bus than on the tram car.

The average speed of the buses is 9.97 m.p.h. and that of the tram car 8.65 m.p.h., that is, 15.26 per cent in favor of the bus. It is necessary, however, that reduced rates for fuel should be secured if the bus is to render most extensive service.

Fig. 159.—Double-decked summer bus for city service.

The following data are obtained from an interurban bus company which is running on a profit basis in Seattle, Wash.:

STATISTICS OF BUS LINE
(Route of 16 miles)

	1917	1916
Bus miles...............................	134,352	113,040
Revenue from operation....................	$27,032.56	$19,213.29
Operation expenses........................	21,045.11	15,551.44
Depreciation..............................	4,142.24	5,193.30
Taxes (covering 1916 expenses).............	126.24	....
Total....................................	$25,313.59	$21,744.75
Deficit...................................	....	2,531.45
Surplus..................................	1,718.97	....

On the basis of the bus-mile unit, receipts in 1916 averaged 17 cts., in 1917, 20.12 cts. Operating expenses, including depreciation, dropped from 19.23 cts. in 1916 to 18.84 cts. in 1917, but excluding the reduced allowance for depreciation the operating expenses for 1917 were 15.66 cts. per bus-mile against 14.64 cts. in 1916.

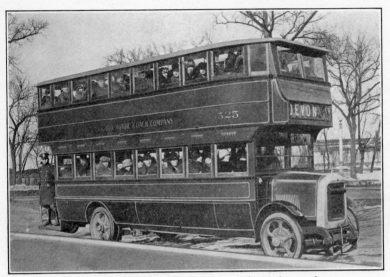

Fig. 160.—Double-decked closed bus, winter city service.

In contrast, the following data are taken from the accounts of San Francisco Municipal Bus Line for 1918. To give the service the company purchased five busses and rented three, all of 19-passenger seating capacity.

PASSENGER TRAFFIC CARRIED IN APRIL 1918

| Line | 5 cent | Tickets | | Trans-fers | Free | Total |
		Q.M.	School			
No. 1 line...............	19,190	1	779	14,654	32	34,656
No. 2 line...............	7,579	....	116	6,649	2	14,346
No. 3 line...............	26,273	1	595	25,182	33	52,089

BUS-LINE OPERATION

Route No. 1......................................	$ 959.90
Route No. 2......................................	378.95
Route No. 3......................................	1,332.25
Total receipts................................	$2,651.10

Repair to busses owned, exclusive of $749.13 for tires which are charged on the mileage basis..........	$ 400.53
Conductor, chauffeur of busses owned.............	1,172.15
Garage expenses of busses owned.................	973.77
Rental of busses................................	747.29
Conductor, chauffeur of busses rented.............	566.05
Operating loss................................	$1,955.98

Reserves:	
Depreciation (18 per cent of receipts).............	$ 477.20
Compensation insurance ($2.39 on $1,738.20)...	41.54
Total reserves..............................	$ 518.74

Gross excess of expenses over receipts, exclusive of tires...	$1,727.43

Revenue credits:	
Two quartermaster's tickets, 10 cts.; 1,490 school tickets, $37.25; and 46,485 local transfers, $1,162.13...................................	$1,199.48
Net excess of expenses over receipts, exclusive of tires......................................	$ 527.95[1]

32,645 miles at 5 cts. per mile (estimated)............	$1,632.25
Net loss for April, 1918.........................	2,160.20
Average net loss per diem.......................	72.01
Bus mileage in April, 1918, miles..................	32.645
Receipts per bus-mile in cents....................	0.081
Operating expenses per bus-mile, except tires and reserves......................................	0.118
Operating loss per bus-mile, except tires and reserves	0.037
Gross excess of expenses per bus-mile..............	0.016
Net loss per bus-mile, tire expense included.........	0.066[1]

Examination of the three instances quoted above show that a number of companies are operating busses to advantage, while others are running at a loss, due probably to faulty management or poorer business possibilities.

[1]After crediting bus line with proportionate transfers and tickets.

In a country with good roads and better weather, where bus transportation can be carried all the year around, there is a very distinct and profitable opportunity for long-haul passenger traffic by auto busses. Such conditions are found in California, where the busses can run throughout the year. As a result, quite a considerable number of long-haul bus companies are running on a profitable basis.

There has been a considerable amount of dissension between the decisions of the commissions as to the regulation of the bus transportation in coordination with the electric railway. Decisions are found both for and against the state regulation,

Fig. 161.—Kuhlman "Delux" Bus (sixteen passenger, one-man front entrance city bus).

as with other public utilities. The following is from a decision of the District of Columbia Public Utilities Commission Order No. 492, F.C. 126, which clearly points out the desirability of motor-bus operation by the street-railway companies, and consequently subject to the state regulation. Both the discussion and the decisions are quoted:

It so happens that certain streets, mostly diagonal, not occupied by car lines, lend themselves by their width or by their direction to more rapid and more direct transportation than it is possible for the street railway lines to afford between the same termini. It is on such routes that bus lines have been established or sought to be extended, and invariably they take from the car companies the cream of their traffic—

the short-haul rider—this notwithstanding the fact that the bus lines pay into the public treasury no gross receipts nor paving taxes and nothing for street crossing policeman, while, on the other hand, they accentuate the congestion on our streets, add to the wear on our roads, and increase the need for the traffic police.

In our opinion, there is a legitimate field for bus service, but this does not lie in the multiplication of lines or of vehicles reaching the heart of the city. It lies rather in providing service in extension to the street car lines into territory so thinly settled as not to justify the large investment necessary for street railway service. The bus lines should be feeders. They should create business and not rob the street railway of the just reward due their heavy investments for the public benefit. An exception to this principle arises when the existing street railway service proves to be inadequate and, for reasons either physical or financial, additional street railway lines cannot be created. In such cases, even in thickly settled territory, the obvious recourse is to the bus line; but, in the absence of legal objections, the best interests of the public will be promoted by causing such lines to be owned and operated by the street railway companies and to coordinate them with the car lines so that transfer privileges and other desirable joint relations may result.

On the other hand, Commissioner Shaw dissents from the majority opinion, saying:

In general, I believe it may be said that regulation contemplates that, as long as a utility renders adequate service at reasonable rates, it should not be subject to competition for the reason that when adequate service is rendered at reasonable rates a duplication of plant and facilities is an economic waste which, in the end, the general public must suffer. However, there is a great difference between a public utility operating motor busses and a public utility operating an electric railway, a gas plant, an electric plant, or a steam railway. The equipment of a motor bus company consists in the main of individual busses to the number required, general offices, and a place to repair and house the busses. It has no large investment in generating plants, distribution systems, track, etc.

Therefore, in my mind, a public utility operating motor busses is not comparable with other utilities subject to regulation. It appears to me that the motor-bus business is more nearly comparable with the taxicab business, over which the commission has heretofore held no jurisdiction.

Plans for the operation of the motor busses in Scranton, Pa., in competition with the lines of the Scranton railway, were

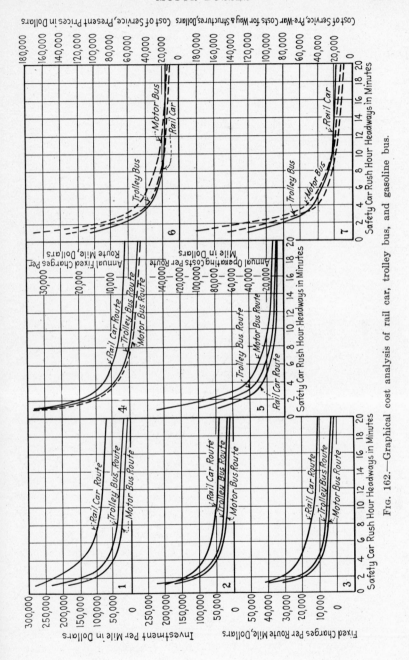

FIG. 162.—Graphical cost analysis of rail car, trolley bus, and gasoline bus.

put to a stop on May 25, 1920, by an order of the state Public Service Commission. The basis of decision was that the establishment of two competing systems of transportation would be contrary to the best interests of the public.

The Trackless-trolley Bus.—The so-called trackless-trolley bus furnishes an important contribution to the art of transportation, because its possibilities enable transportation companies to extend their lines into the suburbs or into the new sections of a city, with an investment 60 to 80 per cent less than is required for a track system to operate cars over the new route

Fig. 163.—Trackless trolley.

for two-thirds the cost of the gasoline busses. Trolley busses are giving excellent service in some of the large cities of this country, but particularly is this true in Europe. The low initial investment, flexibility of service, very economical operation, comfortable riding, and better starting characteristics should prove some of the strong arguments in favor of the trolley bus.

It is true that there is still a broad field of transportation on the city streets for which the rail car is best suited and is the most economical means of carrying a large number of passengers. There is an equally important field in which the trolley bus can furnish an equivalent service at a lower cost than the rail system. Even in comparison with the rail system, the field for the gasoline bus is very limited (on headways of 20 min. or longer), while as compared with the trolley bus it has little to its credit in a city transportation system, except where it is impossible to erect an overhead-trolley line.

The following table shows the cost of overhead construction per mile and per foot of route for trackless-trolley bus and for electric railways.

TABLE XXVIII.[1]—COST OF OVERHEAD CONSTRUCTION PER MILE AND PER FOOT OF ROUTE FOR TRACKLESS TROLLEY BUS AND FOR ELECTRIC RAILWAYS

	Single line		Double line	
	Trolley bus	Electric railway	Trolley bus	Electric railway
Labor..........................	$1,025	$ 930	$1,350	$1,220
Material......................	3,255	2,695	4,265	3,560
Supervision, etc.................	160	140	200	175
Total......................	$4,440	$3,765	$5,815	$4,955
Unit costs on foot basis:				
Unit cost per foot of above items...	$0.841	$0.717	$1.101	$0.938
Curves, 90 deg., per foot..........	0.852	0.722	1.116	0.950
Loops, reverse curves or turn outs, per foot......................	0.934	0.796	1.222	1.041
Cross-overs, etc., per foot.........	0.897	0.775	1.175	1.001

[1] *Bull.* General Electric Company.

In summing up, it may be said that, while the feeder service is the most important use of the bus, there are many other important uses existing in the territory of practically every electric railway. Some of these coordinated uses are:

1. For express or local service, jointly with railway lines.

2. For supplementary service on single-track railway lines, where the railway headway cannot be reduced to meet the demands of the traffic.

3. For supplementing the railway carrying capacity in the rush hours.

4. On the new routes in more thickly populated districts, say, within 2 miles of the business center, designed to serve districts which are not contiguous to the railway lines, to supple-

ment the railway through this zone of maximum loading, and to reach important delivery points which it is not possible to reach by direct railway routes.

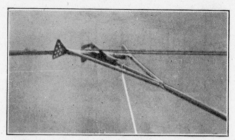

FIG. 164.—Collecter head for trackless trolley equipment.

5. To serve important traffic points, like large factories, where waiting cars would obstruct the track and where the greater flexibility of the bus would permit it to make two or more rush-hour trips as compared with one by car.

TABLE XXIX.—INCREASE IN PASSENGER-CARRYING-CAPACITY OF STREETS IN RUSH HOURS WITH BUS OPERATION

Street Space Occupied		Passenger Carrying Capacity of Street (At Average Load)		Total
		Automobiles	Buses	
100% of Space Occupied by Autos.	No Buses	100%	←100% of Auto Capacity→ ←---200% of Auto. Capacity---→ ←----300% of Automobile Capacity--------→ ←--------400% of Automobile Capacity--------→	100%
99% " " " " "	1% "	99%	24%	123%
98% " " " " "	2% "	98%	48%	146%
97% " " " "	3% "	97%	72%	169%
96% " " " " "	4% "	96%	95%	191%
95% " " " " "	5% "	95%	118%	213%
94% " " " "	6% "	94%	142%	236%
93% " " " " "	7% "	93%	166%	259%
92% " " " "	8% "	92%	190%	282%
91% " " " " "	9% "	91%	213%	304%
90% " " " " "	10% "	90%	236%	326%
89% " " " " "	11% "	89%	260%	349%
88% " " " "	12% "	88%	284%	372%
87% " " " " "	13% "	87%	308%	395%
86% " " " " "	14% "	86%	331%	417%
85% " " " " "	15% "	85%	354%	439%

6. As a substitute for the railway on the lines where the track is worn out and the construction of the new track is not warranted or on lines which do not operate and earn operating expenses.

7. For faulty service. There is real demand in many cities for higher-priced service than the street cars can give.

8. For pleasure riding. This is one of the most important fields for the bus.

9. For special chartered service.

10. For emergency service.

CHAPTER XXIII

MOTORS

Much of the theory underlying the operation of the direct-current, series motors has been discussed in a previous chapter. A brief outline of its construction and selection, together with the principle of operation of the alternating-current motors used in railway systems, will be herein considered.

Direct-current Motor.—The direct-current, series railway motor differs from the stationary type principally in the design of the frame, that of the former motor consisting of an iron casting split in a plane through the center of the shaft and hinged

Fig. 165.—Typical box-type railway motor.

in such a manner that the lower half of the frame with two field poles and windings may be lowered for inspection of the armature with the motor in place on the truck. The larger motors (Fig. 165) are of the so-called "box" type, with the frame in a single casting. The armature is removed from this motor by taking off the end bearing plate and drawing the armature out in a direction parallel with the shaft through the opening thus made. The motor must be removed from the truck for this operation. The frames of both types of motors are provided with openings and moisture proof cover plates for ready access to armature, commutator, and connecting cables. These cables are brought out through insulating bushings in the frame of the motor, which are usually located on the side next to the truck bolster, in order that the movement of these cables may be least when rounding curves.

Railway motors are generally of the four-pole type with the axes of the poles at an angle of 45 deg. with the horizontal in the split-frame types. Field coils are wound with cotton- or asbestos-covered wire with asbestos insulation between layers, or, in the larger motors, with copper strip. The coils are taped, impregnated with insulating compound with the vacuum process, and waterproofed.

Two sets of bearings are provided in the frame, one pair for the car axles and the second for the armature shaft. These are of babbitt-lined cast bronze.

The armature and the commutator are not unlike those of stationary motors, except that the armature is series wound and requires but two sets of brushes. These are placed on the top portion of the commutator and are, therefore, accessible through trap doors in the floor of the car. The brush holders are fixed in position and support the carbon brushes in a radial position on the commutator so that the motor may operate equally well in either direction.

Commutating-pole Motor.—As in the direct-current stationary motors and generators, the rather marked advantages of the commutating poles are applied to the railway motor. These commutating poles are auxiliary poles provided with a winding connected in series with the armature. As the magnetic flux in these poles will vary with the armature current, the serious effects of armature reaction upon commutation are partially neutralized by the flux from these auxiliary poles. The latter are so designed and located that the short-circuit current in the coil under the brush is small and sparking at the brushes, therefore, a minimum. As the output of the motor is often limited by commutation as well as temperature rise, the overload capacity will be increased and its maintenance cost reduced. It is claimed that 100 per cent overload may be suddenly thrown on and off such a motor without sparking at the brushes.

Field-control Motors.—A comparatively recent departure in direct-current railway-motor design is the construction of the field coils in two distinct parts on the core of the pole, the two parts being insulated from each other. The part which is to be in continuous service has the larger number of turns. The smaller coil of a less number of turns is used only in accelerating the car. The four larger coils of the main operating fields are connected permanently in series and the four smaller coils are similarly connected. When the car is being accelerated the eight coils are in series, thus producing a more powerful field and a correspondingly greater tractive effort for the same value of current than if the group of four larger coils alone were in the circuit. When the car has reached nearly full speed the series of smaller field coils is cut out, thus reducing the field and giving higher speed for a given current.

Field control motors may save quite an appreciable amount of energy—from 6 to 10 per cent in frequent-stop city service and from 4 to 7 per cent on elevated lines.

Fig. 166.—Pressed steel motor. (*Westinghouse Electric & Manufacturing Company.*)

Pressed-steel Motors.—Of still more recent development is the pressed-steel motor (Fig. 166). Open-hearth steel plates are pressed into the desired shapes by enormous presses for the yoke, frame, and other integral parts of the motor. These are all assembled and are held together by hot-driven rivets. The result is a motor whose iron parts are 30 per cent less in weight in the 30- to 50-hp. sizes, and still lighter in proportion in larger ratings, whose magnetic circuits can be operated at a higher density on account of the better magnetic qualities of the steel and whose every part is strong, unbreakable, free from blowholes, and in all ways more reliable than the cast-steel parts of the ordinary motor.

The principal drawback to the manufacture of pressed-steel motors is the expensive equipment required for pressing out the motor parts. This factor restricts the manufacture of this type of motor to the most popular ratings.

Single-phase Motors.—With the increase in length of interurban lines, and their large power demands, together with the realization of the high first cost and maintenance charges on the converting equipment necessary for long direct-current roads, came the serious study of the possibilities of alternating-current motors for railway use. It was at once recognized that if a satisfactory alternating-current railway motor could be developed considerable saving could be made in the above factors and a marked simplification in the distribution system effected, as pointed out in the chapter on the distribution system, to say nothing of the possible reduction in distribution-system losses, due to the increase in trolley voltage. As the polyphase motors which have been developed were of the constant-speed type with inherent characteristics unfavorable in most cases for traction, and since the advantages of polyphase transmission at high voltage can be gained without the complication of a polyphase distribution system and car circuits, the attention of American engineers was first turned to the development of the single-phase motor for traction purposes.

This development may be approached either by endeavoring to adapt the direct-current series motor, whose characteristics have proved satisfactory for traction purposes, for use upon single-phase, alternating-current circuits, or the alternating-current induction motor may be studied with a view to redesigning it for railway use. Both of these viewpoints will be considered in the order mentioned.

Adaptation of the Direct-current Series Motor.—Those familiar with the direct-current motor will remember that a reversal of the current in either armature or field alone will reverse the direction of rotation of the motor, whereas a reversal of both field and armature connections will not change its direction of rotation. It might be predicted, therefore, that when a direct-current series motor is connected to an alternating-current circuit of proper voltage, the motor would operate. This was found to be the case, although many effects of the alternating current, which are discussed below, cause the motor to operate unsatisfactorily from a practical standpoint unless several changes are made in its design.

The e.m.f. impressed upon a direct-current series motor is balanced by the sum of counter e.m.f. of revolution E_r and the IR fall of potential in field and armature windings. In addition to these there exists in the series motor operating upon an alternating-current circuit the reactive voltage of the series field and armature windings.

The reactive voltages are due to the self-induction of the respective windings or, better, to the cutting of the conductors by the lines of leakage magnetic flux which encircle one set of conductors only and are, therefore, not useful in producing counter or energy e.m.f. This voltage is 90 deg. in advance of the current and may be treated as though there were an external choke

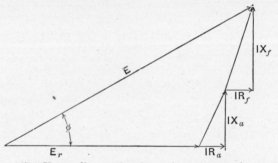

FIG. 167.—Vector diagram for alternating-current series motor.

coil of corresponding reactance connected in series with the motor. It is directly proportional to the frequency of the voltage supply.

With these voltages in mind the vector diagram of the motor may be drawn as in Fig. 167 where

E = impressed voltage.

E_r = counter e.m.f. of revolution.

I = current in armature and field.

R_a = resistance of armature.

X_a = reactance of armature.

R_f = resistance of field.

X_f = reactance of field.

ϕ = angle between impressed voltage and current whose cosine is the power factor of the motor.

From the diagram it will be seen that any change of design that will reduce X_f and X_a will increase the power factor of the motor. This is a desirable change, as a higher power factor results not only in smaller losses and higher torque in the motor, but either lower losses or less copper in the distribution system as well. The reactance voltage of the armature IX_a may be more or less completely neutralized by means of a compensating winding, which will be subsequently explained, while that of the field can only be reduced by reducing the turns on the field or the magnetic flux produced thereby.

Before these possible changes are studied further the question of commutation may well be investigated, for the commutation of a direct-current motor operating upon alternating current

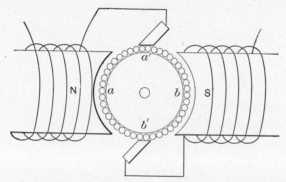

Fig. 168.—Circuit of alternating-current series motor.

is noticeably poor. It will be remembered that in the commutation of direct-current motors care must be taken to have the current a minimum in the coil or coils which are short circuited by the brushes in order that the spark which occurs when the coil is disconnected from the brush by the movement of the commutator may not be serious. Reference to Fig. 168 will show, however, that there is an additional factor to be considered in the commutation of an alternating-current motor. The motor is quite similar to a transformer in that it has a magnetic circuit surrounded by two sets of coils, the field, and the armature. The pulsating flux set up by the field generates an e.m.f. due to this transformer action in the coils of the armature, those coils in the plane $a'b'$ which enclose the greatest number of magnetic lines of force generating the highest voltage and those in the plane ab theoretically zero voltage. But one or more of the coils in plane $a'b'$ are short circuited by the brushes. A large current flows through this coil, therefore, as in a short-circuited secondary coil on a transformer. Unless the design is altered so as to reduce this current, vicious sparking will take place and seriously limit the commutating capacity of the motor.

Two methods of reducing this short-circuit current are in general use. One makes use of an auxiliary stator coil placed 90 electrical degrees from the field coils as in the commutating poles on direct-current motors. This so-called "compensating" coil is in series with the armature and is designed of such strength as to neutralize the combined effect of transformer e.m.f. and armature reactance e.m.f. While such a coil can be made to perform such neutralization for one load and partially neutralize the e.m.f. on all loads, its effect is not complete over the entire range of load, it being particularly faulty at very light loads. One of the large manufacturing companies overcomes this light-load fault by inserting "preventive" leads between the point where connection is made between armature coils and the commutator. These leads are of relatively high resistance and, therefore, tend to limit the short-circuit current to a minimum. As the current circulating through the armature coils encounters the resistance of the preventive leads only as it flows into or out from a brush, the heat loss in the leads is not large. The combination of compensating coils and preventive leads not only puts the commutation of the alternating-current series motor on a par with that of the direct-current motor, but it increases the power factor to a practical operative value as well.

Returning to the question of reducing the reactance e.m.f. of the field in order that the power factor may be still further increased. If this be done by reducing the field flux, the capacity of the motor is correspondingly lowered. It is actually accomplished in practice, therefore, by reducing the number of field turns to from 20 to 25 per cent of those in a direct-current motor of similar characteristics. This is rather difficult with the large-capacity motors having a relatively large number of poles.

Aside from the above changes in design which are necessary in order to adapt the direct-current motor to use with alternating current, the field must be laminated as well as the armature to prevent serious eddy-current losses. The reluctance of the magnetic circuit must be reduced in order that the flux may not be sacrificed with a smaller number of field turns and joints are, therefore, eliminated and the sectional area of the poles increased. Theoretically, the length of the air gap might be shortened to produce the desired reduction in reluctance, but this is not considered advisable from a practical operating standpoint, for with the direct-current motors the bearings often wear to such an extent that the armature rubs on the lower field poles.

Adaptation of Induction Motor.—The evolution of the single-phase induction motor into the alternating-current series railway motor has been very clearly explained from the theoretical standpoint by McAllister.[1] Briefly, the development is as follows: Suppose a single-phase induction motor stator to be provided with an armature similar to that of a direct-current series motor and the stator and armature windings to be connected in series. McAllister shows very clearly that with all possible ratios of field to armature turns the power factor will not exceed 45 per cent and the maximum limit of the ratio of starting to synchronous torque will be in the neighborhood of 125 per cent. Both of these values are too small for a satisfactory railway motor.

If the reluctance of the air gap between polar regions be increased by forming polar projections in the stator fields or by a neutralizing winding such that the ratio of reluctance of the leakage path between poles to that under the poles may be considered as infinite, the power factor and torque ratio may be increased over a wide range by properly proportioning the armature and field turns. The successful railway motor may be considered, therefore, as an induction-motor stator with high reluctance between poles, enclosing an armature similar in design to that of a direct-current series motor.

Construction of the Single-phase Motor.—As the result of the above studies a motor has been developed which is giving very satisfactory results upon single-phase railway systems of low frequency (25 cycles), especially in the larger sizes which have been applied to locomotives.

Such a motor (Fig. 169), does not appear materially different from the direct-current motor, consisting of a cast-steel, box-type frame supporting the laminated-iron stator. The motors are

[1] McAllister, A. S., "Alternating-current Motor."

Fig. 169.—Single-phase series motor.

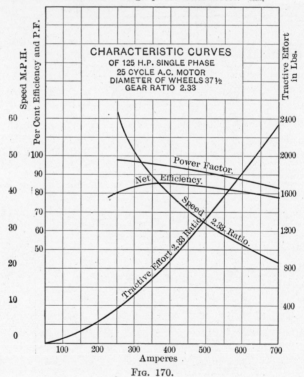

Fig. 170.

provided with four or six poles and their field windings are of the distributed type similar to those of the single-phase induction motor. The winding is of heavy strap copper, however, and consists of relatively few turns. Between the main field windings are located the compensating windings connected in series with the armature. The armature is practically identical with that of the direct-current motor, except that, because of the lower voltage and consequently higher current for which it is designed, it is usually necessary to provide one set of brushes for each pole.

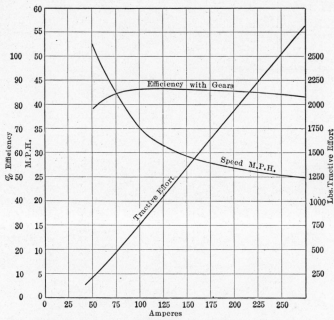

Fig. 171.—Characteristic curves of Westinghouse D. C. 303A, 115-hp. motor, 600 volts, diameter wheels 33 in., gear ratio 2.21.

Characteristics.—The characteristics of the single-phase motor are strikingly similar to those of its competitor, as will be seen by comparing Figs. 170 and 171. The efficiency of the former motor is slightly lower and the torque-current curve slightly more concave, owing to the lower induction for which the alternating-current motor is designed. With the fields unsaturated, therefore, the torque will vary with the square of the current.

Operation on Direct Current.—One of the most important features to commend the single-phase series motor as above described is its satisfactory operation on direct-current circuits. If the changes which have been made to adapt the motor to alternating current are reviewed, it will be noted that no change made impairs its use with direct current. Since it is highly important that interurban roads operate their cars to the center of the terminal cities over the existing direct-current trolley, this

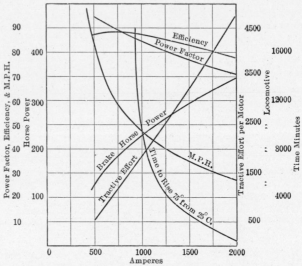

FIG. 172.—Characteristic curves of 250-hp., single-phase, 25-cycle, alternating-current motor, 235 volts, diameter wheels 63 in., gearless.

feature of the series alternating-current motor is of greatest value. Whereas the control system must be duplicated to some extent, as will be seen in the next chapter, the flexibility of operation is well worthy of the slightly added complication.

Repulsion Motor.[1]—When it was found that a corrective current could be made to flow in the armature of an alternating-current motor by means of induction between windings as in the transformer, it was inferred that such a current might be

[1] STEINMETZ, C. P., "The Alternating-current Railway Motor," *Trans.* A. I. E. E., vol. 23.

SLICHTER, WALTER I., "Speed-torque Characteristics of the Single-phase Repulsion Motor," *Trans.* A. I. E. E., vol. 23.

McALLISTER, A. S., "Alternating-current Motors."

made to produce a torque without connection between armature and field as in Fig. 173. Such a motor was found to operate satisfactorily, the brushes being short circuited to allow the torque-producing currents to flow in the armature windings. The characteristics of such a motor are similar to those of the series motor. This motor has been designated as the repulsion motor. Although it was expected that it would find a ready application in the railway field, it has not come into use, largely because of its inability to operate upon direct-current systems and also because it apparently has no marked advantages over the series motor.

Induction Motor.—It will be remembered that the alternating-current induction motor, as its name implies, has no electrical connection between stator and rotor. It is, therefore, a much simpler motor than others used for railway service which involve the use of commutators, and its maintenance expense is, therefore, correspondingly less. The induction motor has the disadvantage, however, of constant speed characteristics similar to those of the direct-current shunt motor which has never proved satisfactory for railway service.

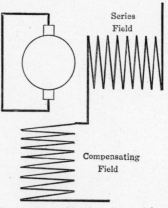

Fig. 173. — Circuit of repulsion motor.

This disadvantage of nearly constant speed at all loads may be partially overcome, however, by making use of one or more of three principles:

A winding may be placed upon the rotor instead of the usual short-circuited, "squirrel-cage" construction and the taps from this winding brought out to slip rings. This permits varying resistances to be inserted into the rotor circuit, which, in turn, produces varying speeds at the expense of lowered efficiency.

Secondly, the so-called "concatenation" method may be adopted, in which the stator of the second motor is connected to the rotor of the first through the agency of slip rings and the rotor of the second motor is provided with variable resistances as in the first case. Thus a low frequency is impressed upon the stator of the second motor, depending upon the speed of the rotor of motor No. 1 and a wider range of speeds produced thereby with less energy lost in heating of resistances.

A third but less used method involves the changing of stator connections in such a manner as to create varying numbers of poles in the stator. Since the speed for a given frequency of supply is dependent upon the number of poles, a series of speeds may be made available in this manner with little sacrifice of efficiency. The complication of control circuits when this method is used makes it prohibitive if many different speeds are required.

Fig. 174.—Rotor of Norfolk & Western induction motor.

Although a rather extensive use of the induction motor has been made abroad for many years, its installation in this country has been confined to two sections of electrified trunk lines, i.e., the Cascade Tunnel of the Great Northern Ry. and a mountain-grade division of the Norfolk & Western R. R. in Virginia. In the former system, although the variation of the number of stator poles was at first considered, it was finally abandoned in favor of the first method of control outlined above. This was further simplified by varying the iron-grid resistances in the various phases of the rotor consecutively instead of keeping the currents balanced. This departure from stationary-motor practice provided several speed changes with a minimum of control connections but was accompanied, of course, by unbalanced currents in the motors. The Norfolk & Western R. R., on the other hand, makes use of a rather unique combination of single-phase distribution for three-phase motors through the agency of a phase converter mounted upon the locomotive. The rotor of this motor is illustrated in Fig. 174. In both of these instances the grades are heavy, the speeds low and the number of required stops very small. For such service only is the induction motor considered advisable at present, in spite of its advantages of simplicity, low maintenance charges, and its ability to regenerate energy upon down grades.

Frequency.—The question of frequency has not been directly referred to in the above discussion. If reference be made again to the factors which were necessarily changed in the direct-current motor to adapt it to alternating-current operation, it will be noted that these factors, principally reactance voltages, are reduced by reduced frequency. The lower the frequency, therefore, the easier it becomes to design a satisfactory alternating-current railway motor and the greater the capacity which it is possible to obtain with a given size and weight of frame and, therefore, the greater the capacity that can be supplied to a single truck or to a single pair of driving wheels.

Motor Design.—Although the details of motor design cannot be discussed at length, a few of the mechanical features which must be given careful consideration by the designer and the railway operator may well be called to mind. Most of the difficult problems in connection with the design and construction of railway motors result from the necessity of crowding a large amount of power into a space necessarily limited by standard wheel gage, demands for light weights, low car floors, and large clearances between motor frame and track. Large gear ratios are usually desirable, especially in city service, in order to keep the energy consumption low and to make use of a high-speed and, therefore, a light and inexpensive motor. Large gear ratios, however, necessitate smaller clearances, thinner bearing sleeves, smaller axles, and low-pitch gears, any one of which results may prove objectionable if not carefully limited. The designer, and the representative of the operating company responsible for motor specifications, must, therefore, adopt a compromise between these extremes.

The selection of bearing metal is also a compromise. A babbitted bearing in a steel shell is cheapest, most easily repaired, and offers a superior wearing surface for high speeds. On the other hand, it is impossible to obtain the intimate amalgam bond between babbitt and steel that exists between babbitt and brass or bronze and the lining is likely to work loose. Further, if there is any play in the box its seat in the frame is apt to be seriously worn if a steel shell is used. Babbitt also wears rapidly and the thickness necessary to line a steel shell may wear sufficiently to cause the armature to drop and rub upon the lower field poles. To overcome these difficulties a bronze shell with a very thin inner sleeve of babbitt or merely a tinned surface has come into rather general favor.

The problem of suitable lubrication has also proved a vexing one for many years. Grease was generally used at first as a lubricant through the agency of separate grease cups first tapped into the bearing shell and later cast integrally with the motor frame. Recently, the use of oil in a journal packed with waste similar to that in the truck journal has been used very extensively, the capillary action of the oil in the waste being depended upon to supply lubricant to the axle.

In the attempt to provide more power in a given space the ventilation of the motor has been studied to advantage recently. Forced ventilation has occasionally been resorted to, but this adds expense and complication to the equipment. Early attempts to provide ducts of large cross-section in the motor, through which air might be forced by the motion of the car, resulted in collecting too much dirt and moisture for the successful operation of the motor. Recently, however, ventilated motors have been furnished, with an air intake at right angles with the direction of motion of the car, which prevents this difficulty. The air enters at the upper and pinion end of the motor and passes between the field coils, over the surface of the armature, under the commutator, back parallel with the shaft through holes in the armature laminations, and is then forced into the atmosphere by means of a radial fan. Such ventilation has been claimed to have increased the possible load per motor for a given temperature rise by 39 per cent with a relatively large number of stops and 42 per cent in service with few stops.

Whereas numerous types of suspensions were designed and used with early motors for supporting the motor upon the truck, the "bar" and "nose" suspensions are now almost universal. It is obviously necessary to provide car axle bearings in the frame of the motor and so to suspend the other side of the motor from the truck that it may swing about the car axle as a center when passing over irregularities in the track in order that the gears may always be kept in mesh. The two suspensions mentioned above differ only in the manner of supporting this free side of the motor frame. The "bar" suspension has a bar or yoke bolted to the frame of the motor which is spring supported from the truck, while in the "nose" suspension a single "nose" or lug is cast upon the motor frame which is supported from the truck by means of a link. In both cases it is now considered desirable to have additional lugs cast upon the motor frame to catch the motor and prevent it from falling to the track in case of the failure of the normal suspension.

Rating.—Railway motors, because of their rather intermittent service at varying loads with a greater amount of ventilation in actual use than upon the testing floor, are rated differently than other electrical machinery.

A great advance has been made recently by the Standardization Committee of the A. I. E. E. in establishing ratings for railway motors.

The "nominal" rating is defined by this committee as "the mechanical output at the car or locomotive axle, measured in kilowatts, which causes a rise in temperature not exceeding 90°C. at the commutator, and 75°C. at any other normally accessible part after an hour's continuous run at its rated voltage (and frequency in the case of an alternating-current motor) on a stand with the motor covers arranged to secure maximum ventilation without external blower. The rise in temperature as measured by resistance shall not exceed 100°C.

The "continuous ratings" of a railway motor are defined as the inputs in amperes at which it may be operated continuously at one-half, three-fourths, and full voltage, respectively, without exceeding the specified temperature rise (Table XXX) when operated on stand test with motor covers and cooling system, if any, arranged as in service.

Since in railway service the loads upon the motors are varying over wide ranges, the "maximum input rating" of the motor becomes of interest.   The Committee states in this connection that:

Railway motors shall be capable of carrying twice the current corresponding to their nominal rating for a period of 5 min., without flash over or mechanical injury.   They shall also be capable of carrying a load of three times their nominal rating for 1 min. under the same conditions.   These overloads shall be applied when the motor is at the temperature which it would acquire when operating at its continuous rating.

Although the temperatures which are permitted in railway motors are based upon the kind of insulating materials used, as previously explained for power-station and substation machinery, the conditions under which the railway motor is operated with respect to ventilation, limited space and weights, etc., have led to a higher allowable temperature for short periods of time than was permitted for other classes of electrical machinery.   Table XXX indicates permissible maximum temperatures and temperature rises for railway motors.

TABLE XXX.—PERMISSIBLE TEMPERATURE RISE IN RAILWAY MOTORS

Insulation	Maximum temperature		Temperature rise on stand test	
	Ther.	Resist.	Ther.	Resist.
Treated cotton, silk, paper and fibrous material, including enamel wire.	85	110	65	85
Mica, asbestos and other high temperature resisting material.	100	130	80	105

It should be noted that, whereas motors were formerly rated in horsepower, they are now rated in kilowatts.   In order to avoid confusion during the period in which the new method is being adopted, the A. I. E. E. recommends that both old and new ratings be given by manufacturers.

Motor Selection.—The method of determining the total power required to operate the car has been explained in a previous chapter.   After the number of motors per car has been decided upon, as outlined in the last chapter, the capacity of the motors to be installed may be approximately determined by dividing the average car demand expressed in horsepower for the various runs by the number of motors per car. If care be taken not to load the motor continuously with its rated load and still make due allowance for its overload capacity for short intervals and the extra demands of abnormal service, this method should permit a correct selection of the nearest standard motor to be made.

In most cases a selection of the proper motor must be based principally upon test data, and the application of results obtained upon the test floor to service conditions is often a difficult problem. The recommendations found in the standardization rules of the A. I. E. E. bearing upon this subject are, therefore, quoted in considerable detail.

In comparing projected motors and in case it is not possible or desirable to make tests to determine mechanical losses, the following values of these losses, determined from accumulated experience, will be found useful. They include axle bearing losses, gear losses, armature bearing losses, brush friction losses and windage.

Per cent of nominal rating	Losses as per cent of input
150	5.0
125	5.0
100	5.0
75	5.0
60	5.3
50	6.5
40	8.8
30	13.3
25	17.0

The core loss of railway motors is sometimes determined by separately exciting the field and driving the armature of the motor to be tested by a separate motor having known losses and noting the differences in losses between driving the motor light at various speeds and driving it with various field excitations.

The core losses at other loads shall be assumed as follows:

At full continuous rated input 1.2 times no load core loss.

At half continuous rated input 1.1 times no load core loss.

The multiplier for other loads shall be in the same proportion.

Selection of Motor for Specified Service.—The following information relative to the service to be performed is required in order that an appropriate motor may be selected.

(*a*) Weight of total number of cars in train (in tons of 2,000 lb.) exclusive of electrical equipment and load.

(*b*) Average weight of load and durations of same, and maximum weight of load and durations of same.

(*c*) Number of motor cars or locomotives in train, and number of trail cars in train.

(*d*) Diameter of driving wheels.

(*e*) Weight on driving wheels, exclusive of electrical equipment.

(*f*) Number of motors per motor car.

(*g*) Voltage at train with power on the motors—average, maximum and minimum.

(*h*) Rate of acceleration in m.p.h. per second.

(*i*) Rate of braking (retardation in m.p.h. per second).

(*j*) Speed limitations, if any (including slowdowns).

(*k*) Distances between stations.

(*l*) Duration of station stops.

(*m*) Schedule speed, including station stops in m.p.h.

(*n*) Train resistance in pounds per ton of 2,000 lb. at stated speeds.

(*o*) Moment of inertia of revolving parts, exclusive of electrical equipment.

(*p*) Profile and alignment of tracks.

(*q*) Distance coasted as a per cent of the distance between station stops.

(*r*) Time of layover at end of run, if any.

Stand-test Method of Comparing Motor Capacity with Service Requirements.—When it is not convenient to test motors under actual specific service conditions, recourse may be had to the following method of determining temperature rise.

The essential motor losses affecting temperatures in service are those in the motor windings, core and commutator. The mean service conditions may be expressed as a close approximation, in terms of that continuous current and core loss which will produce the same losses and distribution of losses as the average in service.

A stand test with the current and voltage which will give losses equal to those in service will determine whether the motor has sufficient capacity to meet the service requirements. In service, the temperature of an enclosed motor well exposed to the draught of air incident to a moving car or locomotive will be from 75 to 90 per cent (depending upon the character of the service) of the temperature rise obtained on a stand test with the motor completely enclosed and with the same losses. With a ventilated motor the temperature rise in service will be 90 to

100 per cent of the temperature rise obtained on a stand test with the same losses.

In making a stand test to determine the temperature rise in a specific service, it is essential in the case of a self ventilated motor to run the armature at a speed which corresponds to the schedule speed in service. In order to obtain this speed it may be necessary, while maintaining the same total armature losses, to change somewhat the ratio between the I^2R and core loss components.

Calculation for Comparing Motor Capacity with Service Require-ments.—The heating of a motor should be determined, wherever possible, by testing it in service or with an equivalent duty cycle. When the service or equivalent duty cycle tests are not practicable, the ratings of the motor may be utilized as follows to determine its temperature rise.

The motor losses which affect the heating of the windings are as stated above, those in the windings and in the core. The former are propor-tional to the square of the current. The latter vary with the voltage and current, according to curves which can be supplied by the manu-facturers. The procedure is therefore as follows:

(*a*) Plot a time current curve and a time voltage curve for the duty cycle which the motor is to perform, and calculate from these the root-mean-square current and the equivalent voltage which with r.m.s. current will produce the average core loss.

(*b*) If the calculated r.m.s. service current exceeds the continuous rating, when run with average service core loss and speed, the motor is not sufficiently powerful for the duty cycle contemplated.

(*c*) If the calculated r.m.s. service current does not exceed the continu-ous rating, when run with average service core loss and speed, the motor is ordinarily suitable for the service. In some cases, however, it may not have sufficient thermal capacity to avoid excessive temperature rises during the periods of heavy load. In such cases a further calculation is required, the first step of which is to calculate the temperature rise due to the r.m.s. service current and equivalent voltage.

Let t = temperature rise ⎫ With r.m.s. service current and equiva-
  $p_o = I^2R$ loss, kw. ⎬   lent service voltage.
  p_c = core loss, kw. ⎭

  T = temperature rise ⎫ With continuous load current corre-
  $P_o = I^2R$ loss, kw. ⎬   sponding to the equivalent service
  P_c = core loss, kw. ⎭   voltage.

Then

$$t = T\frac{p_o + p_c}{P_o + P_c} \text{ approximately.}$$

(*d*) The thermal capacity of a motor is approximately measured by a coefficient equal to the ratio of the electrical loss in kw. at its nominal (1 hour) capacity to the corresponding maximum observable temperature rise.

(*e*) Consider any period of peak load and determine the electrical losses in kilowatt hours during that period from the electrical efficiency curve. Find the excess of the above losses over the losses with r.m.s. service current and equivalent voltage. The excess loss divided by the coefficient of thermal capacity will equal the extra temperature rise due to the peak load. This temperature rise added to that due to the r.m.s. service current and equivalent voltage gives the total temperature rise. If the total temperature rise in any such period exceeds the safe limit, the motor is not sufficiently powerful for the service.

(*f*) If the temperature reached due to the peak loads does not exceed the safe limit, the motor may yet be unsuitable for the service, as the peak loads may cause excessive sparking and dangerous mechanical stresses. It is, therefore, necessary to compare the peak loads with the short period overload capacity. If the peaks are also within the capacity of the motor, it may be considered suitable for the given duty cycle.

Several other methods of making this selection may be adopted, however, and it is always well to check the motor capacity chosen by two or more processes. They will be briefly explained in order of their ease of application.

Selection by Comparison.—A very rough and simple method quite commonly used is to prepare a table from technical journals or the railway census of the equipments of various roads operating under as nearly as possible the same conditions as the proposed road. This table should include number and capacity of motors, average voltage, schedule speed, weight of cars, layover at terminals, stops per mile, average grade, and, if possible, the watt-hours per ton-mile demanded. By comparison with such a table the correct standard size of motor for the new equipment may readily be determined.

Effective-current Method.—It is possible to obtain from manufacturers' test records not only the rating of the motor, but also its continuous current capacity at one or more average voltages, *i.e.*, the current which may be supplied to the motor continuously without exceeding the limit of 75°C. temperature rise. The temperature curves of Fig. 20 may also be obtained, from which the time required to rise to 75°C. above the room temperature from the start with the motor cold can be found for each value of current supplied to the motor, as well as the time required to rise 20° above 75°C. for the various possible overload currents. In making use of these data it should be remembered that the heating of a motor is proportional to the square of the current. The heating value of the current or "effective" current for a given run is not the average ordinate of the current-time curve of that run, but the square root of the average squared current. If, then, the effective current for the various runs as determined from the current-time curves be compared with the continuous

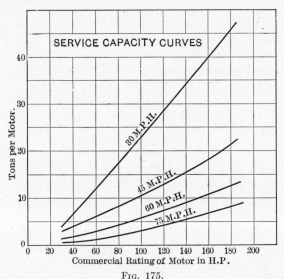

Fig. 175.

current rating of the motors with due allowance for temperature rise of short duration produced by overload currents as determined from the temperature curve, the proper motor may be readily selected. In short, a temperature-time curve is really determined for the various runs and the motor so selected that this curve will not exceed 75°C. rise for other than short intervals of time.

Method Proposed by Armstrong.—In a paper before the A. I. E. E.,[1] Armstrong suggested that a series of curves such as Fig. 175, each representing the motor capacity required for a

[1] ARMSTRONG, A. H., "High Speed Electric Railway Problems," *Trans.* A. I. E. E., vol. 22.

given weight of car per motor and for a certain speed, acceleration, etc., be prepared from theoretical and practical test data and used for quick approximations of motor capacity. Figure 175 is plotted for straight, level track with the following assumed values:

Gross accelerating force, 120 lb. per ton.

Braking retarding force, 120 lb. per ton.

Duration of stops, 15 sec.

Duration of coasting, 10 sec.

Since these data do not take into consideration grades and curvature or other values of acceleration, deceleration, etc., than those listed, either a large number of such charts must be plotted or the results taken from them carefully corrected for any variation of actual from assumed conditions.

Method Proposed by Storer.[1]—This method assumes that a certain motor has been tentatively selected and that it is desired to determine from test under conditions similar to those of actual service whether or not this particular motor will fulfil the requirements.

The effective current for the various runs is determined as explained above, and the average voltage at the terminals of the motor found from the voltage-time curve. If, now, the motor be operated with this effective current and with the average voltage impressed upon it, the motor losses will be the same as in practice and the heating of the motor under service conditions may be determined therefrom. It should be remembered, however, that the ventilation of the motor is better in service and it may usually be depended upon to carry from 20 to 25 per cent more load with the same temperature rise when on the car. This allows a good factor of safety if the motor be selected from test results.

Method Proposed by Hutchinson.[2]—The method employed by Hutchinson, where a large number of motor determinations are to be made by a manufacturing or an engineering company, is one involving mathematical equations based upon a large number of general charts deduced from the typical speed-time curves. In place of assuming the straight-line speed-time curve of Chap. X to be correct, a mathematical correction applying to the

[1] STORER, N. W., *St. Ry. Jour.*, 1901.

[2] *Trans.* A. I. E. E., vol. 21.

difference in area between the accurate and the straight-line, speed-time curve is used and constants derived which, when substituted in the equations given, enable the latter to be solved for correct motor capacity. For further details reference should be made to the original paper.

Regeneration of Energy.—The ability of the induction motor to regenerate energy has been previously referred to. The advantages of such regeneration, which is made possible by coasting down long grades at motor speeds above synchronism, are fourfold:

Less wear in braking equipment and especially in brake shoes.

Furnishing of power to other trains upon the system.

Reduction of power demand on power station with resulting increase in load factor.

Increased life of rolling stock, couplings, and roadbed because of smoother descent of grades by heavy trains.

Whereas these possibilities of regeneration have until recently received little consideration, the fact that upon one three-phase system abroad the train going down grade was able to generate 54 per cent of the energy required by the same train in climbing the grade has led to the study of further possibilities of this regeneration of energy in trunk-line electrification. This has been provided for upon the Norfolk & Western R. R. and the Great Northern Ry., the only two systems in this country employing induction motors. In the latter case the energy regenerated is of secondary importance because of the large amount available from the water power of the mountains, and it is, therefore, dissipated as heat in rheostats. In spite of this fact, however, the advantages of this system of down-grade control of trains are considered sufficient to warrant its installation. This is further proved by tests of actual installations in which 14 per cent of the total energy required by the system was produced by regeneration from down-grade trains, while less than one-third the previous brake-shoe wear was experienced when regenerative braking was used.

Although the direct-current system was thought at first not to lend itself to regenerative control as readily as the induction motor, the 3,000-volt, direct-current installation on the Chicago, Milwaukee & St. Paul Ry. makes use of this principle to good advantage as indicated in Fig 41.

CHAPTER XXIV

CONTROL SYSTEMS

The necessity of starting a car by first impressing a low voltage upon its motors, and then gradually increasing the voltage as the motors speed up until they are receiving their rated voltage, has been previously explained. The advisability of maintaining a constant current through each motor during the constant acceleration period was also pointed out. Means must be provided for regulating the speed of a car and for reversing its direction of motion. It is now necessary to consider the various standard control systems which have been devised to accomplish the above results.

Types of Control.—As regards the method of manipulation of the motor connections and resistances, control systems may be classified either as "hand operated" or "automatic." With the hand-operated type the controller handle is moved notch by notch at the discretion of the motorman, while in the automatic type a current-limiting relay, set for a definite, predetermined value of current, fixes the maximum rate of "notching up." The motorman may move the controller handle to the "full-on" position but the relay will permit the "notching-up" process to go on only at such a rate as will keep the motor current approximately constant. Thus, while the motorman may notch up his controller as slowly as he wishes, the current-limiting relay fixes the maximum rate of "notching up."

The following advantages are claimed for the automatic type of control:

1. It prevents abuse of the motors during the accelerating period.

2. The rate of acceleration is uniform.

3. It allows the motorman to devote his attention to signals and to the track ahead.

The disadvantages are:

1. First cost and maintenance charges are high.

2. The system is complicated.

354

TABLE XXXI.—CLASSIFICATION OF CONTROL SYSTEMS

Elementary type	Method of varying motor voltage	Kind of current	Method of switching	Commercial types	Distinguishing features	Service to which best adapted
Main circuit or drum control	Rheostatic.	A. c. and D. c.	Hand operated drum.	R	Pure rheostatic control.	One motor equipments. (Practically obsolete.)
				K	One set of motors either "shunted out" or bridged during transition.	City cars and light interurban cars.
	Series parallel.	D. c.	Hand operated drum.	L	Motor circuits open during transition.	Heavy interurban cars. (Practically superseded by master control).
				B	Has braking notches on drum, otherwise same as K.	City cars.
	Adjustable ratio transformer.	A. c.	Hand operated drum.	T	Changes motor voltage by cutting in or out different transformer taps.	Light cars on A. c. system.
Indirect or master control	Series parallel.	D. c.	Electromagnetic (G. E. Co's multiple unit) — Hand operated	M and MK	Control circuits energized from line.	Trains of motor cars, heavy cars, locomotives.
			— Automatic	MA	Control circuits energized from line.	
			Electropneumatic — Hand operated	HL	Control circuits energized from line.	
			— Automatic	AB	Control circuits energized from battery.	
	Adjustable ratio transformer.	A. c.	(Westinghouse Elec. & Mfg. Co's unit switch and type PK)	AL	Control circuits energized from line.	Trains of motor cars, heavy cars, locomotives.
				AB	Control circuits energized from battery.	
				PK	Uses a drum main circuit controller equipped with a power operating head.	Light city cars with large passenger carrying capacity.

3. It is difficult to set the limit relay so that the car will be accelerated at the proper rate for all conditions of track and car loading.

In order to prevent the current through the motors from being increased too rapidly with a hand-operated controller, the following method may be used: A mechanical device is attached to the top of the controller, which by means of a ratchet and pawl prevents the forward movement of the controller handle in a single swing, but requires a slight backward movement at each notch to disengage the pawl and thereby allow sufficient time for the current to decrease to its normal accelerating value.

A classification of control systems, based primarily on type of construction, is given in Table XXXI.

Main-circuit Control.—In this type of control, a drum controller, to which is connected the various motor and line circuits, is located on the car platform. For double-end operation, two controllers connected in parallel, one on each end platform, are required. Main-circuit controllers are used on practically all small cars and on some of the older interurban cars.

A few of the more important requirements in the construction of this type of controller are as follows:

1. Finger tips must be of such design that they will not "stub."

2. Ample arc chutes must be provided so as to prevent arcing between the various live parts and between the live parts and the case.

3. Correctly designed magnetic blow-outs must be provided.

4. Switches must be provided so that a disabled motor or pair of motors may be cut out without affecting the operation of the remainder of the equipment.

5. Mechanical interlocks must be provided, so that, (a) the motors cannot be reversed when the controller handle is in an "on" position, (b) the main drum cannot be turned when the reverse handle is in the "off" position, (c) the main drum cannot be turned to the parallel position when one of the motor cut-out switches is thrown.

6. The method of attaching the cables to the contact fingers or terminal board must give good electrical contact and yet permit changes to be made quickly and easily.

Rheostatic Control.—The earliest type of control, which is now practically obsolete, made use of a rheostat in series with the motors, but did not change the motor connections from start to full speed. Two complete revolutions of the controller handle were necessary to cut out all the resistance, but the rheostat was so designed that the controller handle could be left in any position indefinitely and correspondingly small variations of speed obtained.

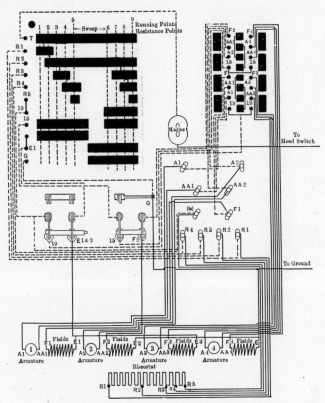

FIG. 176.—K-12 wiring diagram.

Series-parallel Control.—Practically all the control systems in use with direct-current railway motors at the present time, although differing widely in detail, operate upon the series-parallel principle. The two motors of a two-motor equipment or those of each group of a four-motor equipment are first connected in series with one another and also in series with a resistance. This resistance is then reduced by three or four steps until the two motors are alone in series across the circuit from trolley to ground. This notch of the controller is termed a "running" notch, as the controller may be left in this position continuously, resulting in about half speed. With the next step, the motors are changed from series to parallel connection and a resistance again introduced. This resistance is reduced in the succeeding

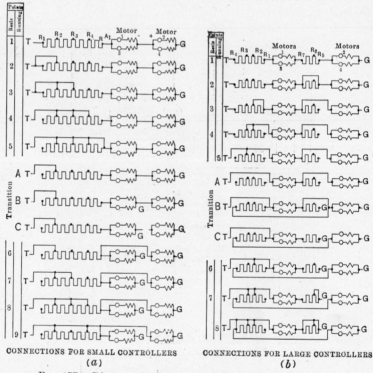

CONNECTIONS FOR SMALL CONTROLLERS
(*a*)

CONNECTIONS FOR LARGE CONTROLLERS
(*b*)

Fig. 177.—Diagram of controller connections in various notches.

steps until upon the last notch all motors are in parallel without resistance. This is ordinarily the full-speed position, although in some types of this control an additional step is employed which either shunts the motor field with a resistance or cuts out part of the motor field coils. In locomotive series-parallel controllers four running notches are sometimes provided:

1. All motors in series.
2. Motors in series parallel.

3. All motors in parallel.

4. Motor fields weakened as above described.

A K-12 controller, which is commonly found on city cars with four-motor equipments, is shown diagrammatically with motor and resistance connections in Fig. 176. The connections for the various notches may be readily traced if the heavy black horizontal bands representing the copper sectors on the control cylinder be assumed to move one numbered notch to the left for

FIG. 178.—K-35-D controller.

each change of connections. Care should be taken to trace out the reversal of armature connections as the reverse cylinder represented by the heavy bands at the right of the figure is turned. The switches numbered (19) and (15) are used in cutting out one set of motors in case of their failure. The resistance steps are so proportioned that if the controller is steadily "notched up" an approximately constant current will be maintained through each motor. A diagrammatic illustration of the various steps is found in Fig. 177.

Figure 177a is also applicable to two-motor equipments, provided the pairs of motors there shown are replaced by single motors. The "bridge" transition shown in Fig. 177b is used in large controllers. Its advantage is that the tractive effort during the transition period is more uniform.

As may have been inferred from the above discussion, the control resistances are designed to remain in the circuit for a short time only and will, therefore, overheat if they be left in circuit continuously.

The mechanical construction of the series-parallel drum controller may be noted from Fig. 178, which shows the interior of a

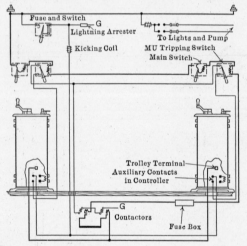

Fig. 179.—Wiring diagram for contactor equipment.

General Electric K-35-D controller with asbestos barrier opened. The main drum with its copper sectors insulated from the shaft and engaging copper contact fingers will be seen in the center and the reverse drum of similar design on the right. On the left at the base of the fingers will be seen the individual blow-out coils. A sufficient magnetic flux is produced by these coils to blow out the arc formed between fingers and sectors as the circuits are opened. In the upper right corner will be found the motor cut-out switches.

In order to prevent the heavy arcing which occurs inside the controller case in large drum controllers, an auxiliary contactor equipment is sometimes employed. Instead of the main circuit

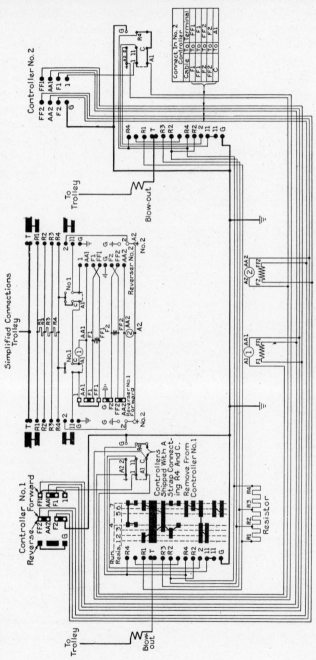

FIG. 180.—Wiring diagram for safety-car-control equipment.

being opened by the drum fingers in the main controller, it is opened by two powerful electromagnetic switches, or contactors connected in series, which are placed in a separate box under the car. These contactors are actuated by auxiliary contacts on the main drum which close or open the operating circuit of the contactors as the controller handle is turned to the "on" and "off" positions, respectively. Figure 179 shows the wiring diagram for the contactor equipment as built by the General Electric Company. The M U tripping switch has an overload coil so that the contactors act as circuit breakers.

FIG. 181.—Controller for safety cars (cover removed).

The necessity for the light-weight controller for use on one-man safety cars was responsible for the development of the General Electric Company K-63 controller. Special attention has been given to the elimination of the unnecessary weight. A large blow-out coil is located on a hinged pole piece at the back of the arc deflectors. The coil is of sufficient length to distribute the flux over all of the main fingers and effectively disrupts the arcs. The deflectors are of tough arc-resisting material and are assembled so as to form a shield preventing the arc from the main terminals coming in contact with other parts at different potentials when the circuit is opened. The cut-out switches are of the knife-blade type and are located on the right-hand side of the controller, midway between the base and the cap plate. When either of the cut-out switches is open, the main cylinder is interlocked so that it cannot be turned beyond the full series position. The main and the reverse cylinders are also interlocked so that it is impossible to operate the latter when the former is in the "off" position, or to operate the former when the latter is in the "neutral" position.

Master Control.—With the rapid increase in the current required by the motors as the size and capacity of electric-railway equipment advanced, it became more and more difficult to design a controller of the type described above to break continually these large currents. As a result, a master controller is often found in the motorman's cab, quite similar in principle to the large controllers, but designed to control an auxiliary circuit only. This auxiliary circuit operates a series of contactors or solenoid-operated main switches mounted under the car. With such a system the contactors may be sufficiently large to control

Fig. 182.—Contactor.

the heavy currents safely and little room is required for equipment above the floor, not to mention the reduction in the amount of heavy cable demanded by such an equipment. The auxiliary circuit may be a high-resistance circuit supplied from the trolley, or in some instances it is supplied by a storage battery of about 14 volts.

As indicated in the classification on page 355, master-control systems may be either hand operated or automatic. At present, on account of their reliability, flexibility, light weight, simplicity, low first cost and maintenance charges, and the fact that the master controller is manipulated in the same way as the type-K controller, the hand-operated types are more popular than the automatic types.

The advantages of master control over main-circuit control for heavy service are briefly as follows:

Fig. 183.—Type C-94-A Master controller. (*General Electric Company.*)

1. Greater safety and reliability.
2. Possibility of making each switch a separate element.
3. Ease with which powerful magnetic blow-outs for each switch may be provided.
4. Flexibility in the arrangement of switch groupings.

5. Rapidity with which contacts may be "made" and "broken."

6. Small amount of space required on car platforms.

7. Elimination of heavy cables running from the motors to the car platforms.

The disadvantages are:

1. High first cost.

2. Greater complication.

With all types of master control a safety device known as the "deadman's handle" may be readily provided. In one form of this device the main controller handle is turned against a spring which throws the handle to the "off" position in case the motorman removes his hand. In another form, the pressure of the motorman's hand on a button in the top of the main controller handle closes a set of contacts which complete the auxiliary circuit. This device may be constructed not only to shut off the power, but also to apply the air brakes automatically if the motorman's hand is removed from the control handle.

Multiple-unit Control.—There is a demand in elevated, subway, and heavy interurban service for the operation of a number of cars in a single train from the motorman's cab of the front car. A marked advance in the design of control equipment was made, therefore, when the multiple-unit control system was developed by Sprague. This system not only embodies the use of the master controller explained above, but it permits the contactors upon all cars to be operated simultaneously by the master controller of a single car, the small auxiliary circuit wires alone extending between cars through the agency of flexible cables and plug contacts. The equipments are all interchangeable, so that any car may be made a control car.

Electromagnetic Control (Sprague General Electric Multiple-unit Control).—In this type of control the main-circuit switching is performed by electromagnetic switches. Each switch is held closed against a heavy spring by means of a powerful solenoid. De-energization of the solenoid causes the switch to open suddenly. The auxiliary circuit is connected through a high resistance directly to the trolley. This system of control is manufactured in both the hand-operated and the automatic types. Figure 184 represents the wiring diagram of both the main and the auxiliary circuits of this type of multiple-unit control in detail, while Fig. 185 illustrates the contactor with

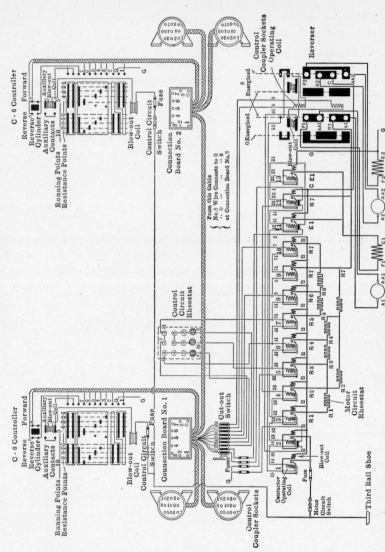

Fig. 184.—Wiring diagram, hand-operated, multiple-unit control.

its relay contacts at the bottom and its asbestos trough for the circuit breaker at the top.

Electropneumatic Control (Westinghouse Unit-switch Control). The unit-switch control is a system developed by another manufacturing company to meet the requirements of master control of single-car equipment or of multiple-unit control. In fact, upon one large railway system cars with the unit switch control and the Sprague multiple-unit control are operating interchangeably in the same train.

The unit-switch control differs from the Sprague multiple-unit system principally in details of operation, the principle of the two

FIG. 185.—Unit-switch group.

being the same. Both systems have the main switches and reversers located under the car, the operation of these switches being controlled by the master controller and an auxiliary or relay circuit. In some types of the unit-switch system energy for the auxiliary circuit is obtained from a 14-volt storage battery which is carried in the car; in other types the auxiliary circuit is energized from the trolley.

The main switches (Fig. 185) are operated by air pressure obtained from the main air-brake reservoir, the air valves being operated by solenoids which are energized from the auxiliary circuit.

The automatic "notching-up" feature of the unit-switch system, which may also be secured with the Sprague multiple-unit control, is accomplished by providing the main switches or contactors with relay contacts which make the proper connections in the auxiliary circuit as they open or close.

The master controller of the automatic unit-switch system (Fig. 186) is provided with three forward and three reverse notches, the function of which will be more clearly seen by referring to

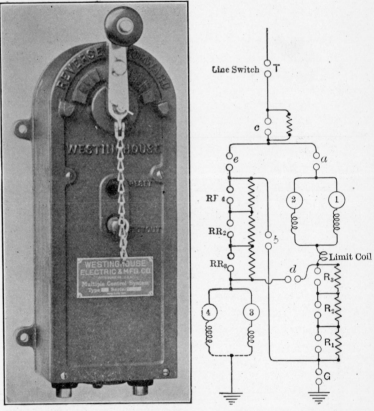

FIG. 186.—Unit-switch master controller.   FIG. 187.—Simplified connection diagrams for unit-switch system.

Fig 187, which is a much simplified connection diagram. The first notch closes the line switch T and the unit switches a and b, thus putting the motors in series with all resistance in circuit. This is not a permanent running notch, but the train may be thus operated at slow speed for switching, etc., for a short time.

The second notch on the controller is the full series running position. This closes switch c, which has interlocking contacts, which, in turn, close RR_1. The latter switch carries inter-locks which close R_1 and so on, closing RR_2, R_2, RR_3, R_3, etc., in order, cutting out corresponding resistance steps until the motors are in series without resistance between trolley and ground.

Notch No. 3, or the full parallel running position, closes switch d, which, in turn, breaks the auxiliary circuit of b and the latter switch opens together with all the resistance switches except c. When b has completely opened, it causes switches e and G to close. When these are fully closed their interlocking relays open switch d. When d is again open the circuits through the resistance switches RR_1, R_1, RR_2, etc. are closed consecutively until the resistance has again been gradually cut out and the motors are finally operating in parallel across the line with no resistance. Limit relay switches described above prevent the resistance switches from closing before the current has decreased to its normal accelerating value. This maintains nearly constant current during the acceleration period.

A complete wiring diagram for the unit-switch, automatic, multiple-unit control system, including both auxiliary and main circuits, will be found in Fig. 188, but because of its complica-tion the simplified diagram of Fig. 187 will be found preferable for all but detail connections.

It must be remembered that in all automatic, multiple-unit control systems the power circuit of each car is complete in itself, with independent contacts with trolley or third rail. Each car, therefore, must have its own limit switch, which may be adjusted for a different value of current for each car to correspond with the equipment upon that particular car. Provision is also made for all the switches to open on any one car in case of failure of power on that particular car, the switches "notching up" auto-matically when the power is again supplied. The latter feature is important with third-rail operation, in which the power is off when passing over each crossing. In order to take care of the preceding condition with the hand-operated, master-control systems, a train "bus line" is provided. This line is a heavy conducting cable running the length of each car and terminating in coupler sockets. As this line is connected directly to the trolley base or third-rail shoes, all collecting devices on the train will be in parallel if the bus line is coupled between cars, and, if one current-collecting device is resting on a live contact line, power will be available on all cars in the train. This bus line is now used in connection with practically all automatic control systems also.

Westinghouse PK Control.—To meet the demand for a light-weight control system embodying the principal features of multiple-unit and master control for use on stepless and other new types of light-weight, low-powered, large passenger-carry-ing-capacity cars, the Westinghouse Electric & Manufacturing Co. has developed a control system known as the PK system. In this system the usual controller-case top of a drum main-circuit controller is replaced by a pneumatically operated notch-ing mechanism. This mechanism is controlled by a master controller similar to that used with the other types of master control. But one main-circuit controller is required and it may be placed under the car.

High-voltage, Direct-current Control Systems.—In general, direct-current control systems for trolley voltages ranging from

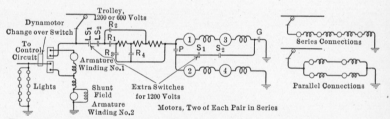

FIG. 189.—Schematic diagram for 1,200-volt equipment with type HL control arranged for half-speed operation on 600 volts.

1,200 to 2,400 volts are very similar to those designed for 600 volts. While drum controllers rated for use with a maximum line voltage of 1,300 volts are on the market, not many of them are being used. The higher voltages require better insulation, greater "creepage" surface, and heavier parts than are required for 600 volts. On account of the tenacity of high-voltage, direct-current arcs, the final break in the main circuit is usually made by operating simultaneously several switches in series. Within city limits high-voltage, direct-current interurban railways usually operate their cars over the tracks of the low-voltage city system. One of the many methods of working out the control problem for the above conditions is indicated in Fig. 189. When the car is operating from the 1,200-volt trolley line a dynamotor is used to furnish 600 volts to the lights, air compressor, and auxiliary control circuit. For 600-volt operation the dynamotor change-over switch must be thrown. Between the ends of the 600-volt and 1,200-volt trolley lines a short section of dead trolley line is usually installed. It is so arranged that this section may be energized either from the 600-volt line or the 1,200-volt line, depending on the direction in which the car is traveling. The car is run under the dead section and the change-over switch thrown to the proper position; the dead section is then energized by closing a pole switch which connects it with the line ahead.

Alternating-current Control.—As the principal advantage in the use of alternating-current motors on the car is the possibility of using high trolley voltages, and as the alternating-current motors are best designed for low voltage, *i.e.*, from 200 to 225 volts, a transformer must be used on the car to reduce the trolley voltage to that suitable for the motors. Since taps may be taken from the various coils of this transformer to furnish still lower voltages useful in starting the car without the resistance loss entailed by the resistance type of direct-current motor control, the principle of alternating-motor control differs somewhat from those previously explained.

Alternating-current control systems may be either of the main-circuit or of the master-control, multiple-unit type. If the former, the controller is similar to the K series-parallel drum controller, except that there are fewer notches, usually five or six only, and no series-parallel connections. The magnetic blow-out coil is also omitted, as the alternating-current arc is not difficult to extinguish without the coil. The various contacts made between controller sectors and the stationary fingers serve to connect the motors, generally permanently connected two in series, to the various taps of the transformer. The reversal of the motors is accomplished in the same manner as in the type-K controller, the reverse cylinder reversing either the armature or field connections.

With the alternating-current master control the principle of operation is the same as before. The magnetic cores of the reverser and contactors must, however, be laminated for use on alternating-current circuits.

In order that connections may be changed from one transformer tap to another without opening the circuit, it is necessary to close a local circuit through a portion of the transformer winding; *i.e.*, if special precautions are not taken a short circuit will be formed in a portion of the transformer coil as two taps of the transformers are connected to the same motor terminal. In order to avoid this difficulty the current is reduced in the local circuit by means of "preventive" resistance or reactance leads, as in the single-phase motor.

The transformers used with the alternating-current motor equipments have been standardized for 3,000, 6,000, and 10,000 volts trolley potential and are connected directly between trolley and ground. On account of the insulation strains liable to be imposed on the motor windings when autotransformers are used, the present tendency is toward the use of two-winding transformers, the secondaries of which are provided with a number of taps. The transformer is mounted under the floor frame of the car.

While the adjustable-ratio transformer-control system works well for single-phase railway motors, polyphase motors require a different system. Where wound rotors are used and but one running speed is required, a type of rheostatic control is used. By arranging the stator windings of the motors so that they may be connected to form different numbers of poles around the stator periphery, other running speeds may be obtained. A controller whose main drum cuts resistance in or out of the rotor circuits as may be desired, and whose auxiliary drum performs the functions of reversing switch and pole-changing switch, meets the requirements where more than one running speed is necessary. As three-phase motors are used only on heavy cars or locomotives, the master-control system is used almost universally; the controllers just mentioned simply control the auxiliary circuits which operate the switches in the main circuits. Liquid resistances are often used for the starting resistances of three-phase locomotive motors.

Combined Alternating- and Direct-current Control.—As previously pointed out, it is desirable that most alternating-current interurban roads operate cars to the heart of the terminal cities. They must, therefore, be able to operate upon both alternating and direct current. In order that the control equipment may be fitted for either, some changes in detail must be made and a considerable complication of circuits results. The various parts of the apparatus, such as controller, reverser, contactors, etc., are used in common by the two systems. A number of changes in connections, however, must be made in shifting from one system to another. These are principally as follows when changing from alternating- to direct-current operation:

Change transformer taps to resistance taps.

Change main fuses or circuit breakers.

Change lightning arresters.

Introduce the magnetic blow-out into the circuit.

Change lighting and heating circuits.

Reconnect fields of air-compressor motor for series operation.

In order that these changes may be made in one operation the cables involved are connected to a second control drum similar to the main controller. This is styled the "commutating switch," the preceding changes being made by a simple movement of the handle. This change may also be made automatically at full speed by providing a release for the switch when no potential is supplied, so that it will open as the car reaches an insulated section in the trolley between the alternating- and direct-current systems. The switch is designed to reset automatically in the opposite direction as the direct-current trolley is reached, and *vice versa*.

As may be inferred from the foregoing, an added complication enters into the problem in operating the air-compressor for the air-brake system. In some installations a motor-generator set of small capacity is installed to furnish 550 volts direct current when supplied with alternating current from the transformer. The standard direct-current air compressor may then be used. Another method more often found is to design the compressor motor for both alternating and direct current, connecting the field coils in parallel for the former supply and in series for the latter.

Whereas the combination of the two control systems upon one car adds considerable complication, as will be seen from Fig. 190, which represents the complete wiring diagram for an alternating-current, direct-current control equipment, and although the first cost and maintenance charges are necessarily increased thereby, several roads have been operating such an equipment.

Regenerative Braking.—Since polyphase motors will act as generators if run above synchronous speed, regenerative braking does not introduce any complications into the system which controls them. Where series motors are arranged for regenerative braking, additional points on the controller and additional contacts are required to take care of the auxiliary windings or connections on the motors.

Controller Selection.—Since the successful operation of railway motors depends largely on the reliability and effectiveness of the control apparatus, it is evident that the problem of controller selection must be studied with care. Direct-current, main-circuit controllers rated at 600, 750, and 1,300 volts maximum are standard products. The capacity of a controller is usually rated in terms of the maximum motor horsepower which it can control without undue heating of contacts and other current-carrying parts. Master controllers are built for all voltages, capacities, and kinds of current.

In the selection of a controller the following are some of the more important points which should be considered:

1. Nature of service, *i.e.*, voltage of line, kind of current, number of cars in train, and weight of cars or locomotives.

2. Capacity of motors.

3. Number and kind of motors.

4. Ground or metallic return.

5. Available floor space on platform.

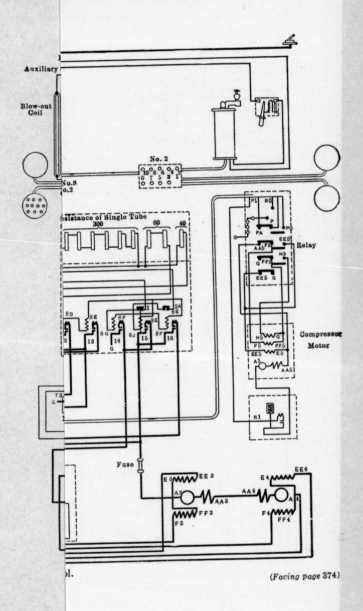

Auxiliary

Blow-out
Coil

No. 2

No.8
o.2

Resistance of Single Tube
300   60   40

Relay

Compressor
Motor

Fuse

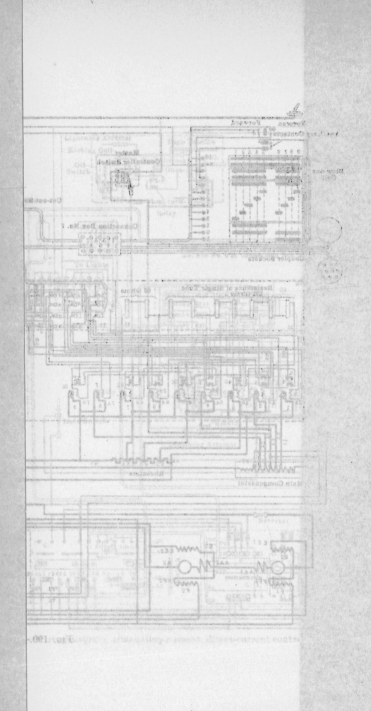

CHAPTER XXV

BRAKES

The problem of stopping a car is quite as important as that of accelerating it. Since the kinetic energy of the car must be overcome in a very few seconds, the power required for braking the car is usually many times that required for accelerating. Whereas the rate of retardation and energy required during the braking period have been already considered, it is now necessary to study the braking forces more in detail, as well as the various types of equipment which have been designed for the production and control of such braking forces.

Electric cars must be accelerated and retarded by virtue of the frictional force between the wheels and the rails. As this force is proportional to the weight on the wheels, the available force is conveniently found from the ratio of horizontal pull in pounds necessary to slide the wheels on the rails to the pressure between wheels and rails. This ratio is commonly termed the "coefficient of friction." It has been found to vary with the materials in contact and the velocity and the length of time during which the force is applied.

While many different devices have been tried out in practice for producing the necessary frictional forces to stop a car, the one which is now almost universally used in both electric- and steam-railroad service is the application of a brake shoe, usually of cast iron or a combination of cast iron and other materials, to the treads and flanges of the car wheels by means of either hand or air pressure transmitted through the agency of a carefully proportioned system of levers.

Coefficient of Friction.—An experimental study of the coefficient of friction between cast-iron brake shoes and steel wheels under practical service conditions was made by Galton and Westinghouse in 1878, and the results of these tests, published in the 1879 *Proceedings* of the Institution of Mechanical Engineers, which are given in the following tables, have been ever since considered as classic, the few later tests which have been made making little if any change therein.

TABLE XXXII.—COEFFICIENT OF FRICTION AT VARIOUS SPEEDS WITH CAST IRON BRAKE SHOES ON STEEL TIRES

No. of tests from which mean is taken	Velocity		Coefficient of friction		
	M.p.h.	Ft. per sec.	Extreme		Mean
			Max.	Min.	
12	60	88	0.123	0.058	0.074
67	55	81	0.136	0.060	0.111
55	50	73	0.153	0.050	0.116
77	45	66	0.179	0.080	0.127
70	40	59	0.194	0.088	0.140
80	35	51	0.197	0.087	0.142
94	30	44	0.196	0.098	0.164
70	25	36.5	0.205	0.108	0.166
69	20	29	0.240	0.133	0.192
78	15	22	0.280	0.131	0.223
54	10	14.5	0.281	0.161	0.242
28	7.5	11	0.325	0.123	0.244
20	Under 5......	Under 7......	0.340	0.156	0.273
....	Just moving...	Just moving...	....	....	0.330

TABLE XXXIII.—EFFECT ON ELAPSED TIME OF COEFFICIENT OF FRICTION

Speed, m.p.h.	Coefficient of friction				
	Start	After 5 sec.	After 10 sec.	After 15 sec.	After 20 sec.
20	0.182	0.152	0.133	0.116	0.099
27	0.171	0.130	0.119	0.081	0.072
37	0.152	0.096	0.083	0.069	....
47	0.132	0.080	0.070	....	....
60	0.072	0.063	0.058	....	....

From the above tables the maximum pressure to be applied to the brake shoes may be determined under the various service conditions in order to provide the required frictional tangential force. To determine what the limits of the latter are, the coefficient of friction between wheels and rail must be known. This value varies widely with the condition of the rail, but may be safely assumed from 0.15 to 0.30 when the rail is wet and dry, respectively. These latter values are coefficients of static friction which are greater than dynamic friction if other conditions are the same, for if the wheels are rolling there is no relative sliding between wheels and rails and the frictional force to be considered is that necessary to start one body from rest upon the other and not that lesser force necessary to keep one body in motion upon the other. The maximum limit of brake-shoe friction is now at once apparent, for it must not exceed the static friction between wheels and track. If it were to exceed that value, the brake shoes would "lock the wheels" and the latter would "skid" on the rails with lessened retardation because of the lower value of dynamic friction thus suddenly brought into play between wheels and track. In fact, this is the cause of the sensation often experienced by passengers who, when barely accustomed to the slowing down of the car during the braking period, suddenly feel the car apparently "shooting forward" as the wheels begin to slide on the track. The decreased frictional resistance offered to the motion of the car under these conditions permits of little if any control of the car by the motorman and serious accidents often result therefrom.

Theoretically, cars should be equipped with braking apparatus which will make it possible to approximate as nearly as possible this maximum value for emergency stops, but since the braking force with hand-brake equipment depends upon the strength of the motorman and with air-brake equipment upon the variable air pressure, it is usually possible to "skid the wheels" on the average car if the brakes are applied too forcibly. Further, since Table XXXII shows that the friction between brake shoe and wheel increases as the speed decreases during the braking period, a force applied to the brake shoes when braking is commenced, which is slightly less than that necessary to lock the wheels, may become sufficiently great to produce that result at lower speeds, since the static friction between wheels and track remains constant. Every experienced motorman understands the results of such an application of brakes and releases and reapplies the braking pressure with less and less intensity as the car comes to a stop. Failure to do this results in too sudden a stop for comfort, a severe chattering of the brake rigging, possible skidding, and, incidentally, marks an inexperienced or careless motorman.

Another factor which must be taken into consideration in stopping a car comfortably and safely is the condition of the track. It is a peculiar fact that when a slight shower causes a very thin film of water on the rail the friction is greatly reduced over that of a dry rail or even a thoroughly wet rail. Again, the crushing of leaves or weeds on the tread of the rail or a too generous supply of track grease often makes it impossible to stop on a section of track thus affected without the use of sand. Cars have been known to slide down long hills with tracks thus covered while the motorman was utterly powerless to reduce the speed, even with the reversal of the motors. Most roads, therefore, not only provide a generous supply of sand on each car, but require the track-repair crew to keep the track free from leaves, grass, and weeds.

Braking Forces.—If the car is to be stopped by the application of pressure to the brake shoes bearing upon the car wheels, as is ordinarily the case, it will be noted at once that the forces tending to move the car forward and those applied as resistances to stop the motion do not lie in the same horizontal plane, the former acting at the center of gravity of the combined loaded car body and trucks and the latter at the contact between wheels and rails. The result is easily seen to be a tendency to raise the rear of the car from the track, the forces acting at the center of gravity of the car having a moment about the front truck. In addition, there is a tendency for the rear wheels of each truck to lift from the track, as the forces at the king pin and center of gravity of the truck have a moment about the front wheels. The resulting effect is that the pressure is lessened between car and rails at the rear and the static friction depended upon for braking is thereby reduced. Either the braking pressure must be reduced upon the rear truck over that of the front truck and that of the rear wheels of each truck over that of its front wheels or else all braking pressures must be lowered considerably below that possible at the front end of the car. That the braking pressures on the rear truck cannot be made less than those of the front truck by any change in the leverages on the car in the case of double-end cars is obvious. With single-end interurban cars such provision is often made. There is, however, a method of hanging brake shoes with the supporting link of the brake shoe out of line with the tangent to the wheel at the center of the shoe which will

vary the pressure between shoe and wheel with the direction of
operation of the car. This may be illustrated by referring to
Fig. 191, where the brake-shoe hanger is 5 deg. out of line with
the tangent. With the car moving toward the right, the fric-

Fig. 191.—Special brake-shoe suspension.

Fig. 192.—Brake-shoe suspension with excessive angle.

tional force at the shoe is balanced by a force of compression
in the hanger plus a force normal to the car wheel proportional
to the sine of 5 deg. This is added directly to the brake-shoe
pressure. If the car be operating toward the left, thus making

the wheel shown in the figure the rear wheel of the truck, the frictional force produces a tension in the brake-shoe hanger and a force proportional to the sine of 5 deg., tending to reduce the pressure exerted by the brake rigging. Whereas this effect may be increased by increasing the angle between brake-shoe hanger and tangent, too great an increase of this angle tends to bind the shoes upon the wheel as in the case of a toggle joint, causing chattering of the brake rigging and flat wheels. Such a condition, often found on car trucks, is illustrated in Fig. 192, where the angle has been increased to 30 deg.

In order to determine the concrete value of the resultant weight upon each wheel of a car, it is necessary to analyze all the forces acting thereon as outlined in Fig. 193 and to balance

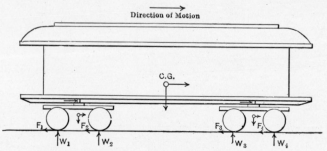

Fig. 193.—Forces acting on car during braking.

the moments of the forces about any single point, as in any problem in mechanics. A sufficient number of equations will result to permit the weights W_1, W_2, W_3, and W_4 to be calculated and the corresponding frictional forces F_1, F_2, F_3, and F_4 determined through the agency of the coefficient of friction. In determining the above equations, it must be remembered that the rotative inertia of the car wheels, axles, and motor armatures must be overcome in stopping the car as well as the translational inertia of car and trucks.

Whereas, the method above outlined will result in a very accurate analysis of the various weights and forces involved, it would be seldom, indeed, that the electrical engineer would make such a calculation before writing specifications for car equipment. The effect of reduction of pressure at the rear of the car may be taken roughly at 15 per cent and the brake rigging designed for a resultant brake-shoe pressure corresponding to 85 per cent of the actual static weight on wheels.

Braking Equipment.—It has been previously stated that the hand- and air-brake systems are now almost universally used in electric-railway service. The former is used alone upon small city cars, while both systems are universally applied to the heavier city, suburban, and interurban equipment. Where both are used, the same brake rigging is installed for both, the leverages in the case of the hand brake being greater to make up for the relatively small pull the motorman can exert as compared

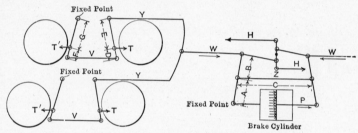

FIG. 194.—Typical brake rigging.

with the air pressure of the brake cylinder. A typical brake-rigging installation may be seen in Fig. 194, the operation of which will be self-explanatory if it be stated that the piston of the air-brake cylinder is forced forward by air pressure, when the proper valve position is provided by the motorman, just as the piston of a steam engine is operated. The principal dimensions of the various parts of the equipment of several interurban cars of the Middle West are given in Table XXXIV, all of which refer to Fig. 194. The ratio between brake-shoe

TABLE XXXIV.—DIMENSIONS OF AIR-BRAKE EQUIPMENT

Interurban car	Dimensions of levers in inches						
	A	B	C	D	E	F	G
1	10.5	9.0	....	5.0	16.0	4.0	13.0
2	9.5	9.5	....	7.0	18.0	7.0	18.0
3	12.0	23.0	....	6.0	16.0	5.0	15.0
4	11.0	17.0	35	5.0	12.5	5.0	12.5

pressure and brake-cylinder pressure may be readily obtained from the following equations. With this ratio known, the air brake pressure per square inch of piston area may be quickly determined for various desired brake-shoe applications.

Let P represent the total force on the piston of the brake cylinder and designate the resultant forces in the various links by the letters appearing upon the links in Fig. 194.

$$P = \text{Air pressure} \times \text{area piston.} \tag{107}$$

From the ratios of lever arms the following equations may be derived:

$$Y = \frac{W}{2} = \frac{PA}{2B} \tag{108}$$

$$T = \frac{Y(D + E)}{D} \tag{109}$$

$$V = \frac{YE}{D} \tag{110}$$

$$T' = \frac{V(F + G)}{G} \tag{111}$$

If the ratio between total pressure exerted by all brake shoes to brake-cylinder pressure be signified by R

$$R \text{ (for a double-truck car)} = \frac{4(T + T')}{P}. \tag{112}$$

Substitution in the above equations of values for the four cars in Table XXXIV results in the forces listed in Table XXXV with a 10-in. cylinder and maximum air pressure of 70 lb. per square inch.

TABLE XXXV.—FORCES ACTING IN AIR BRAKE EQUIPMENT

Interurban car	Pounds						
	P	W	Y	T	V	T'	R
1	5,497	6,400	3,200	13,450	10,250	13,400	19.6
2	5,497	5,497	2,748	9,830	7,080	9,830	14.4
3	5,497	2,860	1,430	5,250	3,820	5,100	7.54
4	5,497	3,550	1,775	6,210	4,430	6,210	9.06

From the above table it will be seen that the multiplying power of the brake levers on four interurban cars taken at random varies from 7.5 to 19.5.

It should not be forgotten that the above forces are based upon an emergency application of air of 70-lb. pressure which is seldom used. For an ordinary service application the forces would average less than one-half the above values.

A further calculation may be made from Table XXXIV, which is of value in determining the adequacy of the equipment for the service. Car No. 4 in this table weighs in the neighborhood of 25 tons. The total brake-shoe pressure exerted on all wheels with a 70-lb. application of air is

$$8 \times 6,210 = 49,680 \text{ lb.}$$

Ratio of total brake-shoe pressure to weight of car is 99.2 per cent. If the coefficient of friction were the same between shoe and wheels that it is between wheels and rails, it would be possible to skid the wheels with an application of air slightly above 70 lb.

Brake Rigging.—The levers by means of which the braking force is transmitted from hand brake or brake cylinder to brake shoes are of heavy strap iron linked together with steel pins provided with cotter pins and supported from the under frame of the car by means of strap-iron stirrups. Links in tension are usually constructed of 1-in. round iron rod. The circle bar between links Y and W (Fig. 194) is provided with the truck together with a clevis which may be welded to rod W and which is so designed as to slide on the circle bar as the trucks swing with respect to the car body when turning a curve.

The hand brake consists of the familiar vertical ratchet crank or wheel in the motorman's cab which winds up a chain under the car vestibule, this chain exerting a tensile force at H (Fig. 194)

Straight Air-brake Equipment.—The air-brake equipment in its simplest form consists of a motor-driven air compressor, a storage reservoir, a brake cylinder, a governor, two engineer's valves with gages for double-end equipment, a system of levers, complete piping equipment, and usually one or more air whistles to act as signals. Figure 195 represents the apparatus above outlined. The compressor, reservoir, brake cylinder, and piping are supported from the underframe of the car. The governor is often placed on the car floor under one of the end seats, while the remainder of the equipment is in the motorman's cab.

The air compressor is a direct-connected pump and direct-current, 550-volt series motor connected between trolley and ground with only a snap switch, the governor switch, and a fuse in circuit. The connection is made between circuit breaker and trolley so that the compressor will not stop when the circuit breaker opens.

The governor is a pneumatically operated switch which can be adjusted to close the compressor circuit and thereby start the compressor when the air pressure falls below a predetermined

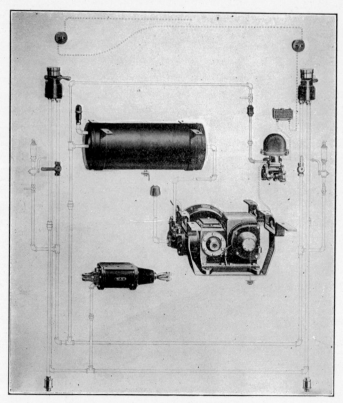

FIG. 195.—Straight air-brake equipment.

value and which will automatically stop the compressor when the pressure reaches the maximum value desired. While there is a considerable range for which the governor may be adjusted, it is generally set to operate at about 70 and 90 lb. per square inch, respectively.

The motorman's valve is of the three-position type. The operating handle, when moved to the "service" position, opens the valve between reservoir and brake cylinder and applies the brakes. The extent to which the handle is moved in this direction and the time during which it is left there determine the pressure applied to the brake shoes. If it be desired to retain this pressure in the brake cylinder the handle may be moved to the "lap" position where all valves are closed. The handle may be removed only when in this position. By throwing the handle to the position opposite to that of "service" into the "exhaust" notch the air in the brake cylinder escapes to the atmosphere and the brakes are released. It is a rather unfortunate fact that two types of air-brake valves apply the air with opposite movements of the valve handle. This is rather confusing when a motorman accustomed to one method changes to another road using the other system.

Emergency Straight-air System.—One of the disadvantages of the "straight-air" system is the length of time required to apply the brakes, due to the relatively long length of pipe through which the air must flow from the reservoir to the brake cylinder. This is, of course, especially objectionable in an emergency application. To overcome this objection for emergency stops and at the same time to avoid the complication and high first cost of the automatic system, the system known as the "emergency straight-air-brake system" has been evolved.

This system adds an emergency valve and a reservoir line to the equipment and provides emergency application and release positions on the motorman's valve. When the valve is thrown into emergency position it allows the pressure of the reservoir line which is higher than that in the emergency valve to compress a spring in the latter and thereby allow a direct passage of reservoir air into the brake cylinder. Connections with the train line and reservoir lines are also simultaneously cut off. The application of the brakes on trailers is made possible by the addition of an auxiliary air reservoir, emergency valve, and reservoir line to the equipment necessary for "straight-air" braking.

In order to release the brakes after an emergency application, the emergency valve must first be returned to its normal position by recharging the reservoir line to reservoir pressure, whereupon the brakes may be released as from a service application

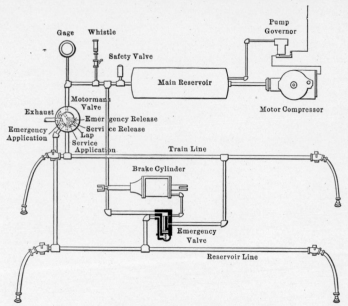

FIG. 196.—Emergency straight air-brake system.

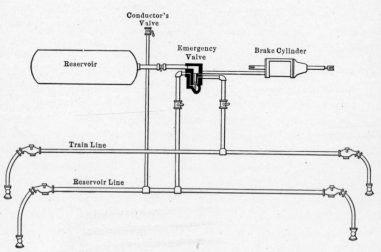

FIG. 197.—Emergency straight air brake for trail cars.

by exhausting the air from the train line. The equipment necessary for motor and trail cars is indicated in Figs. 196 and 197, respectively.

Automatic Air-brake Equipment.—Contrasted with the above "straight-air-brake equipment," which is applicable to single cars only, the "automatic air-brake equipment" (Fig. 198), similar to that used on steam trains, is often found on electric lines, especially in elevated, subway, and heavy interurban service where two or more cars are coupled together. The principal difference between this system and the one previously described is the addition of a second or auxiliary storage reservoir

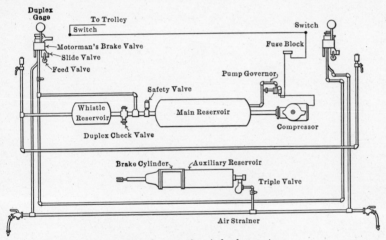

Fig. 198.—Automatic air-brake system.

and the use of a "triple valve." A "train line" or continuous pipe under air pressure is provided throughout the train, rubber-hose couplings with patented airtight knuckle joints permitting the ready closing of the line when shifting cars. The "triple valve," which is the vital part of the entire system, consists of a piston valve ordinarily balanced in a midposition by the auxiliary reservoir pressure on one side and the "train-line" pressure on the other. When the motorman's valve is in the "service" position the train line is momentarily opened to the atmosphere and its pressure reduced sufficiently to cause the auxiliary reservoir pressure to move the triple-valve piston to such a position as to admit air from the auxiliary reservoir to the brake cylinder

and apply the brakes.   This occurs on every car of the train.
To release the brakes, the motorman's valve in the "exhaust"
position allows air to flow from the main reservoir to the train
line and to raise its pressure so that the triple valve is again balanced and the brake cylinder opened to the atmosphere.   One
of the most valuable features about this equipment is the fact
that any leakage or breaking apart of cars, etc. which will reduce
the pressure in the train line will set the brakes upon all cars of
the train.

Quick-action Automatic System.—The automatic air brake
as above described is applicable to trains up to about five cars in
length.   For the longer trains, however, the reduction in train-

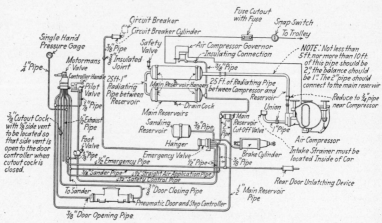

Fig. 199.—Diagram of air brakes and safety-car-control equipment for single-
end operation.

line pressure requires an appreciable time to be felt throughout
the length of the train.   The effect when some cars of the train
are braked while others are free causes severe strains on the draft
rigging, not to mention inconvenience to passengers.   The
"quick-action, automatic air-brake system" is, therefore, applied
to the longer trains.   This is similar to the other, except that the
"triple valve" is so designed as to feed both auxiliary reservoir
and train-line pressure into the brake cylinder.   This procedure
not only causes each car to aid in quickly reducing the train-
line pressure throughout the train, but it decreases the drop in
train-line pressure which must be produced at the head car.

In other words, the action is cumulative throughout the length of the train.

In both the automatic systems the motorman is provided with a duplex gage indicating both train-line and main-reservoir pressure. In the straight air-brake system either a single gage hand is provided to denote the reservoir pressure or two indications are given, the one above outlined and, in addition, a second hand to show the pressure applied to the brake cylinder.

Friction-disc, Electric, and Track Brakes.—Many types of special braking devices have been invented and tried out, involving friction discs bearing upon the planed inside surfaces of car wheels, magnetic brakes supplied with energy either from the trolley or the car motors used as generators, and track brakes consisting of shoes bearing upon the rail instead of the car wheels and often designed to grip the head of the rail with a variable pressure. While some of these devices have served admirably in special instances, especially as an additional safety device upon severe grades, they are not in sufficiently general use to warrant detailed description.

Reversal of Motors.—A method of stopping cars, in cases of emergency, known as "reversing" consists in throwing the reverse lever to the reverse position and applying power to the extent of one or possibly two series notches of the controller. This, of course, tends to operate the car in the reverse direction and not only stops the car with a sudden jolt, but is likely to damage the car equipment. It is, therefore, seldom resorted to, but in case of the failure of the brake rigging, or to avoid a collision, it is sometimes a valuable protection.

Motors Used as Generators.—As a last resort, with no power supplied to the car, and with brake rigging damaged, there is yet another method of stopping the car. The reverse lever may be thrown into the reverse position and the controller handle swung into one of the parallel notches. The resulting connection causes one motor to operate as a generator, driven by the inertia of the car, thus supplying the other motor with power tending to operate the car in the reverse direction. This method may, of course, be used if the power supply be present by throwing the circuit breaker to the open position.

With either of the above methods involving the use of electric power in stopping the car, great care must be taken not to skid the wheels, as this condition not only prevents a prompt stop, but is likely to flatten the wheels as well.

Regenerative Braking.—Closely allied with the last-discussed method of stopping a car is that of "regenerative braking," in which all motors of the car are so connected that they may act as generators delivering electrical energy to the distribution

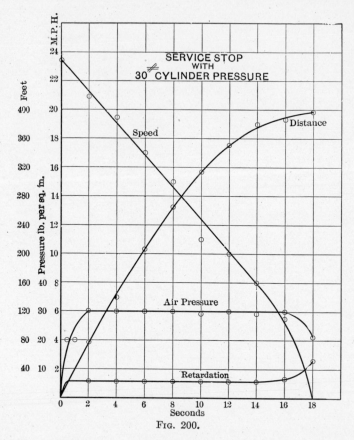

Fig. 200.

system. Although this system of braking is seldom installed for the sole purpose of stopping or controlling the speed of trains on down grades, it has been used to advantage in several instances discussed in the previous chapter and has been found of sufficient value to warrant the extra complexity of control circuits involved therein.

Brake Tests.—It is often of great value to know the time and distance required in which to stop cars of various weights operating at different speeds. This is particularly true in case of accidents and court litigation. Whereas these facts may be predetermined mathematically, as has been previously pointed out, the actual test of a car in service is often required as well.

In order to carry out such a test thoroughly, it is necessary to provide a method of determining the speed of a car, the time

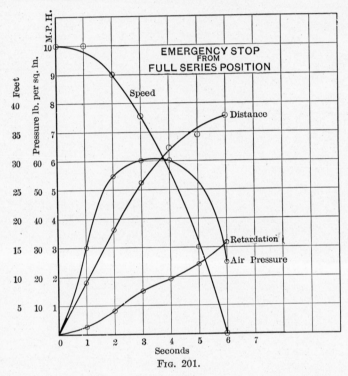

Fig. 201.

between brake signal and stop, and the distance traveled during this period. It is also well in some cases to know the air-brake pressure, the amount of wheel skidding, and the motor current in case either of the reverse methods is used.

One of the most satisfactory methods of determining the speed at any instant is by means of a magneto generator, driven from the car axle, the voltage of the generator read from a voltmeter in circuit being directly proportional to speed.

The distance traveled during the braking period may be roughly determined from the revolutions of the car wheel or a similar wheel driven from the car axle, which may be caused to make electrical contacts every revolution. If any skidding

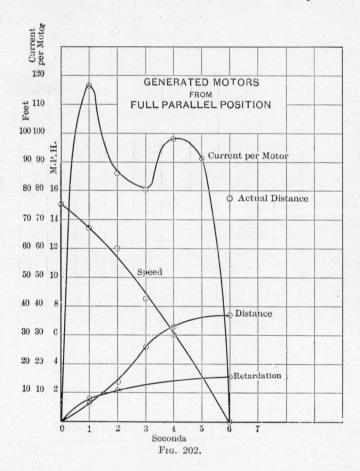

Fig. 202.

occurs, this method becomes valueless. A method which has worked admirably in tests at Purdue University is to give the breaking signal by means of a revolver from which a ball is shot beside the track, thus marking the start of the braking test very accurately. The distance required to stop may then be measured along the track from this point with a steel tape.

All of the data of the test may readily be arranged for an automatic graphical record upon a single paper chart, thus illustrating clearly the desired values at any given instant.

Testing Equipment.—A list of the principal items of the testing equipment with a detailed description of this equipment will be presented here.

Chronograph.—A cut of this instrument is shown in Fig. 203 It consists of:

1. A drum, approximately 6 in. in diameter by 17½ in. long, which held the paper record chart.

FIG. 203.—The chronograph.

2. A spring motor which drove the drum.

3. A Seth Thomas clock with electrical contacts, which is so arranged as to close twice per second.

4. A relay and electrical connections.

5. Two magnet-operated pens.

A diagram of the electrical connections is shown in Fig. 204. It will be noted that the chronograph clock and battery operate the time pens on the trainagraph and speedmeter. One of the chronograph pens is connected in the circuit with a contact maker which is attached to the end of one of the car axles. This contact maker has been adapted from an automobile timer and is so arranged that the contact is "made" for one-half of the wheel revolution and "broken" for the other half. The other chronograph-pen circuit is arranged with a single-pole, double-throw switch so that it can be connected in series, either with the time circuit, or with a special contact placed on the brake valve. In

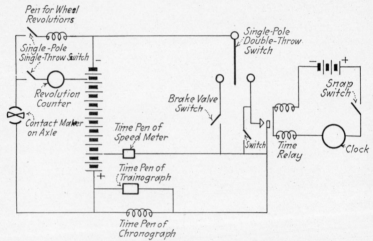

FIG. 204.—Diagram of electrical connections.

FIG. 205.—Electrical contact maker mounted on the end of an axle.

some of the tests on the Birney car the special contact is placed on the controller so that the removal of the motorman's hand from the controller handle permits the handle to spring up and make the contact.

In the air-brake tests the general method of operation is to connect the time-pen circuit to the brake-valve contact a few seconds before the stop signal is given. When the brake valve is thrown to the emergency position the brake-valve contact is broken, thus de-energizing the time-pen magnet and giving an indication on the chart, as shown in Fig. 206. Immediately after this indication the chronograph operator throws the single-pole, double-throw switch, thus connecting the pen to the time circuit and giving the half-second indications shown on the chart. Just before the car comes to a stop the chronograph operator closes the key switch *S*, short circuiting the time-relay contacts. At the instant the car is stopped the operator opens the double-throw, single-pole switch giving the stop indication. The switch *S* is then opened and the double-throw, single-pole switch closes, thus starting the time indications again.

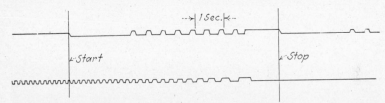

FIG. 206.—A typical chronograph chart.

In the electric-braking tests the operator makes an indication on the chart, similar to that made in the air-brake tests by the brake-valve contact, by manipulation of the double-pole, single-throw switch.

The lower pen record is that of wheel revolutions, each offset in the curve representing a revolution. The slowing down of the car is shown by the longer offsets.

As the chronograph chart is driven at constant speed, both the time interval of stopping and the speed at various times can be calculated from the chart records. The time intervals and speeds so determined are considered more accurate than those determined by other methods and are used extensively in the analysis of test data.

Trainagraph.—The trainagraph is shown in Fig. 207. This instrument is built by the American Steam Gauge and Valve

Fig. 207.—The trainagraph set up in car.

Fig. 208.—The magneto and contact maker attached to car.

Manufacturing Co. and is equipped with three graphic recording pressure indicators and a time pen. The chart is driven by a constant-speed spring motor. In testing, the time pen is energized from the chronograph clock, thus synchronizing the two instruments. Only two of the pressure indicators are used, one measuring brake-cylinder pressures and the other the brake-pipe or main-reservoir pressure, depending on the type of brake being tested. The indicators are connected to the air piping by means of small-diameter, high-pressure air hose. The instrument is also provided with precision pressure gages.

Two sets of tests are run on the cars equipped with straight air brakes. In one set the main-reservoir pressure corresponds to the upper limit of the air-pressure governor range and in the other set to the lower limit of the range. A bleeding cock in the hose line connected to the main reservoir enables the trainagraph operators to reduce the pressure to the proper value for each test.

Speedmeter.—To facilitate the determination of speed while the test is in progress, a graphic recording voltmeter is used in connection with a direct-current magneto. In such a magneto the generated voltage is directly proportional to the speed of the magneto armature. The magneto (Fig. 208) is belted to the driving axle by means of a flat belt and an adjustable resistance is inserted in series with the voltmeter so as to permit adjusting the range of the instrument to fit the different conditions of wheel and axle diameter. The speedmeter is also equipped with a time pen, which is actuated from the chronograph time circuit, thus showing accurately the braking and stop indications on the speedmeter charts.

Revolution Counter.—As a check on the distance traveled over in bringing the car to a stop, an electrically operated, car-wheel revolution counter is used. The connections to this counter are shown in Fig. 204, the axle contact maker used for the chronograph being used for this instrument as well. The circuit to the counter is closed by the observer at the instant the stop signal is given. The number of revolutions counted, therefore, are those occurring from the instant the stop signal is given until the car is brought to a standstill. The observer who operates the counter also measures, with a stop watch, the time necessary to bring the car to a stop.

TABLE XXXVI.—COMPARISON OF STOPPING TIME IN SECONDS AS DETER-
MINED BY SEVERAL METHODS

Run No.	Chrono- graph	Stop watch	Traina- graph	Speed meter	Kind of braking
					E
C- 2	8.6	8.2	8.3	8.8	High Press
C 3	2.7	3.0	....	3.1	High Press
C- 4	4.3	4.3	4.4	4.3	High Press
C- 5	6.0	6.0	5.8	6.1	High Press
C- 6	3.1	2.8	2.9	3.3	High Press
C- 7	7.1	7.2	7.2	7.2	High Press
C-24	2.8	2.6	2.8	3.0	High Press
C-29	4.1	3.9	1.1	4.0	High Press
C-30	3.1	3.4	3.1	3.3	High Press
C-31	5.9	5.4	5.6	5.8	High Press
C-33	7.7	7.8	7.6	7.4	High Press
					E
C- 8	3.2	3.5	3.1	3.5	Low Press
C- 9	4.0	3.4	....	3.1	Low Press
C-10	4.6	4.9	....	4.7	Low Press
C-11	5.1	5.1	4.5	5.1	Low Press
C-12	7.1	7.1	7.1	7.0	Low Press
C-13	8.8	8.8	8.3	9.5	Low Press
C-14	9.8	9.8	9.5	9.6	Low Press
C-34	3.0	3.2	2.8	3.3	Low Press
C-35	6.9	6.7	6.7	7.5	Low Press
C-36	8.7	8.7	8.6	8.6	Low Press
C-15	6.5	6.4	....	6.8	R.M.
C-16	9.4	7.8	....	7.1	R.M.
C-17	....	....	....	....	R.M.
C-18	12.9	12.6	....	13.3	R.M.
C-40	14.6	16.1	....	13.7	R.M
C-41	7.0	7.5	....	5.4	R.M.
C-20	6.0	6.1	....	6.4	B.M.
C-21	9.0	9.8	....	8.5	B.M.
C-23	15.1	15.1	....	14.8	B.M.
C-42	6.0	6.2	....	5.9	B.M.
C-43	12.5	12.5	....	13.0	B.M.
C-44	22.2	22.2	....	22.0	B.M.
C-25	3.6	3.2	3.4	3.6	R.M. + E.
C-26	4.4	4.6	4.1	4.8	R.M. + E.
C-27	6.5	6.3	....	6.3	R.M. + E.
C-28	8.5	8.6	7.5	7.9	R.M. + E.
C-37	3.7	2.5	3.7	3.6	R.M. + E.
C-38	6.2	6.1	6.0	5.8	R.M. + E.
C-39	7.2	7.5	6.9	6.9	R.M. + E.

TABLE XXXVII.—COMPARISONS OF STOPPING DISTANCES AS DETERMINED BY SEVERAL METHODS

Run No.	Measured distance, feet	Distance by chronograph		Distance by revolution counter		Kind of braking
		Revolution of car wheel	Distance feet	Revolution of car wheel	Distance feet	
C- 2	243.1	27.0	220.0	28.0	228.0	E.—High Press
C- 3	29.0	3.0	24.4	4.0	32.6	E.—High Press
C- 4	67.8	8.0	65.2	7.0	57.0	E.—High Press
C- 5	126.0	14.0	114.0	14.0	114.0	E.—High Press
C- 6	27.7	2.0	16.3	3.0	24.4	E.—High Press
C- 7	166.8	19.0	155.0	19.0	155.0	E.—High Press
C-24	26.2	2.5	20.4	3.0	24.4	E.—High Press
C-29	52.4	5.0	42.3	5.0	40.7	E.—High Press
C-30	36.0	3.5	28.5	4.0	32.6	E.—High Press
C-31	100.0	11.0	89.5	12.0	. . . .	E.—High Press
C-33	194.2	21.5	175.0	19.5	228.0	E.—High Press
C- 8	33.8	3.5	28.5	4.0	32.6	E.—Low Press
C- 9	32.0	3.0	24.4	4.0	32.6	E.—Low Press
C-10	66.0	7.0	57.0	7.0	57.0	E.—Low Press
C-11	74.0	8.0	65.2	8.0	65.0	E.—Low Préss
C-12	144.4	16.5	134.2	17.0	138.5	E.—Low Press
C-13	205.6	23.5	191.5	24.0	195.5	E.—Low Press
C-14	266.0	31.0	252.3	31.0	252.0	E.—Low Press
C-34	33.0	3.0	24.4	3.0	24.4	E.—Low Press
C-35	138.9	16.0	130.0	15.0	122.0	E.—Low Press
C-36	213.5	24.0	195.5	25.0	204.0	E.—Low Press
C-15	49.3	5.5	44.7	7.0	57.0	R.M.
C-16	59.0	6.5	52.9	7.0	57.0	R.M.
C-18	138.6	15.5	126.0	17.0	138.5	R.M.
C-40	279.5	. . . .	. . . .	33.0	269.0	R.M.
C-41	67.0	. . . .	. . . .	7.0	57.0	R.M.
C-20	53.0	6.0	48.9	6.0	48.8	B.M.
C-21	122.0	14.0	115.7	14.0	113.0	B.M.
C-23	272.8	32.0	262.1	33.0	269.0	B.M.
C-42	50.0	5.5	44.7	6.0	48.8	B.M.
C-43	191.2	31.0	252.2	30.0	244.0	B.M.
C-44	418.5	58.0	472.0	58.0	471.0	B.M.
C-25	38.4	4.0	32.6	4.0	32.6	E. + R.M.
C-26	69.0	7.0	57.0	8.0	65.2	E. + R.M.
C-27	133.5	14.5	108.1	16.0	130.0	E. + R.M.
C-28	218.1	23.5	191.5	25.0	204.0	E. + R.M.
C-37	28.5	3.0	24.4	13.0	24.4	E. + R.M.
C-38	118.9	13.0	105.9	13.0	106.0	E. + R.M.
C-39	174.5	19.5	159.0	20.0	163.0	E. + R.M.

Report to the Central Electric Railway Association.[1]—As a result of the presentation at the Louisville Convention of the Association, 1922, by H. C. De Camp, of a paper on the subject of "Emergency Stops," the motion was passed:

"That a committee of five be appointed to look into this question very thoroughly."

After several informal conferences and considerable correspondence, the Committee decided to make a series of tests on several types of cars during the week beginning Sunday, May 13, 1923. Emergency-stop tests, extending through this week, were made on:

1. Interurban car, double truck, four motors.
2. City car, double truck, four motors.
3. City car, double truck, two motors.
4. Birney safety car.

Conclusions.—As the result of a careful analysis of the test data, the following conclusions were reached:

1. There is no one best way to stop any car in an emergency. In general, the best way will depend somewhat on the type of brake and motor equipment.

2. As a broad rule, subject to occasional exceptions, it may be said that the best way to stop a car equipped with air brakes is to apply emergency air and sand, simultaneously throwing the controller to the "off" position.

3. The electrical methods of braking, reversed motors and bucking motors, subject the equipment to very severe strains. Because of the abruptness with which the braking force is applied, the value of these methods in emergency braking is more apparent than real, except in those cases in which the air brakes from some cause are inoperative.

4. Of the two electrical methods, reversed motors and bucking motors, the reversed-motors method is the most effective.

5. If the motors are reversed in conjunction with emergency air and sand, skidding invariably results, and even under good rail conditions, the results are not superior to those obtained using air alone.

6. The electric braking methods are more likely to produce erratic results than the emergency air, and for this reason should not be resorted to as a general practice.

[1] EWING, D. D., "Emergency Braking on Electric Cars," *Bull.* 13, Engineering Experiment Station, Purdee University, Lafayette, Ind.

7. Because the rail conditions under which these tests were made were better than those ordinarily obtaining on city streets, the results should be regarded as minima rather than averages or maxima.

8. The best way to stop a Birney safety car in an emergency is for the motorman to raise his hand from the controller handle. This is true only when the car is running with brakes released. With brakes applied, the brake valve should be thrown to the emergency position.

CHAPTER XXVI

CAR-HOUSE DESIGN

As the modern car house not only provides storage for the rolling stock, but also furnishes room for inspection and repairs and often includes the shops and offices of the railway company, much thought must be given to its location and design.

Location.—Too often a lot for a car house is secured before the size or requirements of the latter are determined, thus requiring that the car-house and track layout be fitted to the lot. This procedure results in a limited and unsatisfactory design. A site of sufficient size for all the above functions of the car house, with proper consideration for future growth, should be selected in the most convenient section of the city from an operating standpoint. Care must be taken to make sure that all necessary track privileges may be obtained from the city authorities before the site is finally purchased.

In the case of the interurban car house, a location for the latter, together with the shops, offices, and often the power house or substation, is selected at about the middle of the line, although where the interurban road is operated by the company controlling the traction systems of the terminal cities the cars may be handled by the city car houses. This plan often offers the advantages of lessened fire risk, smaller dead mileage of cars, improved freight and express accommodations, and better or more congenial homes for employees. For the advantages to be gained by locating near the power house, as well as for an outline of many considerations to be taken into account in deciding upon the proper location, reference should be made to Chap. XVI.

The fire risk of a car house is great. Not only should abundant water supply and other fire protection be available, but care should be taken to avoid all fire risk from adjoining buildings. The subsoil should be examined with a view toward determining the foundations and piling necessary, although with the lighter and more equally distributed weight of the car house this is not such a vital factor as with the power station. Good drainage and suitable sewer connections should, however, be available or easily provided.

Layout of Tracks.—One of the first questions to be decided is the percentage of total cars owned for which cover shall be provided. This is a question upon which railway managers differ widely. At the 1907 Convention of the American Street and Interurban Railway Association a committee appointed to investigate this question assumed the case of a car house accom-

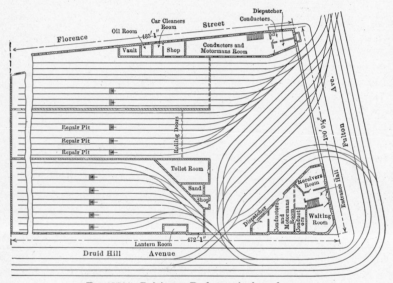

Fig. 209.—Baltimore Park terminal car house.

modating 84 cars under cover as compared with a similar design capable of housing but one-third this number. The estimated costs were $105,000 and $45,000 respectively. With fixed charges at 12 per cent, this represents an annual saving of $7,200, or $85 per car. A study of the requirements of this road showed that all cars not in service between 6 a.m. and midnight could be housed by the small structure and, of course, this would involve different cars on different days. The larger car house and the increased annual outlay includes simply the ability to house two-thirds more cars from midnight until 6 a.m. Since the $85 per car will nearly provide for repainting and varnishing a car each year, and as the added deterioration of the car during this period of day when out of service is not great, this particular case seems to favor open storage. Opposed to this evidence probably the most important argument for complete car storage is the fact that the equipment will certainly receive better attention from inspectors

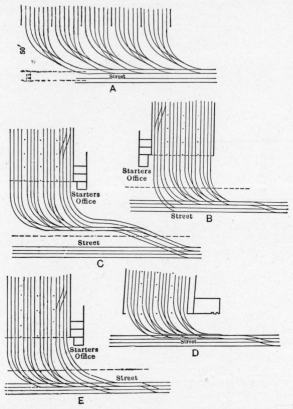

FIG. 210.—Typical car-house track plans.

and repair crew if all cars are stored within the car house, especially in bad weather.

The next question of importance is whether a single- or double-end house is desired. The latter type provides more ready movement of cars through the house and aids greatly in clearing the house in case of fire. Where a whole block or two intersecting streets are available, it is often customary to form an operating loop through the car house for the cars when in regular service, with regular inspections as they stop over the inspection pits. A rather complicated example of this construction is shown in the plan view of Fig. 209, representing the Park terminal car house in Baltimore. The principal objections to the double-end arrangement are the difficulty in keeping tracks

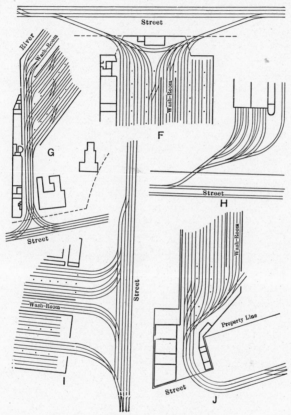

Fig. 211.—Typical car-house track plans.

clear for through operation, the large amount of special track work required, and the added difficulty in heating.

Whichever of the above designs is decided upon, depending largely upon local conditions, the problem remains so to connect the various tracks of the car house with those of the main line that the greatest possible flexibility of car movements within the

yard may be had without interference with main-line traffic and
without obstructing the main track with more special work than
is absolutely necessary.   Figures 210 and 211 illustrate several
typical methods of solution for this problem.   Case *A* intro-
duces several switches into one of the main tracks, but makes no
connection with the second main track.   A more flexible arrangement is shown in case *B*, where a cross-over is provided to the
second main track in addition to one located in the car house.
The latter is often found very useful, but its installation depends
very much upon the availability of the special work in front of the

Fig. 212.—Car house and yard design, remote-controlled track switches.

car house for switching purposes.   If the special work in the
main line be objected to, case *C* may offer a satisfactory solution, requiring, necessarily, more yard room.   The design of case
D uses an extra or "gauntlet" track in the street for switching,
while *E* is similar to *B*, except that the operating tracks are on
the right of the storage house.   If space will permit, *F* (Fig. 211)
offers an ideal arrangement, allowing the through cars to pass
through the car house for inspection or minor repairs if desired
and relieving the main line of all special work.   It may also be
used as a "Y" for turning cars which must operate single ended.
Designs *G* and *J* have been termed "bottle" entrances, involving
the special work within the car house because of building condi-

tions. *H* may be used often in interurban service where land is cheap and the car house may be placed at some distance from the main track. Case *I* involves the use of the third track in the street and, therefore, is limited to use with wide streets only.

The special work required for any of the above entrances should be of girder rail with manganese hardened centers, regardless of the type of rail used in the street and car house. This is especially true in cases in which the regular street traffic must pass over the switches and frogs as well as the cars entering the car house.

Transfer Table.—The use of a transfer table in the car house often does away with much of the special work. This transfer

Fig. 213.—Car house provided with transfer table.

table consists of a large truck operating upon a pair of depressed rails laid across the car house with its upper surface flush with the floor and bearing sections of rail matching those of the storage house and outgoing tracks. A car may be run on this table in either direction, be transported transversely of the car house, and run off on another track. The table may be operated by hand in small installations, but is ordinarily driven by an electric motor. A typical installation may be seen in Fig. 213. Although the transfer table may be found in many city car houses, it is seriously objected to by many because of the time required to shift cars, especially in case of fire, and the space taken up thereby, which might otherwise be available for storage. To obviate these objections the "flush" transfer table is used to some extent, the cars being run up to the table on a slight gradient, the table trucks operating on a transverse track flush with the floor.

Building Design.—With the above questions determined, the design of a suitable building for a car house is a relatively simple matter. The two factors to be kept constantly in mind are ease of handling and repairing cars and fire protection.

Fire Protection.—Car houses are recognized to be considerable of a fire risk and many serious fires have consumed many thousand dollars' worth of rolling stock in a surprisingly short time, the entire duration of several such fires being barely more than 30 min. In many instances where there is a spacious yard room outside, the house rails are sloped toward the entrance so that the cars will coast out of the barn if brakes are released. In other cases many cars have been saved in case of fire by throwing the controller handle to the first notch and allowing them to run out without attendance.

Not more than three tracks should be enclosed without a fire-proof partition and a single fireproof section should not contain more than $200,000 worth of rolling stock as stipulated by the Fire Underwriters. The best design is either brick walls with heavy mill-type roof construction of fireproofed timber or reinforced concrete throughout. For the latter construction see Fig. 213. Steel-truss roof construction has proved very dangerous in cases of fire, as the roof falls in very quickly, thus cutting off all possibility of getting out the remaining cars. Curtain walls of cement plaster on wire lath are often installed in long houses, separating the storage space into several fireproof compartments. The front of the house and these curtain walls are provided with steel rolling doors. Opinion is divided regarding the advantages of timber roof trusses over posts for roof supports. The latter, of course, obstruct the working area somewhat, but are often used to advantage for lighting outlets, sprinklers, and the convenient support for fire-fighting equipment. Automatic sprinkler systems are now being rapidly installed on ceilings and in aisles between cars for additional and prompt fire protection. These are supplied with sufficient head of water either from the city high-pressure system or from a tank especially installed upon the premises. The appearance and relative dimensions of a typical car-house elevation may be noted in Fig. 214.

Pit Construction.—For convenience in inspection and repair, from 30 to 50 per cent of the tracks in the car house are pit tracks, *i.e.*, the floor between the rails is depressed several feet and cemented as shown in Fig. 214 in order that the under portion of the car may be accessible. It has also been found convenient to depress a portion of the floor between adjacent tracks by 1 or 2 ft. for convenience in packing journal boxes, etc.

Heating.—Car houses are heated principally by either steam or hot water, coiled pipes being located in pits and upon the

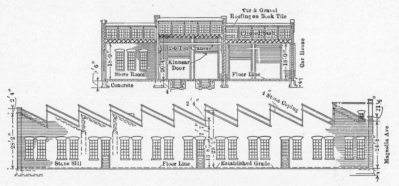

FIG. 214.—Typical car-house elevation.

lower portion of all walls. The boiler room, if not in a separate building, must be carefully protected by fireproof walls. The heating of car houses is at best an unsatisfactory problem, especially where the end doors must be continually open for the operation of cars.

Floors.—The floors in small storage car houses are sometimes of gravel fill. This is not to be approved, however, on account of the impossibility of keeping such a floor in a sanitary condition. Heavy timber flooring is probably most often found, but it should be avoided if the expense of concrete with cement finish can be seriously considered. Often the latter can be constructed with cinders from the power station without great expense and will prove the most satisfactory of all car-house floors. Since substantial piers must be laid for the track in whichever form it may take, the floor is generally supported therefrom.

Lighting.—Incandescent lighting by means of five light series groups of lamps connected between trolley and ground is often used in smaller installations, but a low-voltage, ungrounded supply is much preferable. Lights spaced every car length in aisles are usually sufficient for general illumination if generous provision be made for pit lighting and outlets for portable lamps. Pit lighting particularly should be in conduit, as illustrated in Fig. 215. General illumination for very large areas and for storage

FIG. 215.—Example of good pit lighting.

yards may be furnished by means of arc or large incandescent lamps, but these are not popular for car-house installation.

Offices and Employees' Quarters.—The arrangement of offices, employees' quarters, and storage for raw materials and tools is dependent upon local requirements and will not be discussed in detail. The portion of the building containing the offices and employees' quarters is often of two stories and, where within the city limits, is designed to present a good architectural appearance. Many companies fit up spacious apartments, for the use of employees, rather elaborately with recreation and reading rooms, sleeping quarters, baths, etc. Provision should at least be made, however, for making out reports and for comfortably spending spare time between "reliefs." An average plan may be seen in Fig. 216.

Repair Shops.—It is necessary to decide at first what the policy of the company is to be with regard to car repair and reconstruction. If a large interurban company is to make all repairs, reconstruct damaged cars, and possibly build new cars, a very elaborate series of forge, woodworking, machine, and paint

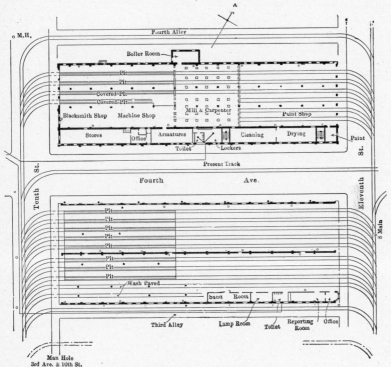

Fig.. 216.—Typical car-house plan.

shops will be necessary. The majority of the smaller companies, however, make only minor repairs, often sending away wheels for replacement or re-turning rather than installing the lathes and hydraulic presses necessary for this work. Whereas the discussion of the former type of shop is beyond the scope of this treatise, especially as comparatively few of the roads are thus equipped, the following average list may be of value in planning the equipment for a small shop. The machines are listed approximately in the order in which they would be added with increased demands upon the repair shops.

1 screw cutting lathe, 14-in. swing.

1 vertical drill press, 24 in.

1 tool-grinding wheel.

4 armature stands for rewinding armatures.

2 forges.

1 automatic power hack saw.

1 oven for baking insulation.

1 commutator slotting device.

1 wheel-turning lathe.

1 hydraulic wheel press.

Whereas the small repair shop as well as the paint shop often occupy sections of the main car house, the large shops are housed in separate but adjacent buildings. Such an arrangement, showing typical floor-plan details, will be found in Fig. 216.

CHAPTER XXVII

ELECTRIC LOCOMOTIVES

With the recent rapid advance in electric traction there has come the successful design, construction, and operation of several types of electric locomotives. While the Baltimore & Ohio R. R. had previously operated electric locomotives in its tunnels for several years, the great impetus in electric-locomotive development came in 1903 as a result of the requirement that the tunnels entering New York City be electrified. This was done largely

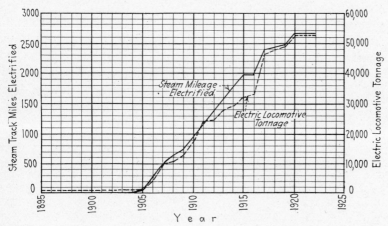

FIG. 217.—Growth of steam railroad mileage electrified and electric locomotive tonnage in heavy traction service in United States and Canada.

as a safety precaution soon after a serious wreck in one of these tunnels due to the inability to read signals on account of the smoke enclosed in the tunnel. Likewise, the Cascade Tunnel of the Great Northern R. R. in Washington was equipped with electric locomotives after a train parted in attempting to mount the severe grade of the tunnel with two steam locomotives, resulting in a delay of the train in the tunnel and the consequent

413

overcoming of the train crew and many passengers by poisonous gases and smoke.

In Fig. 217 are shown the growth curves of electrified track mileage and electric-locomotive tonnage. The effect of the World War on railway-electrification development is clearly shown. A number of railroads which were contemplating electrification of mountain grades or city terminals in 1914 are only now beginning to revive their interest in electrification. In passing, it may be noted further that the curves indicate that each mile of track requires about 20 tons of locomotive capacity.

Advantages of Locomotives over Motor Cars.—With the multiple-unit control of motor cars, which has been previously described, developed to such an extent that long, heavy trains of both motor cars and trailers are being operated successfully in elevated, subway, and interurban service, thus offering a very flexible distribution of motive power and weight on driving wheels throughout the train, it might be expected that this method of propulsion would be applied to the heavier electrification of steam roads. As the traffic demands and the number of cars increased, motor and trail cars could then be added in the proper proportion so as to leave little excess capacity to operate at low efficiency as must often be done when but one or two capacities of locomotives are used for trains of widely varying weights and requirements.

In spite of these advantages of the motor car, the locomotive is still found to be necessary in heavy trunk-line service. Its advantages listed below can be made to overcome those of the motor car by dividing the service into three or four classes, such as switching, suburban, express, passenger, and heavy freight, and designing different locomotives, if necessary, for two or more of these types of service, thus keeping the locomotive loaded approximately to its rated capacity. The advantages of the locomotive in heavy service may be listed as follows:

1. It eliminates the necessity of re-equipping present cars as motor cars.

2. It eliminates the necessity of wiring some of the present cars with train cables for use as electric trailers.

3. It is easy to make up trains regardless of whether they have been electrically equipped or not, *i.e.*, the electric locomotive makes use of present cars without change therein.

4. It is not necessary to make up trains in a certain order with the proper number and location of motor cars therein.

5. Parts in the locomotive are easily reached for repair.

6. The make-up of the train is not affected by the failure of electrical equipment. The locomotive only, and not several cars of the train, must be switched in case of electrical breakdown.

7. The first cost of motive-power equipment is lower.

8. The maintenance expenses of motive power are lower.

At present the motor-car train seems to offer the most advantages for accommodation passenger and suburban service, while the locomotive seems best adapted for the long-haul passenger and freight service.

Granted that an electric locomotive is needed if trunk-line service is to be electrified, a study of the various types of electric locomotives which are in use at the present time is of interest. With the many years of experimenting and practical experience with steam locomotives which have led to a most satisfactory design for the various types of service, advantage was taken of present steam-locomotive design and the electrical equipment added with as little change as possible. To this end the manufacturers of steam locomotives and electrical machinery have cooperated to a marked degree in developing the new product.

Locomotive Ratings.—The standardization rules of the A. I. E. E. require that locomotives shall be rated in terms of the adhesive weight, nominal 1-hr. tractive effort, continuous tractive effort, and corresponding speeds. The nominal and continuous tractive efforts are those corresponding to the nominal and continuous outputs of the motors (see Chap. XXII). The rated speed is the speed expressed in miles per hour when the motors are operating at their full voltage, continuous rating. The tractive effort exerted at 25 per cent coefficient of adhesion is also often given.

Locomotive Data.—The following tables, made up of data collected from many sources, give concisely some of the more important details of the earlier American electric locomotives:

TABLE XXXVIII.—DATA ON EARLIER GENERAL ELECTRIC COMPANY
LOCOMOTIVES

Road	N. Y. C. & H. R. R. R.	Butte, Anaconda & Pacific Ry.	Oregon Electric Ry.	Great Northern Ry.
Electric system	D.c.	D.c.	D.c.	3-phase A.c.
Service	Terminal passenger	Main line freight	Interurban freight	Main line freight
First placed in service	1908	1913	1912	1909
Contact line voltage	600	2,400	600/1,200	6,600
No. of motors	4	4	4	4
Mechanical transmission	Direct	Gears	Gears	Gears
Gear ratio	Gearless	87/18	64/17	81/19
Control	Type M	Type M	Type M	Type M
Motor ventilation	Natural	Forced	Natural	Forced
Underframe	Cast steel	12 in. channels	10 in. channels	Structural steel shapes
Body construction	Steel	Steel	Steel	Steel
Wheel arrangement	4-8-4	0-4-4-0	0-4-4-0	0-4-4-0
Drive-wheel diameter	44 in.	44 in.	37 in.	60 in.
Rigid wheel base	13 ft. 0 in.	8 ft. 8 in.	7 ft. 2 in.	11 ft. 0 in.
Total wheel base	36 ft. 0 in.	26 ft. 0 in.	26 ft. 8 in.	31 ft. 9 in.
Length inside of knuckles	41 ft. 0 in.	37 ft. 4 in.	37 ft 4 in.	44 ft. 2 in.
Total weight	230,000	160,000	100,000	230,000
Weight per driving axle	36,000	40,000	25,000	56,000
Adhesive weight	144,000	160,000	100,000	230,000
T.E. (1 hour)	20,500	30,000	13,300	39,800
T.E. (continuous)	6,700	25,000	8,000	25,000
Speed in m.p.h. (1 hr. rating)	40	15	11.3	15.1
Speed in m.p.h. (continuous rating)	57	16.2	....	15.3
1 Hour hp	2,200	1,200	400	1,600
Continuous hp	1,000	1,080	....	1,000
1 Hour hp. per ton	19.1	15	8	13.9
1 Hour T.E. per ton	178	375	265	346

FIG. 218.—New York Central locomotive.

TABLE XXXIX.—DATA ON EARLIER WESTINGHOUSE LOCOMOTIVES

Road	N. Y., N. H. & H. R. R.	N. Y., N. H. & H. R. R.	Pennsylvania R. R.	Norfolk & Western R. R.
Electric system	A.c.–D.c.	A.c.–D.c.	D.c.	Split phase A.c.
Service	Terminal passenger	Main line term. freight	Terminal Pass.	Main line freight
First placed in service	1908	1909	1910	1914 (building)
Contact line voltage	11,000	11,000	600	11,000
No. of motors	4	4	2	4
Mechanical transmission	Direct (mounted on quill)	Geared to quill	Connecting rods and jack shaft	Gears and side rods
Gear ratio	Gearless	2.32	Gearless	....
Control	A.c.–D.c. Master cont.	A.c.–D.c. Master cont.	H. B.	Master cont. 3-phase
Motor ventilation	Forced	Forced	Natural	Forced
Underframe	Steel channels and girder construction	Structural steel	Cast steel	....
Cab body construction	Steel	Steel	Steel	....
Wheel arrangement	2–4–4–2	2–4–4–2	4–4–4–4	2–4–4–2
Drive wheel diameter	62 in.	63 in.	72 in.	63 in.
Rigid wheel base	8 ft. 0 in.	7 ft. 0 in.	7 ft. 2 in.	11 ft. 0 in.
Total wheel base	30 ft. 10 in.	38 ft. 6 in.	55 ft. 11 in.	43 ft. 0 in.
Length inside of knuckles	36 ft. 4 in.	48 ft. 0 in.	64 ft. 11 in.	52 ft. 0 in.
Total weight	204,000	280,000	314,000	260,000

In Table XL are shown similar details for some of the most recent types of locomotive.

Modern Electric Locomotives.—The New York Central locomotive (Fig. 218) of the direct-current type, a plan view of whose motor is shown in Fig. 219, marked a radical departure in railway-motor design. As will be noted from the figure, the motor is bipolar, the magnetic circuit involving a portion of the truck frame with internally projecting laminated iron poles with vertical faces, between which the armature, mounted directly on the truck axle, might vibrate in a vertical direction with the irregularities in the track. This design, of course, greatly increased the capacity possible in the limited space on the truck, eliminated many of the disadvantages of the small air gap, and gave considerable flexibility to the relative movement of armature and field. It also lowered the center of gravity of the locomotive below that of its steam-railroad competitor and increased the dead load per axle, both of which changes have some disadvantages. A more recent development of the gearless machine has been made by the General Electric Company for passenger service on the Chicago, Milwaukee & St. Paul Ry. A cut of this

FIG. 219.—Plan view, New York Central motor.

FIG. 220.—General electric gearless locomotive. (*Chicago, Milwaukee & St. Paul R. R.*)

locomotive is shown in Fig. 220 and its characteristic curves are given in Fig. 221. This machine operates on 3,000 volts, direct current, and is arranged for regenerative braking (for detailed data, see Table XL).

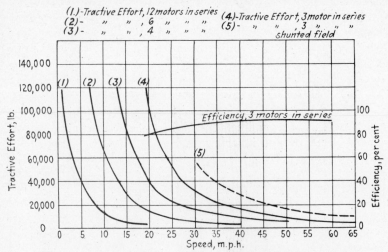

Fig. 221.—Characteristic curves for St. Paul gearless locomotive.

Fig. 222.—Motor and drivers of New York, New Haven and Hartford locomotive.

The locomotives of the New York, New Haven & Hartford R. R., which were developed soon after the above for operation upon the 11,000-volt, single-phase system of the above company and also upon the 600-volt, direct-current system of the New York Central R. R. entering New York City, still retained the motors concentric with the truck axles and between the driving wheels, as will be seen from Fig. 222, but reduced the dead weight upon the axles by supporting the armature upon a quill, concentric with but surrounding the driving axle with a space of $\frac{5}{8}$ in. between axle and inner circumference of quill. The torque

Fig. 223.—Armature and driving pins, New York, New Haven and Hartford locomotive.

was transmitted from the armature to the drivers by means of seven driving pins, spring borne in recesses in the driving wheels, as shown in Fig. 223. This allowed the axle considerable motion, independent of the armature and permitted the motor field and frame to be rigidly supported upon the truck. In order to improve their riding qualities, the pony wheels were added to each of these locomotives in 1908.

The Pennsylvania locomotives (Fig. 224) were built for service through the New York tunnels and yards of the Pennsylvania R. R. The locomotives are of the articulated type, two similar sections being set back to back, and articulated together with a heavy hinge which permits horizontal movements only. Each

TABLE XL.—DATA ON RECENT ELECTRIC LOCOMOTIVES

Road	Paulista (Brazil)	Chilean-State	Mexico	Baltimore & Ohio	Chicago Milwaukee & St. Paul (G. E.)	Chicago Milwaukee & St. Paul
Electric system	D.C.	D.C.	D.C.	D.C.	D.C.	D.C.
Service	Freight	Freight	Passenger & Freight	Passenger & Freight	Passenger	Freight
Built or building	1921	1923	1923	1923	1920	1920
Contact line voltage	3,000	3,000	3,000	600	3,000	3,000
Number of motors	6	6	6	4	12	6-Twin
Mechanical transmission	Flex. Gear	Flex. Gear	Twin Gear Flex.	Twin Gear	Gearless	Geared Quill
Gear ratio	16:83	15:63	18:90	24:78		
Motor ventilation	Forced	Forced		Forced	Forced	Forced
Wheel arrangement	0-6-6-0	0-6-6-0	0-4-4-4-0	0-4-4-0	2-4-8-8-4-2	4-6-2-2-6-4
Drive wheel diameter	40 in.	42 in.	46 in.	50 in.	44 in.	68 in.
Rigid wheel base	14 ft. 0 in.	13 ft. 9 in.	9 ft. 2 in.	9 ft. 6 in.	13 ft. 9 in.	16 ft. 9 in.
Length inside knuckles	50 ft. 2 in.	49 ft. 9 in.	52 ft. 11 in.	39 ft. 6 in.	76 ft. 0 in.	88 ft. 7 in.
Total weight (1000 lb.)	234.3	230.0	309.0	240.0	521.2	600
Weight per driving axle (1000 lb.)	39.05	38.3	51.2	60.0	38.15	63
Adhesive weight (1000 lb.)	234	230.0	309.0	240.0	457.8	378
T.E. (1 hr. rating)	32,400	31,400	54,000	25,000	48,500	78,000
T.E. (continuous)	21,600	24,400	48,500	12,800	42,250	48,100
Speed in m.p.h. (1 hr. rating)	20.8	21.8	19.0	16.4	27.1	22.6
Speed in m.p.h. (continuous rating)	23.4	23	19.5	19.6	28.4	26.4
1 hour hp	1,800	1,800	2,736	1,100	3,500	4,680
Continuous hp	1,350	1,500	2,520	670	3,200	3,400
1 hour hp. per ton	15.4	15.6	17.7	9.2	13.5	15.6
1 hour T.E. per ton	277	273	350	208	186	260

Table XL.—Data on Recent Electrical Locomotives. *(Continued)*

Road	New York Central	Detroit & Ironton	New York, New Haven & Hartford	Norfolk & Western	Pennsylvania	Virginian
Electric system	D.C.	A.C.	A.C.	A.C.	A.C.	A.C.
Service	Passenger	Freight	Passenger	Freight	Freight	Freight
Built or building	1914–1918	1924	1923	1924	1917	1924–1925
Contact line voltage	600	11,000 / 22,000	11,000 / 600	11,000	11,000	11,000
Number of motors	8	one Trans. 8 (series D.C.)	6-twin	2	4	2
Mechanical transmission	Gearless	Twin Gear flex.	Geared Quill	Flex. Gear-Jackshaft side rod	Gear-Jackshaft side rod	Flex. Gear-Jackshaft side rod
Gear ratio				21:100	21:106	20:100
Motor ventilation	Forced			Forced	Forced	Forced
Wheel arrangement	0-4-4-4-4-0	2-6-6-2	2-6-2-2-6-2	2-4-4-2	2-6-6-2	2-4-4-2
Drive wheel diameter	36 in.	42 in.	63	63	72	62
Rigid wheel base	5 ft. 0 in.	11 ft. 0 in.	14 ft. 3 in.	16 ft. 6 in.	13 ft. 4 in.	16 ft. 6 in.
Length inside knuckles	56 ft. 10 in.	58 ft. 6 in.	66 ft. 10 in.	48 ft. 7 in.	76 ft. 6 in.	50 ft. 9 in.
Total weight (1000 lb.)	267.5	340	358.0	414.0	516.0	430.0
Weight per driving axle (1000 lb.)	33.43	42.5	40.0	74.5	73.3	78.0
Adhesive weight (1000 lb.)	267.5	340	240	298.0	439.5	312.0
T.E. (1 hr. rating)	20,000	47,000	19,100	54,000 / 31,500	88,000	56,600 / 33,000
T.E. (continuous)	14,000	40,000	13,100	45,000 / 26,300	73,000	47,300 / 27,600
Speed in m.p.h. (1 hr. rating)	49.0	16.0	48.0	14.1 / 28.3	20.4	13.4 / 27.0
Speed in m.p.h. (continuous rating)	53.5	17.0	58.8	14.2 / 28.4	20.5	13.5 / 27.1
1 hour hp	2,600	2,000	2,508	2,030 / 2,375	4,800	2,030 / 2,375
Continuous hp	2,000	1,750	2,052	1,700 / 2,000	4,000	1,700 / 2,000
1 hour hp. per ton	19.4	11.8	14.0	11.5	18.8	11.1
1 hour T.E. per ton	150	277	107	260	341	263

section of the locomotive contains a single large motor which is mounted in the cab and has a maximum rating of 2,000 hp. at 600 volts. At starting, the current input to the locomotives sometimes reaches 7,000 amp. The motors are of the field-control type and have four efficient running speeds:

1. Series connection with full field.
2. Series connection with normal field.
3. Parallel connection with full field.
4. Parallel connection with normal field.

Fig. 224.—Pennsylvania R. R. locomotive.

The characteristic curves of this locomotive are given in Fig. 225.

The Butte, Anaconda & Pacific locomotive, whose characteristic curves are given in Fig. 227, is a freight locomotive and was built for operation in connection with a 2,400-volt, direct-current trolley line. It is equipped with four commutating-pole motors. The motors are wound for 1,200 volts and insulated for 2,400 volts, and are operated with two motors permanently connected in series (for detailed data, see Table XL).

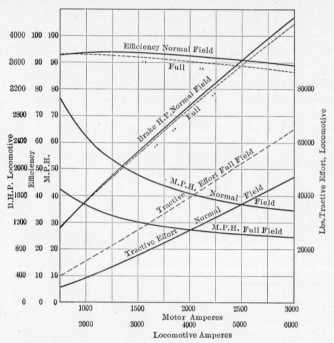

Fig. 225.—Characteristic curves, Pennsylvania locomotive.

Fig. 226.—Direct-current freight locomotive. (*General Electric Company.*)

The locomotive illustrated in Fig. 228 is a typical interurban freight locomotive (for detailed data, see Table XL).

Split-phase Locomotive.—This type of locomotive is equipped with polyphase motors which receive their energy supply through a phase converter from a single-phase contact line. Figure 229 illustrates the phase converter which has been developed by the Westinghouse Electric & Manufacturing Co. Essentially,

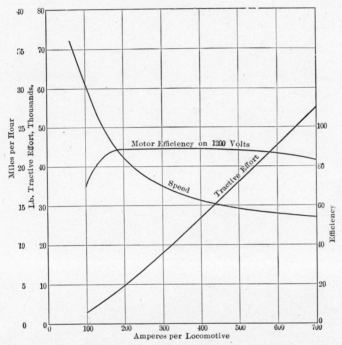

FIG. 227.—Characteristic curves, Butte, Anaconda & Pacific locomotive.

it consists of a high-speed, single-phase synchronous motor on the stator of which is placed a second winding in electrical space quadrature with the main winding. This second winding has 87 per cent as many turns as the main winding. One end of this winding is connected to the midpoint of the secondary winding of the locomotive transformer. The outer secondary terminals and the remaining terminal of the second stator winding form the three-phase terminals to which the motors are connected. This connection of windings is similar to the well-known Scott two-phase to three-phase system of transformer connections, the quadrature voltage required being furnished by the second winding of the phase converter. The small motor

Fig. 228.—Interurban locomotive. (*General Electric Company*).

Fig. 229.—Synchronous phase converter with single-phase starting motor and direct-current exciter. (Norfolk and Western and Virginian electric locomotive.)

which is direct connected to the phase converter is a series single-phase motor and is used in starting the phase converter.

The earlier form of phase converter was of the induction type. The chief objection to this type of converter is that its power factor is inherently lower than that of the synchronous type and that it does not permit of power factor adjustment as does the latter type. A view of the type of locomotive on which this converter is used is afforded in Fig. 230, while the characteristic curves of a typical locomotive are indicated in Fig. 231.

Motor-generator Locomotive.—The most recent type of locomotive is that developed for Henry Ford's Detroit, Toledo & Ironton R. R. (Fig. 232). This locomotive is equipped with direct-current series motors which receive their energy supply from a motor generator located in the cab of each locomotive unit. The trolley voltage is 22,000 volts, single-phase, 25-cycle, alternating current and the motor side of the motor-generator

Fig. 230.—Norfolk and Western locomotive descending a heavy grade.

set is a single-phase synchronous motor. A transformer changes the trolley voltage of 22,000 volts to 1,250 volts for the motor. The motor rating is 2,100 hp., 25 cycles, four pole, and the generator rating is 1,500 kw., 600 volts, 2,500 amp.

The traction motors are rated at 225 hp., 600 volts. They are geared to the driver shaft with a 22–98 gear ratio. The motors are controlled for adjusting the field strength of the generator and are also arranged for regenerative braking. This method of control is very flexible from the standpoint of speed adjustment permitting with these locomotives 45 different running speeds between standstill and maximum speed. This type of control, eliminating as it does all series-rheostat losses, is highly efficient.

A double-unit locomotive of this type, such as is shown, weighs 340 tons.   It can develop 5,000 hp. at 17 m.p.h. and at starting exert a tractive effort of 225,000 lb.   It can deliver 3,600 hp.

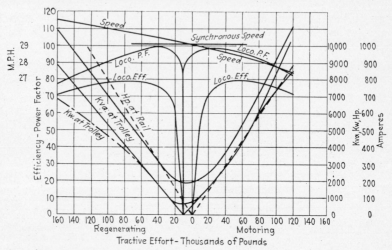

FIG. 231.—Characteristic curves of an induction-motor locomotive.

FIG. 232.—Westinghouse motor-generator locomotive. (*Detroit, Toledo and Ironton Railroad.*)

continuously, the corresponding speed and tractive effort being 25 m.p.h. and 54,000 lb., respectively.

Motor-generator locomotives of somewhat different type have been constructed recently by the General Electric Company for the New York, New Haven & Hartford R. R.

Combining economical transmission and distribution with a motor of high economy, both in energy and weight, and possessing great flexibility in speed control, the development of the motor-generator locomotive seems to mark the beginning of a new period in electric-locomotive design.

Design Requirements.—The electric locomotive is not an absolutely interchangeable machine, but, like the motor car, it gives the most satisfactory results when designed for the particular service in which it is to be used. Briefly stated, some of the more important requirements for a given service are:

1. Ample motor and mechanical transmission capacity.
2. High factor of safety of mechanical parts.
3. Economy in operation.
4. Safety and reliability in operation.
5. Accessibility for inspection and repairs.
6. Adequate control system.
7. Locomotive non-destructive to the track structures.

Some of the factors which are affected by the preceding requirements will now be considered.

Motor Mountings and Transmissions.—In the early locomotives it was believed to be necessary to mount the motors on the driving axles between drivers, as in motor cars, with the consequent limitation in capacity of motors on account of gage of track and short wheel base. The change of track gage was, of course, practically impossible with the present installation of standard-gage roads in the country, and an increase in the length of wheel base introduced difficulties in rounding curves. In fact, any limitation upon the flexibility of the truck and the free and independent vertical and transverse movement of individual axles with irregularities in the track tends to move the entire mass of the locomotive, thus introducing bad riding qualities and vibrations which become dangerous at high speeds. An attempt was first made, therefore, to vary the design of the large interurban motors to gain greater capacity upon the limited size of trucks and later to remove the motor from the truck axles, as will be shown hereinafter.

After some few years of experience with the operation of the earlier locomotives and a careful study of their characteristics as compared with steam locomotives, the principal problem in design seemed to be resolved to that of the transmission between

motor axle and driving wheels. Storer and Eaton, in a paper
before the A. I. E. E.,[1] have presented this problem in a very
concise form, and because of its importance in electric-locomotive
design, and as designing engineers in both this country and abroad
are at variance regarding the best method of transmission to
adopt, a statement of the various types in use, taken from the
above paper together with illustrations of each, is herein included.

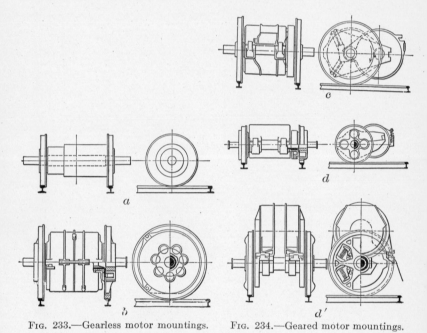

FIG. 233.—Gearless motor mountings.   FIG. 234.—Geared motor mountings.

(a) Gearless motor with armature pressed onto driving axle. "New
York Central" (Fig. 233a).

(b) Gearless motor with armature carried on a quill surrounding axle,
and driving the wheels through flexible connections. "New Haven
Passenger" (Fig. 233b).

(c) Geared motor with bearings directly on axle and with nose
supported on spring-borne parts of locomotive. "St. Clair Tunnel"
(Fig. 234c).

(d) Geared motor with bearings on a quill surrounding axle, and (1)
nose supported on spring-borne parts of machine. "New Haven Car"

[1] STORER, N. W. and EATON, G. M., "The Design of the Electric Locomotive," *Trans.* A. I. E. E., vol. 29.

(Fig. 234*d*), and (2) motor rigidly bolted to spring-borne parts of machines, the quill having sufficient clearance for axle movements. "Four-motor New Haven Freight" (Fig. 234*d'*).

(*e*) Motor mounted rigidly on spring-borne parts, armature rotating at same rate as drivers, power transmitted to drivers through cranks,

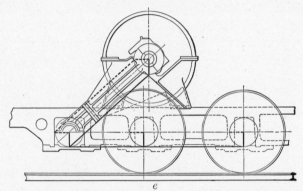

Fig. 235.—Motor mounting on Pennsylvania locomotive.

connecting rods and counter-shaft on level with driver axles. "Pennsylvania" (Fig. 235).

(*f*) Motor mounting and transmission as in (*e*) but motor fitted with double bearings one part for centering motor crank axle and the other for centering the armature quill which surrounds and is flexibly connected to

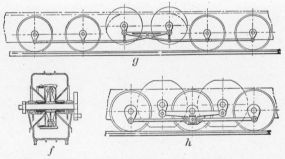

Fig. 236.—New York, New Haven and Hartford and foreign motor mountings.

the motor crank axle. "Two-motor New Haven Freight," (Fig. 236*f*).

(*g*) Motors mounted on spring-borne parts, armature rotating at same rate as drivers, power transmitted to drivers through offset connecting rods and side rods. "Latest Simplon Locomotives " (Fig. 236*g*).

(*h*) Motors mounted on spring-borne parts, armature rotating at same rate on drivers, power transmitted to drivers through Scotch yokes and side rods. "Valtellina Locomotives" (Fig. 236*h*).

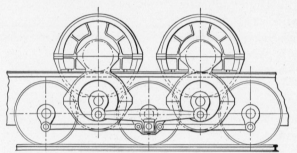

FIG. 237.—Mounting with both gears and connecting rods.

(*i*) Motors mounted rigidly on spring-borne parts, power transmitted through gears to counter-shaft, thence to drivers through Scotch yokes and side rods (Fig. 237).

FIG. 238.—Arrangement of transmission. Norfolk and Western locomotive.

It will be seen from the preceding that the locomotives of the Pennsylvania R. R. were a rather radical departure from the other designs previously described, having their motors above the trucks in the cab and returning to the connecting rods of the steam locomotives for transmission to the drivers. This design raises the center of gravity and permits practically unlimited motor capacity in a single unit, as its dimensions may be increased longitudinally at will and transversely by overhanging the driving wheels.

The gearing of the combined gear and side-rod drive used on the Norfolk & Western locomotives is illustrated in Fig. 238. This design has been developed to a satisfactory point and is now being used on the latest locomotives purchased by the same company and also on the new locomotives of the Virginian Rys.

In general, it may be said that gears offer a very satisfactory transmission for a low-speed locomotive, such as is used in freight and switching service, but they do not seem to be able to stand up under the heavy impact strains which accompany high-speed operation. On the other hand, slow-speed gearless motors are excessively large and heavy, because the peripheral speed of the armature is below the most economical value. Motors are, therefore, best adapted for high-speed operation.

Within recent years there has been a marked tendency toward the use of flexible gears where the geared drive is adopted. In these gears the rim of the gear is connected to the center through heavy springs. This arrangement greatly minimizes the impact strains on the gear teeth.

Locomotive Weights.—The locomotive weights used in various classes of electric-railway service have been indicated in Chap. XI. The weights and dimensions of interurban locomotives are usually limited by roadway conditions, such as strength of bridges, weight of rail, spacing of ties, overhead and side clearances, and by the maximum peak loads allowed on the power-distribution system and power plant. It is feasible to build locomotives for heavy traction service in very large sizes, but it is not necessary to do so, as the multiple-unit control system permits any desired number of locomotives to be operated as a single unit. Besides, small units may be more readily shopped, and while in the shop do not tie up as much capital as do the larger units.

A study of Tables XXXVIII and XXXIX indicates that the weight per driving axle varies considerably in the different designs. Axle loads up to 72,000 lb. have been used in steam-locomotive practice, but such loads make roadway maintenance very costly. In well-designed heavy electric locomotives the driving-axle loads usually range between 35,000 and 65,000 lb. The weight on drivers must be sufficient that the adhesion of the locomotive will permit the motors to be worked up to their overload rating, yet must not be so great that the motors will be dangerously overloaded before the drivers slip.

Drive Wheels.—Drive-wheel diameters vary from 33 to 72 in. Small drive wheels cannot be used with gearless motors, because they limit the diameter and, therefore, the capacity of the motor armatures. Other considerations which tend to fix the minimum size of the drive wheels have been given in Chap. XI. Considerations of motor, transmission, and frame design fix the maximum limits of drive-wheel diameter.

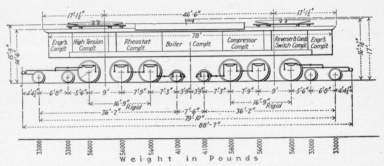

FIG. 239.—Diagram showing equalization plan and weight distribution of a Westinghouse locomotive. (*Chicago, Milwaukee & St. Paul R. R.*)

Drive wheels for large locomotives are usually constructed with a steel tire shrunk on a cast-steel core. Either solid rolled-steel or cast-iron wheels with chilled treads are used on the smaller locomotives. The treads are usually made to conform to the specifications of either the Master Car Builders' Association or the A. E. R. A.

Trucks.—The length of the rigid wheel base of a truck is limited by the sharpest track curve which must be negotiated by the locomotive. Many different truck designs are in use. A modified form of the Motor Car Builders' type is much used for small locomotives. Trucks for heavy locomotives are usually articulated or hinged in order to prevent "rearing up" of the ends of the trucks when the motors are exerting large tractive efforts. Since the trucks transmit the entire tractive effort of the locomotive, they must be heavy and strong. As has already been intimated, the design of the main trucks is usually dependent to a greater or less extent on the type of motor mounting used. For speeds above 40 m.p.h., or for operation over track which has many sharp curves, pony or guiding trucks are usually necessary. These trucks must carry sufficient weight in order that they may properly perform their functions.

Cab Underframing.—The cab underframing is a vital part of the locomotive. In most cases it transmits the tractive force developed by the motors to the drawbar and supports the cab and a great part of the locomotive equipment. It must be strong enough to withstand enormous bumping strains and shocks. For heavy service, the frames are often designed to withstand bumping forces equivalent to a static load of 500,000 lb. In general, the underframing is similar to that used in steam locomotive tender construction. Heavy channel or I-beams are used for the longitudinal members or sills. These are riveted to heavy cast-steel end sills. The body bolsters and steel sheet floor are also riveted to the sills, thus making an exceedingly strong platform construction. Since standard structural shapes may be used, this form of construction is very economical. Some engineers advocate the use of frames built up of plate metal as they are a little more flexible in the vertical plane and permit a little better equalization of the load on the drive wheels. Such frames are much used abroad, but have not been used to any considerable extent in this country.

Cabs.—Cabs may be either of the box or steeple type. For heavy-road locomotives the box-type cab is commonly used. Control positions are located at each end. The air compressor, blower for motor, ventilating system, switch groups, and other auxiliary apparatus are conveniently located on the cab floor.

Cabs are built of either wood or steel. The latter is preferable, but is more expensive. For service in cold climates, steel cabs should be lined with wood or some heat-insulating composition, and both steel and wood cabs should be provided with heaters. Locomotives designed for passenger service sometimes carry an oil-fired steam boiler in the cab for heating the cars.

Interurban and switching locomotives are often equipped with steeple-type cabs. In these cabs the auxiliary apparatus is

placed under the steel hoods at either end.　On switcher locomotives only one control position need be installed.

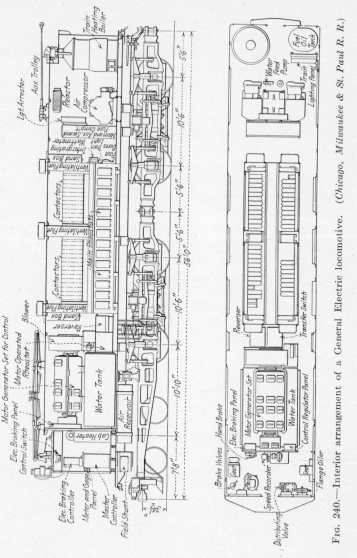

Fig. 240.—Interior arrangement of a General Electric locomotive.　(Chicago, Milwaukee & St. Paul R. R.)

In general, the cab should be well lighted, have convenient
doors and lookout windows, and be so constructed that the cab
itself can be removed with a minimum derangement of apparatus.

Riding Qualities.—Not only must a locomotive be able to start a train and have sufficient power to haul it at the required speed, but it must perform these duties with the maximum safety and the minimum destruction of roadway. Track hammering and "nosing" of the locomotive are the principal causes of track destruction and resulting wrecks. Heavy dead weights (non-spring-borne weights) and unbalanced rotating parts cause hammer blows to be delivered to the rail head. The excessive vibration which occurs when an improperly designed locomotive is operated at high speed is also very destructive to the roadway. Nosing, or the swinging back and forth of a locomotive in a direction transverse to the track, tends to loosen the spikes and overturn the rails, either by the direct pressure of the wheel flange against the rail head or by impact blows. While it is impossible to eliminate nosing entirely, various results may be prevented by the following means:

1. The use of pilot trucks. Pilot trucks tend to guide the locomotive around curves and prevent transverse movements of the ends of the locomotive. The lateral thrust of the wheels against the rails acts as a guiding force, which has for its lever arm the horizontal distance from the center of gravity of the locomotive to the effective turning center of the pilot truck.

2. Restraining the transverse movements by means of springs. Oscillations around the vertical center-of-gravity axis are thus dampened and impact blows on the side of the rail heads prevented.

3. Permitting a certain amount of vertical and transverse movements of the individual axles. Movements imparted to the individual axles by uneven track or small obstacles will be taken up by axles themselves and not imparted to the entire mass of the locomotive.

4. Massing the bulk of the weight as near the center of gravity of the locomotive as possible. When this is done, only a small guiding force will be necessary to keep the locomotive body in its proper position relative to the track, and transverse oscillations are easier to dampen out. The excessive nosing often noticed when single-truck cars and switcher locomotives are operated at fairly high speeds is largely due to the large amount of overhanging weight.

5. Keeping the center of gravity high. The distance from the point of restraint to the center of gravity is thus increased, thereby decreasing the movement which tends to cause oscillations about the center of gravity.

The first passenger locomotives built for both the New York Central & Hudson River R. R. and the New York, New Haven & Hartford R. R. gave much trouble on account of their serious nosing. The riding qualities of both types were greatly improved by the use of pilot trucks. Locomotive builders, profiting by the experience gained in the operation of these locomotives, are now building locomotives which have very excellent riding qualities.

Costs.—Since most of the locomotives now in service were at first more or less experimental and had large development charges included in their first costs, authentic information regarding locomotive costs is difficult to obtain. Cost data that have been published from time to time indicate that at present the first costs range from 25 to 40 cts. per pound. Locomotive maintenance and repair costs largely depend on the nature of the service in which the locomotive is operated. A study of Interstate Commerce Commission reports and other published data indicates that these costs range from 3 to 12 cts. per locomotive-mile, with an average value of about 5 cts.

Although some arguments in favor of the electric locomotive as compared with its steam rival will be considered in a later chapter, it may be said in the conclusion of this discussion that the electric locomotive has accomplished thus far all that has been required of it, i.e., to operate as satisfactorily as the steam locomotive under all conditions of service and to eliminate the disadvantages coincident with the smoke and dirt of the latter. It has also shown itself capable of accelerating more rapidly than its competitor, which particularly commends it where headway is short and stops are frequent. It can readily be designed for a drawbar pull far in excess of that of the largest steam locomotives. It has, therefore, found a permanent place in the electrification of terminals. Its future now seems to be one of further adaptation and adoption, although its depreciation and maintenance in comparison with the steam locomotive can hardly be intelligently compared at present.

CHAPTER XXVIII

ELECTRIFICATION SYSTEMS

The problem to be discussed under the above caption is one that has received much attention during the past few years by steam- and electric-railroads officials, consulting engineers, and electrical manufacturing companies. It has been the target of much discussion before technical societies and in the technical press, at times involving rather heated criticisms based upon both accurate engineering data and the enthusiastic prophecies of more or less prejudiced engineers. To sift out the salient factors in the case and outline the present status of the problem in a few words becomes, therefore, a difficult task.

Electric Systems.—The systems which have sufficient advantages and for which complete power-station, distribution, and rolling-stock equipment have been sufficiently developed to warrant consideration in this problem are the following:

1. Direct-current system.
2. Single-phase, alternating-current system.
3. Three-phase, alternating-current system.
4. Combined systems.

The preceding systems of electrification, classified either as to kind of motors or as to kind of contact line used, are:

1. Direct current.
2. Single-phase alternating current.
3. Three-phase alternating current.

Most of the component parts of the above systems have been described in previous chapters. For convenience, however, in the study of this chapter a brief description of each system is here given.

Direct-current System.—This system was the first one developed. It is used on practically all city lines, most interurban lines, and on a large percentage of the trunk-line electrifications in this country. The contact-line voltages range from 500 to 3,000 volts. The contact line, which may be either an overhead trolley or a third rail, and its feeders receive energy from substations located along the line. The motor cars and locomotives are equipped with direct-current series motors.

Single-phase System.—Either series or modified-repulsion, commutator-type, single-phase motors are used. Contact-line voltages range from 3,300 to 25,000 volts. The contact line receives energy from transformer substations located along the line. This system has been used only in interurban and trunk-line service, the high contact-line voltages being considered too dangerous for operation on city streets.

Three-phase System.—The locomotives are equipped with three-phase induction motors. Two overhead contact lines are used, the track rails forming the third conductor of the three-phase circuit. Transformers on the locomotive are used to lower the contact-line voltage to a value suitable for the motors where high contact-line voltages are used, although for voltages up to 3,000 the transformers are often dispensed with. The contact lines receive their energy supply from transformer substations, as in the single-phase system. While the great majority of railways now using electric motive power use either the direct-current or the single-phase systems, three phase locomotives with an aggregate rating of approximately 600,000 hp. are in use at the present time, chiefly on the mountain-grade railways of Italy.

Combined Systems.—Several combined systems have been proposed. The most important of these are the split-phase and motor-generator systems. In both of these systems a single-phase contact line is used, so that the distribution system is identical with that of the single-phase system.

The locomotives in the split-phase system are equipped with three-phase motors and a phase converter for converting the single-phase energy received from the contact line to the three-phase energy required by the motors.

This system, which is a recent development, has been adopted by the Norfolk & Western Ry. and the Virginian Rys. in their mountain-grade electrifications.

The motor-generator system is being used on the Detroit, Toledo & Ironton R. R., a portion of which is now being electrified. It is fundamentally a type of locomotive rather than a separate system of electrification. The same thing is largely true of the split-phase system.

Comparison of Systems.—The various systems will now be compared upon as nearly the same basis as possible. The peculiarities of each system, which may result in advantages or disadvantages depending upon local conditions in each installation, will be discussed in connection with the several determining and distinctive functions of the complete railway system.

Power Station.—The present tendency is all in the direction of purchased power rather than the operation of power houses by the railway companies themselves. Experience has demonstrated that, by reason of better load factor and larger power units, the power companies can sell power to the electric railways at a lower rate than the railway companies can generate it in power houses of their own. Of course, this power is all generated in three-phase machinery. Where the railway requires a different number of phases or a different frequency, suitable conversion apparatus is necessary. This apparatus may be owned and operated by either the power company or the railway company. The power station itself has, therefore, ceased to be a matter of pertinent interest to the railway engineer.

Transmission Lines.—No material difference exists between the systems in regard to transmission, so long as three-phase transmission is adopted. The costs of these lines for all systems are, therefore, practically identical. In the comparatively few installations where single-phase transmission might be adopted, the design and the construction of the line are simplified by the use of two wires in place of three, but for a given power transmitted and a fixed efficiency of transmission the cost of copper in the three-phase system is 25 per cent less.

Substation.—One of the most marked variations in the systems is found in the design of the substation. As explained in the previous chapter, the direct-current system requires the installation of transformers, synchronous converters, or motor generators and switchboards in the substation, whereas the alternating-current systems call for the transformers and automatic-control switches only. This greatly reduces the first cost and maintenance in the latter systems. The elimination of this converting equipment will be found, from the tables listed on page 451, to lower the first cost of a single-phase substation to 27 and 37.5 per cent of the 600- and 1,200-volt substations, respectively, while the operating costs are reduced, respectively, to 26.2 and 58.2 per cent of the direct-current substations. This is not clear gain on the part of the single-phase system, however, as it is partially balanced by the cost of rolling stock in the latter system.

In the relatively few instances in which the increase in distribution voltage in the single-phase system is sufficient to permit the economical transmission for the entire length of the line at trolley potential, the substation cost and maintenance is not only entirely eliminated, but the step-up transformers at the power station may usually be eliminated as well and the switchboard considerably simplified in consequence.

The first cost of the 1,200-volt, direct-current substation is but 73 per cent of the 600-volt station because of the lower current value necessary for the same output, thereby reducing the size and cost of converters, cables, and switchboard.

While the comparisons here made are based on the equipment of an interurban railway, the percentages given may be considered as approximately representative of the values which would obtain for heavier service where proportionately higher voltages would be used.

The substation cost per mile of track is somewhat higher for the three-phase system than for those systems using a single-phase contact line, for reasons which will be discussed in the next article.

Distribution System.—As would naturally be expected, the first cost of the distribution system decreases with increase of contact-line voltages, thereby favoring those systems in which high contact-line voltages are used, especially where the traffic is heavy.

Commutation and insulation difficulties limit the voltage which may be used across motor terminals and, therefore, the contact-line voltage in the direct-current system. Since the contact-line voltages are necessarily low with this system, the distribution system is required to handle large currents, and in order that these large currents may be handled without excessive voltage drop, auxiliary lines or feeders are required. These lines complicate the overhead work and greatly increase the cost of the distribution system. Stray currents from the track return circuit may cause electrolysis troubles which are difficult and costly to mitigate.

High contact-line voltages are easily obtained and readily utilized in the systems employing a single-phase contact line. The overhead line construction is extremely simple, as feeders are usually not required. The transmission system and even the transformer substations may be omitted if the road is comparatively short and the traffic is not too heavy. The distribution system efficiency is higher than with any of the other systems. Murray[1] gives 97 per cent as the efficiency of the distribution system of the New York, New Haven & Hartford R. R. The operation of a single-phase circuit, one side of which is a grounded track rail, produces serious inductive disturbances in paralleling telephone and telegraph lines. These disturbances are usually even more difficult and costly to mitigate than the electrolysis troubles caused by the direct-current system. The impedance drop in the track rail becomes practically prohibitive if frequencies higher than 25 cycles are used. This objection to the use of the higher frequencies is very important, particularly where the railway company desires to purchase electrical energy from a commercial power company, since the generating equipment for commercial power and lighting purposes is becoming pretty well standardized at 60 cycles.

The complicated overhead work necessary in the three-phase system constitutes a very important objection to that system. The difficulty of adequately insulating the complicated overhead structures limits the contact-line voltage which may be used to a comparatively low value. Consequently, the number of substations, and, therefore, the substation cost per mile of track, are higher than for a single-phase contact line, although still much lower than for the direct-current system. Practically all of the objections which apply to the single-phase system also apply to this system. As a result, American engineers have not given it very much consideration.

Of the two most practical systems of distribution, direct current and single-phase alternating current, the single-phase alternating-current system permits the greatest interchangeability of rolling stock. This feature of interchangeability will be discussed further in connection with the article on rolling stock.

Motors.—With the equipment of rolling stock, the pendulum of efficiency, first cost, and possibly of maintenance, swings in

[1] *Trans.* A. I. E. E., vol. 31, p. 154.

the other direction, favoring those systems using direct-current motors.

Single-phase motors in their present stage of development are generally believed to be slightly inferior to the direct-current motor in efficiency and quick accelerating qualities for a given rating. They are also considerably heavier for a given output, thus increasing the weight of car to be accelerated for a given traffic return. The above are general conclusions which will probably be conceded by both factions that have entered the rather extended controversy regarding the relative advantages and disadvantages of the single-phase motor for traction purposes. That this question if far from being decided is illustrated, however, in the following discussions of the subject before the A. I. E. E., which have been quoted herein for the double purpose of pointing out the unsettled condition of single-phase motor development as well as illustrating the various details of design under question.

Sprague points out the following differences between the single-phase and direct-current motors:[1]

1. The input of current in one is continuous, in the other intermittent.

2. One has a single frame, the electrical and mechanical parts being integral; the other has a laminated frame contained within an independent casing. Hence there is not equal rigidity, or equal use of metal.

3. One has exposed and hence freely ventilated field coils; the other has field coils embedded in the field magnets.

4. One has a large polar clearance, and consequently ample bearing wear; the other has an armature clearance of about only one-third as much, and hence limited bearing wear.

5. One is operated with a high magnetic flux, and consequently high torque for given armature conductor current; the other has a weak field, and consequent lower armature torque.

6. One has a moderate sized armature and commutator, and runs at a moderate speed; the other, with equal capacity, has a much larger diameter of armature and commutator, and runs at a much higher speed.

7. One permits of a low gear reduction, and consequently a large gear pitch; the other requires a higher gear reduction, and a weaker gear pitch.

[1] SPRAGUE, FRANK J., "Some Facts and Problems Bearing on Trunk Line Operation," *Trans.* A. I. E. E., vol. 26.

8. The windings of one are subject to electrical strains of one character; in those of the other the strains are of rapidly variable and alternating character.

9. The mean torque of one is the corresponding maximum; the mean torque of the other is only about two-thirds of the maximum.

10. The torque of one is of continuous character; that of the other is variable and pulsating, and changes from nothing to the maximum fifty times a second.

11. One has two or four main poles only, two paths only in the armature, and two fixed sets of brushes; the other has four to fourteen poles, as many paths in the armature, leading to unbalancing, and as many movable sets of commutator brushes.

12. One can maintain a high torque for a considerable time while standing still; the other is apt to burn out the coils, which are short circuited under the brushes.

13. In one, all armature coil connections are made directly to the commutator; in the other, on the larger sizes resistances are introduced between the coils and every bar of the commutator, some of which are always in circuit, and the remainder always present.

14. In one the sustained capacity for a given weight is within the reasonable requirements of construction; in the other it is only about half as much.

15. Finally, the gearless type, with armature and field varying relatively to each other, is available for one, but this construction is denied to the other.

Consideration, then, of the characteristics peculiar to each class of motor indicates not that the single-phase motor cannot be used, but that if adopted the weight or number, and the cost of locomotives or motors required to do the work must be much greater; that the depreciation of that which is in motion will be much higher; and that there will always be an excess weight of fixed amount per unit which must be carried irrespective of the trailing or effective loads. We must, therefore, in many cases be led to the selection of the direct current motor, that motor which has the higher weight capacity, the greater endurance, and the lower cost per unit of power.

In discussing this paper, Storer criticizes each point in turn as quoted below:[1]

1. "The input of current in one is continuous, in the other, intermittent." Quite true, but the drawbar pull is quite as effective in one case as in the other.

2. The direct current motor has a solid frame like the single-phase motor. It has, further, two or more laminated poles bolted in, and if

[1] STORER, N. W., discussion of above paper, *Trans.* A. I. E. E., vol. 26.

the interpole construction is used has as many more relatively small and delicate poles. The alternating current motor as built by the company with which I am connected has, in all sizes up to a diameter of 38 in., field punchings made in a single piece and built up and keyed in the frame, making it as solid a construction as an armature on its spider. The claim for less rigidity in the single-phase motor is, therefore, not sustained.

3. "One has exposed and hence freely ventilated field coils; the other has field coils embedded in the field magnets." It is known to most motor designers that coils in contact with iron will dissipate heat much faster than when in the open air. This is especially true of coils in an enclosed motor. I have repeatedly noticed that motor field coils which have been removed on account of roasting have shown the insulation in contact with the pole pieces to be in good condition, while other sides were badly roasted. I know, therefore, that, in respect to ventilation of field coils, the single-phase motor is superior to the direct current motor. Smaller cross section of coils also allows the heat to be radiated better in single-phase motors, and the fact that a large part of the loss in the motor is concentrated in the field iron will enable the motor to dissipate a much larger amount of heat for a given temperature rise than will a direct current motor.

4. Concerning "polar clearances." Many thousands of direct current motors are to-day in operation with a clearance of $\frac{1}{8}$ to $\frac{3}{16}$ in. between poles and armatures, and in practically all cases where more than $\frac{3}{16}$ in. clearance is used it is for electrical reasons. Further, while the smaller air gap used for single-phase motors was at first much feared, the fears have proved to be without foundation and the present clearances of from 0.1 to 0.15 in. have proved to be ample and fully as good as 0.15 to 0.25 in. in direct current motors, because there is no unbalanced magnetic pull.

5. Concerning "torque." The torque of an armature is the pull it will exert at 1-ft. radius. Therefore, it makes no difference in the result whether it is obtained with large flux and few armature conductors, or *vice versa*.

6. "A much larger diameter of armature and commutator, runs at a much higher speed." This is a very general statement; what are the facts? The armature diameters ordinarily run from 5 to 15 per cent larger than for direct current motors of corresponding output. It is undoubtedly true that the armature speeds of the earlier single-phase motors were much higher than the speeds of corresponding direct-current motors; at the present time, however, the speed at the nominal rating of the motor is practically the same as that of direct current motors, and the maximum operating armature speeds are within the safe limits set for direct current motors.

7. Concerning "gear reduction and gear pitch." The gear reduction depends, of course, upon the speed; and as far as gear pitch is concerned, I wish to say that the same gear pitch is used for single-phase motors as for direct current motors of the same capacity.

8. "The windings of one are subject to electrical strains of one character; in those of the other the strains are of rapidly variable and alternating character." No conclusion is drawn from this. It may be of interest to know that there have been a number of instances where the single-phase motor has broken down in service on a direct current section of the line, necessitating cutting it out of the circuit; but when the car reached the alternating current section of the line it has been again connected in circuit and operated satisfactorily, thus indicating that the electrical strains with alternating current are less severe than with direct current.

9 and 10. Concerning the "variable torque of the single-phase motor." No comment is made as to the relative merits of uniform or pulsating torque. In a recent discussion before the Institute, Mr. Porter called attention to certain characteristics of the torque exerted by an alternating current motor, especially when it reaches the slipping point of the wheels. It was stated that there is an apparent advantage in the pulsating torque, because, when the motor starts to slip it does not immediately decrease its mean torque, as is done in the case of the direct current motor, but slips in a series of jerks, apparently regaining the hold on the rail at every pulsation.

11. Concerning the "number of poles." The paper states that the direct current motor has "two or four main poles only." No direct current motors built in the last 15 years except those on the New York Central locomotives have less than four poles. The paper states that the alternating current motor has "eight to fourteen poles." The single-phase motors built by the company with which I am connected have four poles for all sizes up to and including 125 hp. The largest single-phase motor thus far built has a capacity of 500 hp. It has but 12 poles.

12. Concerning "a high torque while standing still." As we understand the matter, railway motors are designed to move a train rather than to hold it at rest. At the same time we know that the single-phase motor is amply protected against mistakes of motormen in leaving the current on the motor for a half-minute or so with brakes set.

13. Concerning "resistance in commutator leads." It is well known that the resistance leads used in single-phase armatures are for the purpose of reducing to a minimum the loss due to the transformer action in the short circuited coil. Their presence is fully justified and the efficiency is higher than it would be if they were not used.

14. This refers to relative weights concerning which I shall have something to say farther on.

15. On this point I agree absolutely with the author. There is one type of construction to which the single-phase motor is not adapted. This is so far employed in only a single case.

Per cent of full load torque	Direct current 90 hp. motor	Alternating current, 25 cycle, 100 hp. motor	Direct current 200 hp. motor	Alternating current, 15 cycle, 200 hp. motor
125	86.25	82.0	88.8	87.3
100	86.8	85.0	89.0	88.0
80	87.0	86.0	89.2	88.3
60	86.5	86.8	88.8	87.7
40	85.0	86.0	87.0	85.0
25	82.0	82.5	84.0	82.0

More or less is said in the paper concerning the lower efficiency of the single-phase motor, and inference might be drawn that it is about 10 per cent lower than that of the corresponding direct current motor. Just to show what modern motors are capable of doing, I give above in parallel columns the efficiencies of corresponding sizes of direct and alternating current motors at different percentages of their full load torque.

Referring to the 1,200-volt, direct-current system for interurban service, the motors are similar to the 600-volt type which has been well standardized. Upon the city systems they operate as standard 600-volt equipment connected in parallel for full speed, while upon the 1,200-volt trolley they are connected two in series for full-speed operation. Where only half-speed operation is required within the city limits, 1,200-volt motors similar to the 600-volt type are used, the current capacity, of course, being less for a given car and extra insulation being provided for the higher voltage.

A number of interurban roads, whose contact-line voltages range from 1,200 to 1,500 volts, have been in operation for several years and the equipment for these voltages has become pretty well standardized. Motors designed for 1,200 to 1,500 volts and connected two in series for operation in connection with contact lines whose voltages range from 2,400 to 3,000 volts have not been tried out to the extent that the lower voltage equipment has, but those now in service are apparently not giving much more trouble than is experienced in the operation of 600-volt equipment. The increased insulation necessary for successful operation on the higher voltages increases the size, weight, and cost of the motors, thus diminishing to a certain extent some of the advantages direct-current motors are assumed to have over single-phase commutator motors.

In the matters of electrical efficiency, simplicity, and ruggedness, three-phase motors rank first. They are lighter in weight and for a given amount of space have greater continuous output than any other form of motor. All three-phase motors now used in railway service are of the induction type and, therefore, have shunt-type motor characteristics. They operate at approximately constant speed for all conditions of load. This feature is of value where high schedule speeds must be maintained over roadway which has comparatively short, heavy grades. Viewed from the standpoint of the power plant, however, this feature is objectionable because of the peak loads imposed upon the plant when heavy trains are being hauled at high speed over the grades. The motors act as generators if operated slightly above their synchronous speed, thus permitting regenerative braking on the down grades. Their starting characteristics are inferior to those possessed by series-type motors and, therefore, they are not so well adapted for use in a service where the number of stops per mile is large. This, and the fact that small inequalities in drive-wheel diameters result in serious overloads on the motors geared to the wheels with the larger diameters, practically precludes the use of this type of motor for all classes of service except that of long-haul, locomotive-drawn trains.

Rolling Stock.—Two classes of rolling stock, namely, motor cars and locomotives, will be compared.

The added weight and the lower acceleration for a given capacity of motor are not the only disadvantages of the single-phase, alternating-current system from the standpoint of motor-car rolling stock. As has been pointed out, it is often desirable that cars equipped for alternating-current service be able to enter cities upon direct current. While the alternating-current, single-phase series motor makes an excellent direct-current motor, the control equipment for use upon either system is at best rather complicated and its first cost, weight, and maintenance relatively high. The added complication of this combined control is at once obvious if a comparison be made of Figs. 184 and 190 (pages

366 and 374), while the tables in the following section, First Cost, Maintenance, and Operating Expense, prove the rolling stock thus equipped to cost 28 per cent more, with a probable maintenance charge of 49 per cent more, than the 600-volt, direct-current equipment.

Since the three-phase and split-phase systems make use of three-phase motors, they are not very well suited for motor-car operation.

In the matter of locomotive weights, there seems to be little difference between the direct-current and the three-phase systems. Single-phase, split-phase, and motor-generator locomotives are somewhat heavier, although the differences are not great. Inasmuch as it is sometimes necessary to ballast electric locomotives in order to get sufficient adhesive weight, the slightly greater inherent weights of the single-phase and split-phase locomotives are not so much of a disadvantage as they might seem on first thought.

As regards flexibility, single-phase and motor-generator rolling stock rank highest, since they may be used with any kind of a distribution system. When used with the direct-current distribution system, however, additional control equipment must be provided. Since the voltage over the motors in these two systems may be varied by means of adjustable ratio transformers or other efficient methods, the control losses are minimum and a large number of efficient running speeds are possible.

Alternating-current rolling stock costs more and has higher maintenance charges than direct-current rolling stock. Also as regards reliability, published reports indicate that the direct-current rolling stock has the advantage, although on account of the widely different operating conditions which exist on the different roads, fair comparisons are hard to make. Some data on the reliability of electric motive power are given in the next chapter.

Power Factor.—One of the disadvantages of the alternating-current systems is the low, uncontrollable power factor. The direct-current system has no apparatus on the car or between the car and the converters which can lower the power factor and its converters may even permit the power factor of the transmission line to be raised. The alternating-current systems which have no synchronous converting apparatus offer no means of power-factor control, while the power factor is lowered still further beyond the substation by car motors, transformer, steel messenger or trolley, if used, and rails. A lower power factor means higher proportional current for a given capacity with increased first cost of equipment and percentage losses.

First Cost, Maintenance, and Operating Expense.—The relative merits of the direct-current and single-phase systems for inter-

TABLE XLI.—COMPARATIVE COST PER MILE SINGLE TRACK

	D.c. 600 v.	D.c. 1,200 v.	A.c. 6,600 v.
Roadbed complete, including grading, ballasting, etc..............	$15,000	$15,000	$15,000
Trolley and feeder installed........	3,800	3,000	2,100
Track bonding...................	600	530	480
Transmission line installed........	1,500	1,500	1,300
Substation installed..............	2,200	1,600	600
Power station installed............	2,450	2,450	2,570
Cars and equipment..............	1,800	1,970	2,300
Telephone......................	120	120	120
	$27,470	$26,170	$24,470
Saving over 600 volts d.c.......	....	1,300	3,000

TABLE XLII.—RELATIVE OPERATING COST PER MILE SINGLE TRACK PER ANNUM
(One hour headway)

	D.c. 600 v.	D.c. 1,200 v.	A.c. 6,600 v.
Car miles per day................	64	64	64
Kw.-hrs. per day at power house...	275	275	245
Cost of coal per annum............	$470	$470	$419
Cost of substation attendance......	175	79	46
Maintenance of motors and control.	94	117	140
Total........................	$739	$666	$605
Saving over 600 volts direct current exclusive of fixed charges........	....	76	134
Saving in fixed charges............	....	137	315
Total annual saving.............	....	$213	$449

TABLE XLIII.—PROMINENT AMERICAN STEAM RAILROAD ELECTRIFICATIONS[1]

Name of road and section electrified	Character of service	Specific cause of electrification	Began electric operation	Length of route, miles	Length of track, miles	System of electrification	Trolley or third rail	Transmission to sub-stations
Baltimore & Ohio, Baltimore Md. tunnels............	Heavy pass. & freight	Tunnel and terminal	1895	3.3	8.4	600-v., d.c.	Third rail	13,200 v., 25 cycles
N. Y. Central & Hudson River R. R., N. Y.-Harmon.	Heavy passenger	Terminal	1906	34.0	351.0	600-v., d.c.	Third rail	11,000 v., 25 cycles
N. Y. N. H. & Hartford R. R., New York-New Haven	Heavy pass. & freight	Terminal economy	1908	74.0	269.0	Single-phase, 11,000 v., 25 cycle 600 v. d.c., N. Y. C.	Catenary trolley, third rail	22,000 v., 25 cycle, single phase
Grand Trunk Ry. Co., Port Huron Mich. St., Clair Tunnel.	Heavy pass. & freight	Tunnel	1908	2.5	12.0	Single-phase 6,600 v. 25 cycle	Catenary trolley	Direct feed
Great Northern R. R., Cascade Tunnel, Washington..	Heavy pass. & freight	Tunnel	1909	4.0	10.0	Three-phase 6,600 v., 25 cycle	Two wire direct suspension	33,000 v. 25 cycle
Mich. Central R. R., Detroit River Tunnel..........	Heavy pass. & freight	Tunnel & terminal	1910	6.25	24.0	600 v. d.c.	Third rail	4,600 v., 60 cycle
Boston & Maine R. R., Hoosac Tunnel, No. Adams, Mass.	Heavy passenger & freight	Tunnel	1911	7.92	22.0	Single-phase, 11,000 v. 25 cycle	Catenary trolley	Direct feed

Penn. Tunnel & Terminal R. R., P. R. R. into New York City.	Heavy passenger	Tunnel & Terminal	1912	15.0	95.0	600 v., d.c.	Third rail	11,000 v., 60 & 25 cycle
Butte, Anaconda & Pacific R. R., Butte–Anaconda, Mont.	Heavy pass. & freight	Economy	1913	30.0	90.5	2,400 v., d.c.	Catenary trolley	100,000 v., 60 cycle, part of network
Norfolk & Western Ry., Bluefield–Elkhorn, W. Va....	Heavy pass. & freight	Tunnel Heavy grade Economy	1915	55.5	164	Split-phase 11,000 volt	Catenary trolley	33,000 v., 25 cycle, single phase
Canadian Northern, Montreal, Can..........	Heavy pass.	Tunnel & Terminal	1915	9.0	25.0	2,400 v., d.c.	Catenary trolley	11,000 v., 60 cycle
Chicago, Milwaukee & Puget Sound Ry..........	Heavy pass. & freight	Heavy grade & economy	1916	648	848	3,000 v., d.c.	Catenary trolley	110,000 v., part of hydroelec. network

Abstracted in part from DEWHURST, J. A., "A Review of American Steam Road Electrifications," *Gen. Elec. Rev.*, November, 1914.

urban service from the standpoint of first cost, maintenance, and operating expenses can best be illustrated by means of Tables XLII and XLIII taken from a very able discussion of the subject before the A. I. E. E. by W. J. Davis, Jr.[1]

The above comparative costs are based upon the following data:

Length of road, 50 miles or more.

Cars, 52 ft. overall, weighing 21 tons without equipment or load and seating 56 passengers.

Car equipment, four 75-hp. motors.

Maximum speed on tangent level track, 45 m.p.h.

Schedule speed, 24 m.p.h., including stops and slow running through towns.

Headway, maximum service, $\frac{1}{2}$ hr.

Frequency of stops, one in 2 miles.

Average energy, 85 watt-hr. per ton-mile at car.

	D.c. 600 v.	D.c. 1,200 v.	A.c. 6,600 v.
Spacing of substations............	10 miles	22 miles	32 miles
Maximum trolley voltage drop.....	25 per cent	25 per cent	10 per cent
Efficiency, generator bus bars to cars.........................	71 per cent	71 per cent	84 per cent
Average efficiency car equipment...	75 per cent	75 per cent	73 per cent
Average power factor of system....	96 per cent	96 per cent	85 per cent

Several steam railways in the United States have electrified certain sections of their lines, yet very little authentic detailed cost data have been published. In some cases steam locomotives still operate over certain portions of the electrified sections, making it almost impossible to segregate operating costs. Many of the installations have been more or less experimental and their first costs contain heavy development charges. A study of the scattered data relative to American railways which have been published indicates that:

1. The energy costs for the various systems are not far from equal, favoring if anything the alternating-current systems.

[1] DAVIS, JR., W. J., "High-voltage Direct-current and Alternating-current Systems for Interurban Railways," *Trans.* A. I. E. E., vol. 26.

2. In the direct-current system a large portion of the installation cost is in the feeder system and converting apparatus, and substation maintenance and attendance expenses are important items in the list of operating expenses.

3. The locomotive first costs and maintenance for the single-phase system are higher than for the direct-current system.

4. The first cost of the single-phase system is from 5 to 15 per cent less than that of the direct-current system.

5. The operating expenses for the two principal systems, single phase and direct current, are approximately the same.

Operating conditions in Europe are different than in America, nevertheless it is interesting to note that the Swiss Railway Commission, in their report to the administrative council of the Swiss Federal States Railway, made early in 1914, recommended the installation of a 10,000-volt, 15-cycle, single-phase system. The Commission, which was composed of eminent engineers, after an exhaustive study which extended over a period of 5 years and in which consideration was given to direct current with the contact-line voltages up to 3,000, three phase up to 8,000, and single phase up to 15,000 volts, concluded that, both from the technical and the economic points of view, the recommended system was best adapted to the particular needs of the Swiss State Railways. They found that the ultimate first costs of the systems were approximately the same, that locomotives of adequate power could be obtained with any of the systems above named, and gave preference to the single-phase system on the ground of its greater flexibility. Commissions for the Prussian, Bavarian, Austrian, and Swedish governments have turned in very similar reports. It seems, therefore, that in continental Europe, Italy excepted, the single-phase system is likely to become pretty well standardized.

The present tendency everywhere is toward the use of higher contact-line voltages. This is markedly true for the direct-current system, in which voltages proposed for use today are five times the values used a decade ago. Single-phase, alternating-current apparatus has been greatly improved during the last few years and the introduction of the various combined systems has tended to broaden the field of the single-phase contact line. Most electrical engineers agree that no one electric system is best adapted to all classes of service and they disagree most markedly as to the type of system which should be used for any given set of operating conditions. The fact remains, however, that any one of the systems will do the work of any railway in a very satisfactory manner. The need of standardization is urgent, for if the electrified terminal and tunnel divisions of trunk lines expand to the point where they desire to merge and exchange equipment to give through service over several roads, the use of 600-volt, direct-current third rail by one railway, of high-voltage alternating current by a second, of three-phase by a third, of high-voltage direct current by a fourth will result in a situation fully as serious as the attempted combination years ago of roads of different track gages and of cars with and without standard air-brake equipment. George Westinghouse did not sound the warning of standardization any too early, therefore, in his paper before the joint meeting of the A. S. M. E. and the British Institution of Mechanical Engineers, held at London in 1910, when he said:

For the present it may be a matter of little moment whether different systems have their contact conductors in the same position, or whether the character of the current used is the same or different. As previously stated, in the early days of railroading it was of little consequence whether the tracks of the different systems in various parts of the country were alike or unlike, but later it did make a vital difference and the variation resulted in financial burdens which even yet lie heavily on some railways. It is this large view into the future of electrical service which should be taken by those responsible for electrical-railway development.

CHAPTER XXIX

ELECTRIC TRACTION ON TRUNK LINES

A study of Table XLIV, in which are listed the more important steam-railway electrifications, indicates that in the earlier electrifications electric motive power was adopted to meet special requirements or to solve peculiar problems in traction, such as the necessity of increased service in large terminals, avoidance of smoke in tunnels, increase in safety of operation, and increase in track capacity on mountain grades, but that in later electrifications economy of operation has been one of the chief reasons.

Probably, the two paramount questions in the minds of steam-railroad directors in connection with this problem are:

1. Can the service be improved with electric traction?

2. What will it cost to change and to operate and maintain the new system when installed?

While it seems advisable to consider these questions more in detail subsequently, a few of the minor advantages of electric traction which are involved in the first question of possible improved service will be first considered. The outline which forms the basis of the following brief discussion on these advantages is one presented in great detail in the very valuable paper by Stillwell and Putnam before the A. I. E. E.[1]

The factors which contribute to the earning power of the electrified road to a greater extent than the steam railroad are:

Frequency of service.

Speed.

Comfort of passengers.

Safety.

Reliability of service.

Increased capacity of line.

Frequency of stops.

Convenient establishment of feeder lines.

[1] STILLWELL, LEWIS B. and PUTNAM, HENRY ST. CLAIR, "On the Substitution of the Electric Motor for the Steam Locomotive," *Trans.* A. I. E. E., vol. 26.

Frequency of Service.—Experience with high-speed interurban lines paralleling steam lines, but offering much more frequent service, leads to the conclusion that frequent service creates traffic and, therefore, increases earning power. The frequent service offered by an electrified system is usually impractical with steam operation.

Speed.—Higher average speeds are possible and practical in electric service for four principal reasons:

1. The absence of reciprocating parts reduces the danger of the locomotive leaving the track.

2. The absence of reciprocating parts reduces the maintenance of the track and the liability of broken rails.

3. The more rapid acceleration permits higher average speed with the same number of stops, or more stops with the same schedule speed.

4. For heavy trains requiring two locomotives, high speeds can be maintained by means of the multiple-unit control system. This is unsafe with two steam locomotives, as both engines cannot be controlled by a single engineman.

Higher speeds can be maintained over mountain grades with electric locomotives than can be maintained with steam locomotives. On ascending grades, the speed at which a steam locomotive can haul a given weight of train is limited by its boiler capacity and by the fact that a great deal of power is required to haul the heavy locomotive itself when it is operated at high speed on a heavy up grade. On the other hand, exceedingly powerful motors can be mounted on a comparatively light electric locomotive. These motors can carry large overloads for short periods of time and they receive their energy supply from a large power station. On down grades regenerative braking is possible, thus permitting the air brakes to be reserved for emergency service and higher speeds to be used with safety.

Comfort of Passengers.—The general comfort of passengers is greatly enhanced by the following features of electric traction:

1. Elimination of smoke and cinders.

2. Improved ventilation, because of the absence of smoke and cinders.

3. Easily controlled car heating.

Safety.—Several very notable elements of danger which are present in steam traction are eliminated when electric motive power is used.

1. The results of the absence of reciprocating parts which permit higher speeds to be maintained, as outlined under Speed, also reduce the probability of accident.

2. The absence of the intense fire of the locomotive reduces the probability of fire in the wreckage.

3. The elimination of hot water and steam in locomotive and heating system reduces the dangers often resulting from such sources.

4. The absence of smoke and steam prevents errors in reading signals from these causes.

5. The presence of a source of electrical power along the roadway and the necessary employment of electrically trained maintenance crews should decrease the first cost and maintenance, and therefore increase the use of automatic block signals.

6. The locomotive driver can give his entire attention to driving; he is not required to engineer a large steam power plant. His seat can be so located that both sides of the track are in full view at all times.

As has been noted under a preceding caption, regenerative braking is possible, and since the air brakes then are used only in stopping the train, car wheels and brake shoes are not heated by long-continued applications of the brakes while the train is descending a heavy grade. The number of wrecks due to broken wheels cracked by such heating is thus reduced.

Excessive wheel loads, which are common causes of track failure, can be avoided. Fire risks on property adjoining the right-of-way are decreased and there are no stray sparks to cause prairie or forest fires.

It must be remembered, however, that in contrast to these advantages, the electrical-distribution system, especially the third rail, offers a danger not present in steam-railroad operation. Whereas the third rail may be protected, thereby reducing the danger under normal operation to a minimum, such protection would avail little in the case of a wreck. Under these circumstances the automatic circuit breakers must be relied upon to disconnect the section from the source of supply before serious physiological effects are produced or fires started in the wreckage.

Reliability of Service.—Comparison of the train delays from all causes, both electrical and mechanical, before and after electrification upon the few roads which have been operating sufficiently long by electricity to guarantee dependable results, points to the conclusion that the service is more reliable after electrification than before.

For example, upon the Manhattan division of the Interborough Rapid Transit system of New York after electrification, the delay during the most severe months of the year for the exposed third-rail system was but 72 per cent of that under steam operation, expressed in train-minutes, although an increased car mileage of 37 per cent was maintained with the electric service.

Upon the electrified section of the New York, New Haven & Hartford R. R. during the heaviest traffic day of the year, occasioned by the annual football game at New Haven, 128 regular trains and 30 special trains were operated between New York and New Haven in 1908 with but two delays totaling 17 min., while, in 1909, 155 trains were run with no delays whatever.

The following table[1] compares the total delayed time on the Butte, Anaconda & Pacific Ry. for the month of June, 1913, steam operation, with the month of June, 1914, electrical operation:

TABLE XLIV.—COMPARISON OF TRAIN DELAYS

	Number of trains		Total delay				Grand total	
			Freight		Pass.			
	Freight	Pass.	Hr.	Min.	Hr.	Min.	Hr.	Min.
1913	357	272	497	34	20	46	518	10
1914	280	280	296	28	7	10	301	38
Per cent decrease..	21.57	2.94[a]	40.4		75.12		41.78	

[a] Increase.

On the Chicago, Milwaukee & St. Paul Ry., it is reported that with electric operation delays on account of extra-heavy trains are only one-ninth[2] as great as with steam and that, in general, electric operation is much more reliable than steam operation.

[1] Abstracted from Cox, J. B., "The Electrical Operation of the Butte, Anaconda & Pacific Ry.," Trans. A. I. E. E., November, 1914.

[2] BEEUWKES, New York Railroad Club, 1917.

For the year 1912 the average locomotive mileage per train detention chargeable against motive power on the electrified division of the New York Central & Hudson River R. R. was 48,271 miles, and the maximum mileage made by any one locomotive without detention was 249,423 miles.[1] A comparison of many published reports indicates that, on the average, train detentions chargeable against motive power with electric operation are only about 50 per cent of the number occurring with steam operation.

Increased Capacity of Line.—One of the marked advantages of electric traction is its large tractive effort for a given size and weight of equipment. While this feature is pronounced in the electric locomotive because of the elimination of the tender and the possible use of such a design as to throw practically all the weight of the locomotive upon the drivers, the effect is still more marked if motor cars be used, thus making practically the entire weight of train available for tractive effort between wheels and track. With this relatively great tractive effort much higher rates of acceleration are possible, which, in turn, permit smaller headway between trains and increased traffic capacity for a given track.

This is of particular value upon heavy grades of the single-track roads of the West, where electrification permits so great an increase in traffic over an existing single track that it obviates the necessity of double tracking the road for some time to come. In this case the cost of electrification may be balanced directly against the cost of a second track, which in the mountains of the West becomes a formidable figure.

In tunnels, the capacity of the track is increased because no time interval between trains is required for tunnel ventilation. With steam locomotives the vitiated air so affects the operation of the furnace that the locomotive capacity is often considerably reduced.

Further, the length of freight trains using the steam locomotive is limited by the strength of the draft gear. With the use of two or more electric locomotives at the head of a train, or if the limit of the draft gear is reached, possibly the introduction of several locomotives throughout the length of the train, all operated by means of the multiple-unit control from the leading

[1] QUEREAU, in *Proc.* Ry. Master Mech. Assoc., 1913.

engine, will probably make possible a greatly increased freight traffic over a given road, thus increasing the freight as well as the passenger capacity of the line.

In a steam-railway electrification the increase in track capacity will, of course, depend greatly on operating conditions. Most of the present electrifications are but short sections of line and the electric motive power is restricted by having to meet the requirements of steam operation on the balance of the road. With complete electric operation better results may be expected than are now usually obtained. Despite this condition the increase in track capacity resulting from electrification ranges from 50 to 100 per cent.

Frequency of Stops.—The ability of the electrically operated train to make more frequent stops and thus better accommodate the riding public without reducing the schedule from that of the steam road has already been explained.

In addition to the above advantage, in some instances it is possible to interconnect the local railway system with the electrified road in such a way as to transport passengers more nearly to their destination without change.

Both of the above features tend to increase the traffic and resulting earnings of the road.

Convenient Establishment of Feeder Lines.—With the reduced cost of power possible with an electrified trunk line, short branches of present steam roads or existing suburban or interurban lines may be operated electrically much more economically than at present. The large and efficient organization of the trunk-line system also adds materially to this possibility. These short branch roads then become valuable feeders to the through trunk line.

Still further economy and convenience to passengers in such branch-line operation may often be brought about by adding branch-line motor cars to the through train at junction points, operating the entire train thus made up by the multiple-unit system.

Improvement of Service.—It is believed that the first question to be asked by the directors of a steam road, to which reference was made early in the chapter, has been satisfactorily answered by the above improvements in the service, which have been shown to be possible upon electrified roads.

The factors, adaptability to service, possibility of increased drawbar pull, and more rapid acceleration, should, however, have more detailed analysis, for it is largely with regard to these features that service may be improved and earnings increased, and, therefore, it is these features to which the present steam railroad officials look at a time when service can no longer be

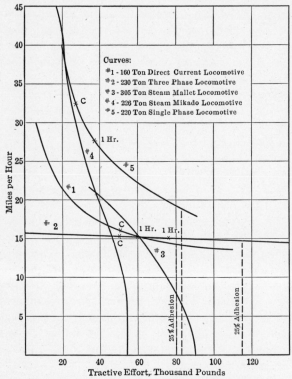

Curves:
#1 - 160 Ton Direct Current Locomotive
#2 - 230 Ton Three Phase Locomotive
#3 - 305 Ton Steam Mallet Locomotive
#4 - 226 Ton Steam Mikado Locomotive
#5 - 220 Ton Single Phase Locomotive

FIG. 241.—Locomotive speed-tractive effort curves.

increased with present locomotives, since the latter have practically reached their maximum size and efficiency.

Tractive Effort and Drawbar Pull.—In Fig. 241 are plotted the speed-tractive-effort curves for several modern steam and electric freight locomotives. The weight of the tender is included in the steam-locomotive weights and all of the electric locomotives are double-unit machines. The data, from which the curve for the steam Mallet was plotted, were taken in the course of some tests by the Southern Pacific Ry. on one of its largest oil-burning locomotives.[1] The curve for the Mikado-type locomotive was calculated from the dimensions of a typical locomotive of that type as built in the year 1913. The single-phase locomotive units are of the type used by the New York, New Haven & Hartford R. R. for mixed service and are geared for higher speeds than are usually practicable in heavy mountain freight service. The three-phase units are of the type used by the Great Northern Ry. in its Cascade tunnel electrification and the direct-current units are the Butte, Anaconda & Pacific, type which were described in Chap. XXVII.

The three-phase locomotive has but one running notch on the controller; the direct current has two, and the single-phase, with its adjustable-ratio transformer control, has thirteen. The single-phase locomotive can, therefore, economically exert its rated tractive effort through a very wide range of speeds. The curves for the steam locomotives are for the condition of maximum continuous boiler output with boiler new and clean. As the tubes and other heating surfaces quickly become fouled in service, the curves for average working conditions would show lower tractive efforts. Leaky tubes also seriously affect the boiler's capacity and it seems to be a difficult matter to keep the tubes perfectly tight on account of the high furnace temperatures used in the operation of modern boilers.

The points marked C and "1 Hr." on the electric-locomotive curves indicate the continuous and 1-hr. ratings, respectively. The Mallet, direct-current, and three-phase locomotives are low-speed machines designed for hauling heavy trains over mountain divisions. On account of the numerous sharp curves it is impracticable to operate heavy trains at higher speeds over these divisions.

A study of the curves leads to the conclusions:

1. The curves for the electric locomotives are more nearly horizontal than those of the steam locomotives. The physical significance of this is that a change in the drawbar pull of a steam locomotive is accompanied by a much greater change in speed than a similar change causes in the speed of an electric locomotive. Roughly classified, electric locomotives are constant-speed machines.

[1] Ry. Age Gaz., Jan. 14, 1910.

2. For a given weight of locomotive the starting tractive effort of the electric locomotive is much higher than that of its steam competitor.

3. The electric locomotive can exert a tractive effort up to the limit fixed by adhesion when running at a comparatively high speed.

By reason of its constant-speed characteristics and its light weight for a given tonnage rating, the electric locomotive maintains its speed while ascending grades much better than does the

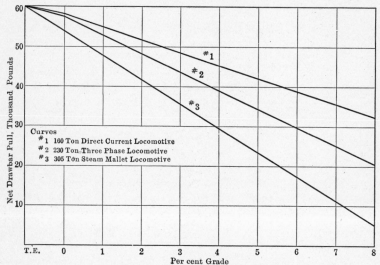

FIG. 242.—Effect of grades on drawbar pull.

steam locomotive. Uniformity of speed tends to simplify train schedules, reduce the danger of collision, and increase the capacity of the track. Where the profile of the road is undulating, a short heavy grade often fixes the tonnage rating of a steam locomotive. The electric locomotive, by reason of its ability to carry large overloads for short periods of time, is not so badly handicapped in this respect. It is not only able to start its train on a heavy grade, but it is also able to carry it over the grade at nearly rated speed. On the other hand, the steam locomotive maintains its tractive effort over a wide speed range much better than does the electric, and thus enables the same locomotive to be used successfully in hauling trains whose scheduled speeds are widely different.

Figure 242 shows the effect of grades on the drawbar pulls of the three locomotives which are shown in Fig. 241 as having practically the same speed when exerting a tractive effort of 60,000 lb. On account of its great weight, the drawbar pull of the steam locomotive decreases very rapidly as the per cent

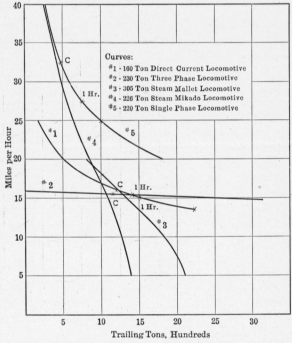

Curves:
#1 - 160 Ton Direct Current Locomotive
#2 - 230 Ton Three Phase Locomotive
#3 - 305 Ton Steam Mallet Locomotive
#4 - 226 Ton Steam Mikado Locomotive
#5 - 220 Ton Single Phase Locomotive

FIG. 243.—Locomotive tonnage ratings.

grade increases. On a 3 per cent grade the drawbar pull of the electric locomotive is 35 per cent greater than that of the Mallet.

Tonnage Ratings and Service Capacities.—The tonnage ratings, on a 1½ per cent grade, at various speeds of the locomotives whose speed-tractive-effort curves were given in Fig. 241 are plotted in Fig. 243. The points C and "1 Hr." have the same significance as in Fig. 241. Tonnages lower than the continuous rating may, of course, be hauled continuously, but tonnages higher than the 1-hr. rating can be hauled only for a short time.

The continuous tonnage rating of the 160-ton, direct-current electric locomotive is practically equal to that of the 305-ton Mallet at 16 m.p.h. The thing of most interest to the operating man, however, should be not the tonnage which can be hauled by a single locomotive, but rather the service capacity or the number of ton-miles per hour which the locomotive can haul over a given track. The service capacity may be calculated by the equation

$$\text{Service capacity} = \text{Tonnage} \times \text{miles per hour} \times \frac{\text{running time}}{\text{total time}}.$$

The service capacities, on a $1\frac{1}{2}$ per cent grade, of the locomotives

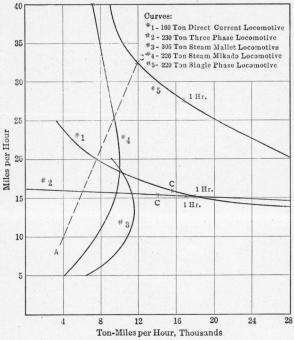

Curves:
#1 - 160 Ton Direct Current Locomotive
#2 - 230 Ton Three Phase Locomotive
#3 - 305 Ton Steam Mallet Locomotive
#4 - 226 Ton Steam Mikado Locomotive
#5 - 220 Ton Single Phase Locomotive

Fig. 244.—Locomotive service capacities.

under discussion have been plotted in Fig. 244. The ratio of running time to total time is affected by a great many factors, most of which are more or less variable, so that only an average ratio can be determined for a given road. The ratios here used, $\frac{6}{10}$ for steam and $\frac{8}{10}$ for electric, are probably high for many roads, but are the values found to obtain approximately in at least one electrification study.

It will be seen from the figure that the curves for the two kinds of locomotives are very different. The curves for the steam locomotives reach maximum values at definite values of speed, while those of the electric locomotives have no definite maximum values except those fixed by the ratings of the respective locomotives. The same statement may be made regarding the tonnage rating curves in Fig. 243. The service capacity of the Mallet is greatest at a speed of about $12\frac{1}{2}$ m.p.h. and at this speed it has only about three-fourths of the continuous capacity of 160-ton electric locomotive.

The curves for the direct-current and single-phase locomotives are plotted for the operating conditions which obtain when the controller handles are in the last running notch. It will be remembered that the single-phase locomotive has twelve and the direct-current one other running notch. Curves for the lower-speed notches will be located to the left and downward from the curves here given. The locus of the continuous-rating point C of the single-phase locomotives is the line AC. The intersection of AC and the curve for the Mikado locomotive gives the speed at which these two locomotives, which have about the same weight, have the same service capacity. If the gear ratio, drive-wheel diameter, and rated motor speed of the single-phase locomotive had been the same as those of the direct-current locomotive, their service-capacity curves would be approximately coincident. If, therefore, it is desired to change the speed at which an electric locomotive has its maximum continuous-service capacity, it may be readily done (within certain limits) by changing the gear ratio of the locomotive.

Accelerating Qualities.—The ability of the electric locomotive to accelerate a train quickly is well illustrated in Fig. 245. These curves were calculated for a trailing load of 750 tons, consisting of seven steel Pullman cars, three steel coaches, and two baggage or express cars, ascending a $\frac{1}{4}$ per cent grade. The locomotives used are among the latest and most powerful of their respective types. The curves show that the electrically hauled train is pretty well up to the balancing speed in 100 sec. and practically reaches that speed in 200 sec.

The Pacific-type steam locomotive has approximately the same balancing speed but does not reach it until about 900 sec. after starting. The Atlantic-type locomotive balances at a lower speed and does not accelerate as rapidly as the heavier Pacific type. The curves show clearly the great advantages possessed by electric locomotives when operating in a service which requires a large number of stops.

A most inspiring and graphic demonstration of the ability of the New York Central locomotive, particularly in rapid acceleration, was the often-quoted test carried out in 1904 on the New York Central R. R. when electric locomotive No. 6000, drawing eight Pullman coaches with a total train weight of 478.5 tons,

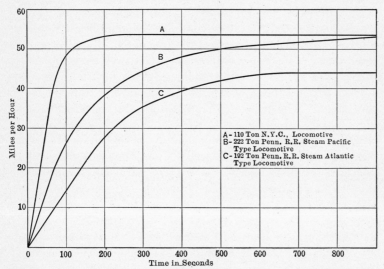

Fig. 245.—Passenger train speed-time curves (750 trailing tons on $\frac{1}{4}$ per cent grade).

after reaching the same speed as the New York Central fast express was allowed to attain its maximum speed and was found to gain a full train length in the distance of 1 mile.

General Suitability for the Service.—In many respects the electric motor is better adapted for railway service than the steam engine. The motions of the moving parts are simpler and all moving parts can be readily balanced. The weight and volume per horsepower output are much lower.

In cold weather the drawbar pull necessary to haul a given train at a given speed is greater than in warm weather. Cold weather decreases the drawbar pull of the steam locomotive because of the increased heat radiation from the boiler and engines, while the drawbar pull of the electric locomotive, for a given temperature of the motor windings, is increased.

The coefficient of adhesion is higher with electric than it is with steam locomotives, because the torque of the electric motors is uniform and there are no unbalanced forces tending to lift the locomotive from the track.

Steam locomotives must carry their own supplies of fuel and water and these supplies must be renewed at frequent intervals. Stops for this purpose lower the schedule speeds and tend to congest traffic.

Experience gained in the practical operation of existing electric locomotives indicates that they require inspection once in from 1,200 to 2,500 miles of operation. To keep steam locomotives in equally good condition, they must be inspected and cleaned at the end of each run.

Service does not decrease the efficiency of an electric locomotive, while, on account of the fouling of heating surfaces, the efficiency of the steam locomotive may be seriously impaired.

On the other hand, electric locomotives are still in the development stage, while steam locomotives are quite well standardized. The steam locomotive is an independent unit. Its operation is in no wise affected by the proximity of other locomotives, nor does it depend on an outside source for its supply of energy.

Long-continued overloads injure electrical equipment and do not seriously affect the life of steam equipment. Electric locomotives designed for operation in connection with one electric system cannot usually be operated in connection with a different system. Steam locomotives have, therefore, a much higher degree of interchangeability.

Electrification Increases Real Estate Values.—One of the most important by-products of electrification is the great increase in the value of the real estate which is covered by the terminal tracks in large cities. Office buildings may be constructed over the tracks, as has been done at New York City. The salvage value of such land is very great. Real estate adjoining the right-of-way also increases in value on account of the elimination of the smoke and the partial abatement of the noise nuisance.

Cost of Electrification and Operation.—Granted that the service can be improved and the capacity of a road increased with electric traction as pointed out above, an answer to the second question must be found, *i.e.*, "what will it cost to change and to operate and maintain the new system when installed?"

The first cost of the charge will vary greatly with local conditions and in any case would probably be prohibitive if undertaken for a complete trunk-line system at once. Experimentation, if necessary at all, should be carried out upon some of the less important branches and the electrical rolling stock secured a portion at a time. It has even been suggested that, as the purchase of new steam locomotives to replace those worn out or considered obsolete is usually treated by steam roads as an operation charge and not a charge against capital, the electrical rolling stock, or a large portion of it, might be secured in like manner and no great capital investment made for this portion of the new system.

As has been pointed out in a preceding chapter, there is a growing tendency on the part of railway companies to purchase from commercial power companies the electrical energy required for the operation of their trains—particularly in the West where water power is plentiful and coal is costly. By so doing, the first cost of electrification is greatly reduced; the annual costs for energy are usually less and the fact that the energy supply is often received from a transmission network insures better continuity of service.

The A. I. E. E. was particularly fortunate at its 1911 annual convention to have presented by the Pennsylvania R. R., through B. F. Wood, a very detailed statement of the first cost and operating expenses of the electrification of the West Jersey and Seashore R. R. While the figures for a larger trunk line operating locomotives in place of motor-car trains would vary somewhat from those applying to this road as illustrated in the discussion which follows, the costs of this particular electrification, which were the first to be made public in complete detail, are well worthy careful study. With present price levels, the costs would be about twice those given in the accompanying tables.

Tables XLV and XLVI give total and unit costs of electrification, while operating expenses are well analyzed in Tables XLVII to LI, inclusive. The costs apply to a total of 150 miles of single track upon which 47- to 52-ton cars are operated in trains with two 200-hp. motors per car controlled with the multiple-unit equipment. The power station is of 8,000-kw. capacity supplying power to eight substations ranging from 1,000 to 2,500 kw. each. The distribution voltage on the third-rail system is 675 volts direct current.

TABLE XLV.—COST OF ELECTRIFICATION[1]

Power stations:

Building, stacks, coal- and ash-handling machinery	$354,000	
Equipment	640,900	
Total		$ 994,900
Transmission line		241,500
Substations:		
Buildings	$ 72,000	
Equipment	419,560	
Total		491,560
Third rail		557,636
Overhead trolley		80,500
Track bonding		102,659
Cars		1,135,900
Car repair and inspection sheds		46,674
Right-of-way, additional		592,100
Reconstructing tracks		763,800
Constructing new tracks		2,071,000
Terminal facilities and changes at stations		252,400
Signals and interlocking plants		561,900
Changing telegraph and adding telephone facilities		105,100
Fencing right-of-way, cattle guards, etc		88,400
Miscellaneous items		44,200
Total		$8,130,229

TABLE XLVI.—UNIT COSTS OF ELECTRIFICATION[1]

Power station, cost per kilowatt	$ 124.36
Transmission line, cost per mile	3,485.00
Substations, building and equipment cost per kilowatt	28.90
Third rail, cost per mile	4,235.00
Overhead trolley, cost per mile	4,120.00
Track bonding, cost per mile	684.50
Cars, including electrical equipment, each	12,214.00

[1] WOOD, B. F., "Electrical Operation of the West Jersey & Seashore R. R.," *Trans.* A. I. E. E., vol. 30.

TABLE XLVII.—POWER STATION OPERATION AND MAINTENANCE COST[1]

			Year 1910	
		Items	Total	Cent per kw.-hr.
Operation	Labor	Boiler room...............................	$14,742.36	0.052
		Turbine.................................	10,010.81	0.035
		Electrical................................	1,661.02	0.006
		Supervision janitors and watchmen..........	2,756.23	0.010
		Total operating labor.....................	$29,170.42	0.103
	Material	Coal....................................	102,715.31	0.363
		Water.................................	500.00	0.002
		Lubricants..............................		
		Miscellaneous material...................	2,238.44	0.007
		Miscellaneous charges...................	1,700.49	0.006
		Total operating material................	$107,154.24	0.378
		Total operation.....................	$136,324.66	0.481
Maintenance	Labor	Building.................................	326.29	0.001
		Boiler room.............................	1,550.44	0.005
		Turbine.................................	836.11	0.003
		Auxiliary apparatus.......................	844.17	0.003
		Electrical................................	195.30	0.001
		Piping.................................	691.94	0.002
		Miscellaneous...........................	187.30	0.001
		Total maintenance labor................	$4,631.55	0.016
	Material	Building...............................	$146.63	0.001
		Boiler room.............................	2,493.23	0.009
		Turbine.................................	1,597.52	0.006
		Auxiliary apparatus.....................	2,066.13	0.007
		Electrical...............................	3,046.44	0.011
		Piping.................................	383.97	0.001
		Miscellaneous...........................	599.06	0.002
		Total maintenance material.............	10,332.98	0.037
		Total maintenance...................	14,964.53	0.053
Summary		Total labor...............................	33,801.97	0.119
		Total material............................	117,487.22	0.415
		Total labor and material station proper..............	151,289.19	0.534
		Other items charged to station accounts.............	2,160.60	0.008
		Total.................................	153,449.79	0.542
		Net output...............................	28,312,500	
		Pounds coal per kw.-hr............................	3.246	
		Cost of coal per 2,000 lb...........................	$2.235	

[1] WOOD, B. F., "Electrical Operation of the West Jersey & Seashore R. R.," *Trans.* A. I. E. E., vol. 30.

TABLE XLVIII.—AVERAGE COST OF TRAIN OPERATION PER CAR-MILE[1]

Year	Repairs electric equipment of cars	Repairs passenger cars	Other maintenance of equipment costs	Electric power at car shoes	Yard service shifting costs	Motormen	Trainmen	Train supplies and expenses	Total	Other expense	Total expenses	Car miles, total	Average cars per train
1909	0.63	1.10	0.25	4.30	0.33	0.88	1.44	0.69	9.67	9.08	18.75	4,107,609	3.457
1910	0.65	1.01	0.27	3.33	0.43	0.91	1.52	0.67	8.80	9.39	18.19	4,552,532	3.518
1912	0.96	1.07	0.22	5.10	0.43	0.90	1.61	0.79	10.08	9.95	20.03	4,647,236	3.598

[1] WOOD, B. F., "Electrical Operation of the West Jersey & Seashore R.R.," *Trans. A. I. E. E.*, vol. 30 and *Gen. Elec. Rev.*, November, 1913.

TABLE XLIX.—COST OF TRANSMISSION SYSTEM MAINTENANCE[1]

(Total and average per mile per month)

Year	High tension		Overhead trolley		Third rail		Running track bonding	
	Total	Per mile	Total	Per mile	Total	Per mile	Total	Per mile
1910	$3,444.57	$4.10	$4,895.16	$36.70	$10,864.13	$6.46	$2,445.72	$1.36
1912	5,060.67	7.30	6,161.03	64.01	14,045.73	9.91	3,228.84	1.79

[1] *Ibid.*

TABLE L.—COST OF SUBSTATION OPERATION AND MAINTENANCE

Year	Total for eight substations				
	Operation	Maintenance	Total	Cost per kw. hr.	Substation output kw. hr., 675 volts direct current
1910	$20,852.31	$3,607.30	$24,459.61	$0.001082	21,972,300
1912	20,953.92	2,729.55	23,683.47	0.000967	24,481,100

Kahler has estimated the cost of a single-phase electrification of 467 miles of steam railroad located in the mountainous regions of the West and handling a traffic of 2,814,407,580 ton-miles annually, as follows:[1]

[1] KAHLER, C. P., "Trunk Line Electrification," *Trans. A. I. E. E.*, vol 32, p. 1209.

Item		
High-tension lines (steel tower), 450 miles........		$2,250,000
Trolley and feeder wire:		
3/0 grooved copper trolley, 468 miles at $650..	$ 304,200	
Steel trolley wire, 156 miles at $320...........	49,920	
2/0 feeder wire, 468 miles at $550.............	234,000	
		588,120
Overhead construction:		
Bracket-arm construction, 420 miles at $1,650..	$ 693,000	
Span construction, 92 miles at $2,600.........	239,200	
Steel bridges, 4 miles.......................	36,000	
Section breaks.............................	6,600	
Additional for curved track, 100 miles at $300..	30,000	
		1,004,800
Track bonding, 624 miles at $450..............		280,800
Substations:		
14 substations, 56,000 kv.-a..................	$ 616,000	
3 portable substations, 6,000 kv.-a. (complete)	96,000	
		712,000
Rolling stock:		
14 motor cars at $18,000.....................	$ 252,000	
10 passenger locomotives at $45,000...........	450,000	
43 freight locomotives at $50,000.............	2,150.000	
11 switching locomotives at $35,000...........	385,000	
		3,237,000
Changing block signals and telegraph, 468 miles..		561,600
Engineering and supervision, 5 per cent..........		431,716
Contingencies, etc., 10 per cent.................		905,964
Total......................................		$9,972,000
Credit for steam equipment:		
140 locomotives...........................	$2,520,000	
241 coal cars.............................	241,000	
14 passenger cars.........................	112,000	
Give credit for 70 per cent of new value.........	$2,873,000	2,012,000
Net estimate.............................		$7,960,000
Cost per mile of track.......................		17,200

The data presented by J. B. Cox in "The Electrical Operation
of the Butte, Anaconda & Pacific Ry.," *Proceedings* of the
A. I. E. E., November, 1914, are of interest from an operating
standpoint. The Butte, Anaconda & Pacific Ry. is an ore road
and has a route mileage of 25.7 miles and track mileage of 90.5
miles. The traffic, which is very heavy, was formerly handled

by 27 steam locomotives. It is now handled by 17 80-ton, 2,400-volt, direct-current electric locomotives[1] and five steam locomotives. The electric locomotives operate about 80 per cent of the total annual locomotive mileage. The electrical energy required is purchased of a hydroelectric power company which operates a high-tension transmission network in the vicinity of the railway. Coal for the steam locomotives costs $4.25 per ton delivered at the railway-company bins. The total cost of electrification was $1,201,000. No reduction was made for the salvage of the 22 steam locomotives which were displaced. In the following table the operating expenses for 1914 include the expenses of the five steam locomotives which are still in service on tracks not yet electrified. Presumably still greater economy will be effected when the electrification is complete, the operating forces better trained, and the equipment a little farther removed from the experimental stage.

TABLE LI.—OPERATING EXPENSES OF BUTTE, ANACONDA & PACIFIC RY.

Item of operating expense	Steam, 1913	Electric, 1914	Decrease	Per cent. decrease
Fuel and power............	315,235.74	164,508.70	150,727.04	47.81
Repairs..................	124,787.90	92,278.08	32,509.82	26.05
Enginemen's wages........	104,461.18	71,225.28	33,235.30	31.81
Engine house expenses.....	29,907.80	18,638.38	11,269.42	37.68
Water..................	4,953.66	1,193.70	3,759.96	75.90
Lubricants..............	9,751.44	4,942.32	4,809.12	49.30
Other supplies............	5,823.52	4,552.36	1,271.16	21.83
Total locomotive performance..................	594,921.24	357,339.42	237,581.82	39.93
Trainmen's wages........	147,632.30	116,486.00	31,146.30	21.10
Grand total..........	742,553.54	473,825.42	268,728.12	36.19
Ton miles hauled.........	158,917,720	172,855,856	13,938,136[1]	8.77[1]

[1] Increase.

After subtracting from $268,728.12 a sum necessary to cover depreciation charges and distribution-system maintenance expenses, the total net saving with electric operation was $242,-299.12, or 20.2 per cent on the cost of electrification. This net

[1] See chapter on Electric Locomotives.

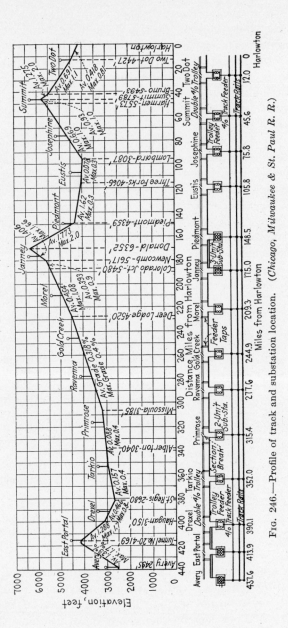

Fig. 246.—Profile of track and substation location. (*Chicago, Milwaukee & St. Paul R. R.*)

saving was made in spite of the fact that 8.77 per cent more ton-miles were hauled in 1914 than in 1913.

Of the more recent electrifications the data published relative to the Chicago Milwaukee & St. Paul Ry. are the most complete. The profile and substation locations for the Rocky Mountain electrification of this road are shown in Fig. 246, while Fig. 247 shows the graphic time table and load curve of the Rocky Mountain division.[1]

TABLE LII.—COST DATA, CHICAGO, MILWAUKEE & ST. PAUL RY.

Item	Average cost per route mile	Various average unit costs	Per cent item cost to total, excluding locomotives
Trolley system complete...........	$ 8,390	....	47.7
Transmission system complete.....	0.2360	....	13.3
Per mile of transmission line.......	....	$ 2,835	....
Substations......................	6,050	....	34.4
Per station......................	....	189,400	....
Per kilowatt.....................	....	45	....
Miscellaneous: right-of-way—minor building, etc................	265	....	1.7
Engineering and administrations...	514	....	2.9
Total...........................	17,579	....	100.00
Locomotives			
Road engine...................	....	122,500	....
Switch engine.................	....	37,700	....

Certain cost data for this road are shown in Table XLIII.[2] In a recent official statement[3] published by the railroad the total cost of the electrification of the 440 miles over the Rocky Mountains is given as $11,661,773, the value of the displaced steam equipment being $3,535,265. The electrical costs are as of the time of electrification, 1914, 1915, and 1916. The great increase in first cost occasioned by the World War is indicated by the fact that the 208-mile Cascade Mountain electrification of this company cost $113,284,811 in 1917, 1918, and 1919. Here the value of the displaced steam equipment as of the same date was $3,829,-250. From these figures it appears that the first costs increased

[1] BEEUWKES, A. I. E. E. Jour., September, 1920.
[2] Report to the N. E. L. A. Convention, May 21, 1920.
[3] Elec. Ry. Jour., Feb. 28, 1925.

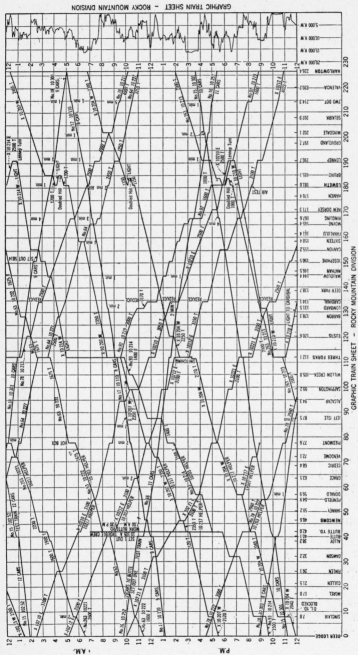

Fig. 247.—Graphical time table and load curves for a division of the Chicago, Milwaukee and St. Paul R. R.

100 per cent and that the cost of electrification is about three times the value of the displaced steam equipment.

An extended study of operating expense and fixed charges, in which all expenses were considered as of the price levels of 1923, shows that the saving in operation due to electrification of the Rocky Mountain divisions during the period 1916 to 1924, inclusive, amounts to $11,868,247, while the saving in the Cascade Mountain division for the period 1920 to 1924 amounts to $531,760. The total saving in both sections amounts to $12,400,-007, or one-half of the total cost of electrification. With increase in traffic volume the savings will be still larger.

In the matter of fuel consumption it is interesting to note that during the last three months of 1915 with steam operation the coal consumption was 276 lb. per 1,000 ton-miles, while during the last three months of 1916 with electric operation the energy consumption was 39.4 kw.-hr. per 1,000 ton-miles. Thus the coal consumption on a kilowatt-hour basis is 7 lb. per kilowatt-hour. The electrical energy came from hydroelectric plants, but if it had come from steam plants it is quite probable that the coal per kilowatt-hour would have been considerably less than one-half of seven. The energy measurement from which the 39.4 kw.-hr. was computed was made at the meters of the power company which furnishes the energy and not at the locomotive. Records for several years show that the ratio between the watt-hours registered on the locomotive meters and those registered on the power company's meters is about 0.67. The difference between the aggregates of the two sets of readings consists of all the losses of transmission, conversion, and distribution less the regenerated energy.

A study of these and other data lead to the general conclusion that the fuel consumption with electric operation is only about one-half of that with steam operation. It is true that the steam locomotive is being constantly improved in thermal efficiency, but central-station plants are improving still more. Recently a large steam plant operating under test conditions produced 1 kw.-hr. per 11,600 B.t.u. This corresponds to a thermal efficiency of 34 per cent. Modern steam locomotives under test conditions have attained a thermal efficiency of about 9 per cent. Thus, if a 50 per cent loss between the coal pile and the drawbar of an electric locomotive be allowed, the ultimate thermal efficiency of the electric power is 17 against 9 per cent for the steam power.

On account of the high first cost of electrification and, therefore, the high fixed charges, it is evident that it would not pay to electrify a road over which the traffic is light. Only a very careful study of each particular case will enable an engineer to decide whether electrification will justify itself or not. With steam motive power, the first cost and fixed charges are low, while with the electric motive power the possibility of low operating expenses and the increase of gross earnings is presented.

In conclusion, it may be said that the greatest objection to electrification is the high first cost, and its most important advantages are safety, increased capacity of track, and economy.

INDEX

483